Tiling for Contractors

How to Prep, Set, and Finish Like a Pro

By Michael Byrne and Michelle Griffoul

A Journal of Light Construction Book

www.jlconline.com

hanley▲wood

Cover Design: Jennifer Griffiths
Cover Photo: Michael Mesikep

Project Editors: Steven Bliss, Clayton DeKorne
Editorial Direction: Sal Alfano, Don Jackson
Managing Editors: Leslie Ensor, Emily Stetson
Technical Review and Index: Ted Cushman

Graphic Designer: Jennifer Griffiths
Illustrators: Tim Healey, Charles Lockhart
Production Director: Theresa Emerson

International Standard Book Number: 978-1-928580-44-7

Printed in the United States of America

A Journal of Light Construction Book
The *Journal of Light Construction* is a trade name of Hanley Wood, LLC.

The Journal of Light Construction
186 Allen Brook Lane
Williston, VT 05495

Dedication

No one has helped more in the production of this book than Michelle Griffoul, whose tiles grace the cover. She unselfishly gave everything to allow me the freedom to write, and without her unwavering support, not a single page of this book could have been completed. She demonstrated what it means to be a real partner, and it would be unfair not to recognize her inspiration and innumerable contributions. This book is dedicated to Michelle; her name deserves to be on the cover as much as mine.

Thank you, Michelle, for all you have given me.

Acknowledgments

Writing a book takes time, energy, resources, and isolation from family and friends. Writing is a solitary effort, but no book can be written without help from others. I am indebted to my editor, Steve Bliss, who weathered my delays, moods, excess words, bad grammar, and all the blind alleys I dragged him through. His editing and organizational skills were instrumental in getting this book finished; and his kindness, encouragement, generosity of time, and good humor will always be remembered and appreciated.

Thanks are also in order to Don Jackson at JLC, who suggested I write this book, and Sal Alfano, my publisher at Hanley Wood, who never lost faith in me. Emily Stetson and Leslie Ensor, the book's managing editors, kept the wheels turning; illustrators Tim Healey and Charles Lockhart rendered my rough scribbles into clear, informative drawings; layout artist Jennifer Griffiths showed infinite patience with me and made the book beautiful; and to JLC art director Barb Nevins and production director Theresa Emerson for accommodating schedule delays and coordinating with the press. Mike Mesikep shot the cover and many of the photos inside and let me into his house so I could play with tiles. Paul Winn waited long hours for my setups so he could shoot the remaining photos. Clayton DeKorne stepped in at the last minute and helped get this book finished, and Ted Cushman read through the book at least twice to ensure accuracy and continuity. I am delighted they were the people who produced this difficult book. Any omissions or oversights belong to me—not this persistent, dedicated, and talented team. Thank all of you for your hard work and patience.

For supplying tile and materials, I want to thank the following people and companies for their cooperation and generosity: Kevin McFadden at Bonsal ProSpec, Bosch, Collomix, Beth Scott at Custom Building Products, DeWalt, Handi-shim, Laserjamb, Dan Louis at Laser Products Industries, Marshalltown, Michelle Griffoul at Michelle Griffoul Studios for providing tiles for the leaf inlay floor and the impressed bamboo and Koi tiles seen on the cover and in Chapter 3, MK Diamond Products, Eric Edelmeyer at Noble Company, Pacific Laser Systems, RotoZip, Simpson Strong-Tie, Stabila, Noah Chitty at Stonepeak Ceramics, Tajima Tools, Steve Rausch at USG Corporation, Roger Brouard at Veto Pro Pac, Joel Beaton at WaleTale, and Russ Rose at Watts Radiant (thanks for the wine and cheese, Russ).

Warm thanks and appreciation to Nancy and Bob Daniels. To Bob for his good counsel and bad puns, and to him and Nancy for their friendship, support, hospitality, and unconditional love.

And last, but not least, a very special thank you to Zoë and Gabriel Carter, for teaching me about life.

Contents

How To Use This Book

When I set out to write this book, I did not want to write it solely for either a professional or a do-it-your-selfer because for quality results, there is absolutely no difference between how a pro or D-I-Yer should install tile. Another thing I wanted to do was to alert readers of this book to tile installation information that is found in a booklet called *American National Standard Specifications for the Installation of Ceramic Tile* and to tile installation methods found in another booklet, the *TCA Handbook for Ceramic Tile Installation*. Architects, designers, contractors, tile installers, and others in the construction industry regard these booklets not as recommendations but as minimum quality standards.

Minimum standards—the point below which an installation will fail—are essential to the tile industry because they set useful benchmarks, but they are not best practices. For that reason, I have endeavored to present techniques and methods that exceed minimum standards and that have enabled me to produce high-quality installations. These installations are stronger, easier to maintain, and last longer than installations built to minimum standards. In the following pages, you will not find shortcuts or methods that make the work easier to perform. Whether you decide to produce quality work or a hack job, tile installation requires hard work. Instead of quick and dirty, the installation techniques presented in this book will enable any installer—pro or D-I-Yer—to produce quality results he or she can be proud of.

Unlike my first two books, which presented background information first and projects second, this book starts with techniques and projects that anyone in good health, with a reasonably stocked tool kit, and basic construction knowledge and skills can handle. Many pro installers and amateur enthusiasts with some experience can start right away with the project chapters and refer to the information chapters as needed. I kept this in mind when the different chapters were put in order so this group did not have to wade through a lot of background material. For beginning professionals and do-it-yourselfers, I recommend starting with the information chapters to gain basic knowledge and referring to the project chapters for a broader view before attempting an installation.

The most popular installations—floors—lead off the projects, followed by walls, shower stalls, and countertops. The information chapters are laid out in an order that follows normal installation sequences, but I did not intend the reader to start in any particular order. Whether you are a pro or D-I-Yer, I recommend you begin with chapters that reflect where you are weak and proceed through to chapters that reflect your particular strengths. However you read this book, I hope the information and techniques presented here will help you build quality installations with confidence.

Chapter 1
HOW TO INSTALL FLOOR TILES

Successful tile floors are beautiful, long lasting, and easily maintained. These qualities are the result of a strong underlying structure, the proper materials and methods, good styling, and careful execution. The most beautiful and durable tiles, however, will never shore up a weak structure, and even the best installation materials will break down if used improperly. The trick is to find the right combination of materials and methods for each installation and then to adhere to the product manufacturers' instructions throughout the installation. Starting with the right materials and methods can be a problem in itself, however, since most installers do not have full control over material selection.

With floor installations, material selection is especially important because floor tiles, unlike those installed on walls or ceilings, must support the weight of furnishings and people and endure the traffic that passes over them. But even the best tiles can fail when installed over a bed of thinset mortar that is pocked with voids or has a loss of bond (Figure 1-01). The best tile installations can also fail if the grout is soft and porous.

All the projects described in this book meet or exceed tile industry standards, and they represent my approach to installations as a consultant and tile setter: trouble free and built to last. Please refer to the following review of floor-tile installation basics to help plan and execute your next installation. Also refer to the materials list within each project to see if the performance rating I assign to it is suitable for the work you are considering. For more information on how to incorporate these specs into your own projects, see "How to Use This Book," page vii.

Floor Tile and Installation Materials

Use special care when selecting ceramic, stone, and other hard tiles, because floor tiles must support the weight of all furnishings and equipment, plus foot traffic, and in many cases, wheeled traffic. The ideal is to start with the materials best suited for the job and then to install them with careful and consistent techniques.

It should be obvious that only floor tiles should go on floors. Nevertheless, many floors are tiled with materials that are totally inappropriate. Glazed wall tiles are often used on floors, but their relatively soft glaze can scratch and wear, and their soft bodies have a relatively low compressive strength. Some stone tiles should never be used on commercial or high-traffic floors or at residential entryways, and some are not recommended for use in wet areas.

In addition to the tile itself, all installation materials are vital to the performance of a tile floor. For this reason, I only use products that were designed specifically for use with ceramic tile, and to the greatest extent possible, I try to obtain all the installation materials from a single manufacturer so there are no

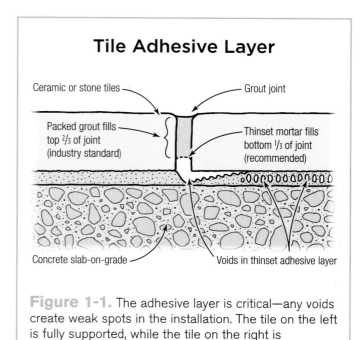

Tile Adhesive Layer

Ceramic or stone tiles — Grout joint

Packed grout fills top 2/3 of joint (industry standard)

Thinset mortar fills bottom 1/3 of joint (recommended)

Concrete slab-on-grade — Voids in thinset adhesive layer

Figure 1-1. The adhesive layer is critical—any voids create weak spots in the installation. The tile on the left is fully supported, while the tile on the right is unsupported on one end and is further weakened by notch-trowel voids in the thinset.

compatibility issues. From a practical point of view, unless your project is very large or involves a tract of homes rather than a single dwelling, the difference in cost between the best and worst adhesive mortar and grout is minimal.

Floor Installation Methods

There are numerous materials and methods for installing floor tiles, and some are better suited to a particular job than others. As a contractor, I prefer the mortar-bed method because it allows me to correct out-of-plumb floors and to produce finished tilework that is exceptionally smooth and flat. However, mortar-bed skills require significant training and practice. The thinbed installation methods described in this book enable most reasonably tool-friendly people in good health to construct high-quality, long-lasting tile installations.

The chief drawback of the thinbed method is that the finished tile surface reflects the condition of the setting bed: If floors are out of plane or beyond industry standards, the tiles covering the setting bed will also be out of plane and will be marked with lippage, out-of-level surfaces, and other unattractive signs of

an unprofessional installation. To avoid these problems, thinbed installations have to be built carefully at each stage to yield the best possible results. Self-leveling and featheredge compounds are recommended for bringing a floor into level. Thinset mortar should never be used to correct a flawed subsurface.

This book focuses on thinbed installation methods. This chapter covers two different approaches for tiling floors: tiles installed over concrete slabs and tiles installed over plywood. Within these two basic types are literally hundreds of variations that run the gamut from basic floors to floors built with a variety of nail-on setting beds; membrane systems; and even built-in, computer-controlled, tile-warming systems. There is not enough room in this or any single book to cover all floor tile installation methods, but I am going to explain the methods and materials I recommend and specify the most and show you how to use basic skills to tile practically any floor surface.

Interior tile floors need to be flat, level, and smooth to eliminate *lippage*, the name given to a significant and noticeable difference in height between two neighboring tiles. For tiles less than 10 inches on edge, all structural surfaces receiving tile or tile installation materials should be flat, level (or evenly sloped), and

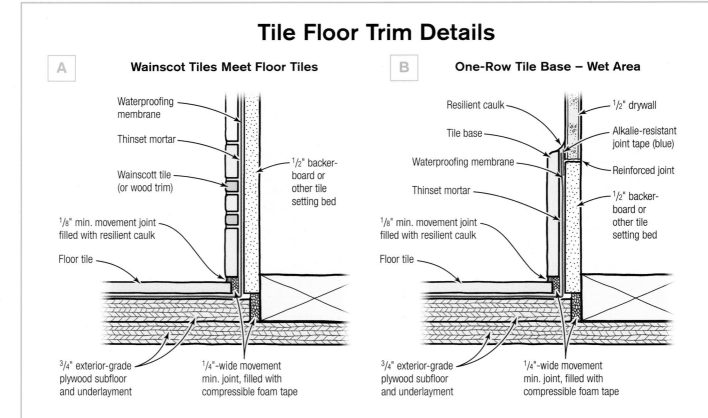

Tile Floor Trim Details

| A | **Wainscot Tiles Meet Floor Tiles** | B | **One-Row Tile Base – Wet Area** |

Figure 1-2. For the neatest appearance, wall tiles should lap over floor tiles (A). This applies to ceramic, stone, glass, and mosaic tiles. Note that wall/floor junctions in Details A, B, and C all require two separate movement joints: an upper one between the wall trim and floor tiles and a lower one between the floor tile and wall surface.

smooth to within 1/4 inch in 10 feet (see Table 6-1, "Recommended Setting Bed Flatness," page 155).

For larger tiles, the setting bed needs to be flatter to reduce lippage. It is important that the 1/4-in-10 (or more stringent) standard be used during framing or concrete placing to reduce the need for repair carpentry or self-leveling compounds. For thinbed work, whatever flatness standard is used to determine the finish of the tiles must also be applied to all stages of concrete slab or wood construction supporting and surrounding the tiles.

Of course, if you are tiling over an existing surface, repairs or corrections may be unavoidable. "Surface Tolerances for Tiles and Membranes" (page 162) shows the tolerance range I use, regardless of tile size, to ensure smooth tiling on wood and concrete floor surfaces. As for lippage, manufacturing tolerances allow for almost 1/8-inch warpage with 12-inch tiles, so it may be very difficult to avoid excessive lippage if the tiles themselves are not flat. Nevertheless, the job-site standard for lippage has always been the thickness of a dime. Exceed that and your work begins to look sloppy (Table 10-2, page 256). If you are unsure of industry standards regarding workmanship and finish, refer to ANSI A108 4.3 and 4.4.

Trim Options for Tile Floors

The perimeter edges and borders of any ceramic tile floor are greatly enhanced by the addition of trim. This can be done with matching factory-made trim pieces if they are available or with trim from another manufacturer. With stone tiles, if matching trim is required but not offered by the manufacturer, it is possible to create trim on site with a profile blade (see Figure 4-46, page 126). Or you can provide stock to a stone fabricator, who can make it for you.

Tile floors can also be trimmed with a wide variety of non-tile materials, including wood, synthetic trim boards, and other materials. Figure 1-2 shows how to finish a tile floor with a variety of trims and how to detail the all-important movement joints that are required around the perimeter of every floor tile application.

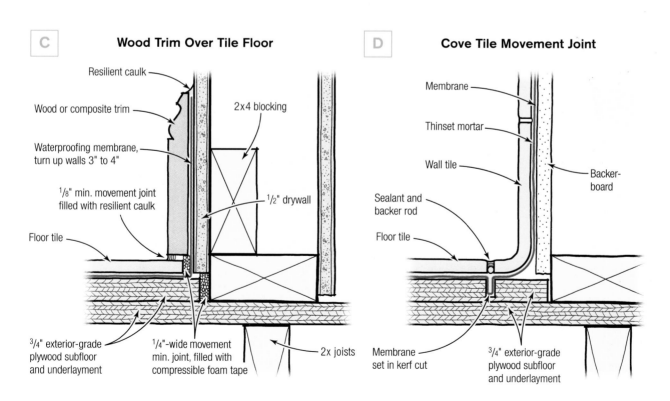

C   Wood Trim Over Tile Floor

Resilient caulk

Wood or composite trim

Waterproofing membrane, turn up walls 3" to 4"

1/8" min. movement joint filled with resilient caulk

Floor tile

2x4 blocking

1/2" drywall

3/4" exterior-grade plywood subfloor and underlayment

1/4"-wide movement min. joint, filled with compressible foam tape

2x joists

D   Cove Tile Movement Joint

Membrane

Thinset mortar

Wall tile

Sealant and backer rod

Floor tile

Backerboard

Membrane set in kerf cut

3/4" exterior-grade plywood subfloor and underlayment

The lower movement joint extends below the drywall or backerboard and down to the subfloor. All sides of a wood baseboard (C) should be painted or sealed prior to installation in areas likely to get wet. With cove tile base (D), the joint between field and cove tiles must be filled with a resilient caulk or sealant to prevent cracking.

Floor Project 1:
Tiling Over Plywood

On wood-frame construction, where strength is important, my first choice is to install a thick, traditional mortar bed. Where height limitations won't allow a 2-inch-thick mortar bed, however, the next best option is to use a double plywood floor as a base for tile. A single layer of nominal ¾-inch exterior-grade plywood underlayment (APA rating Exterior or Exposure 1) is very strong—much stronger than most backerboards. When it is glued and fastened with screws every 6 inches over a layer of ¾-inch exterior-grade T&G plywood subflooring, you have one of the strongest wood platforms available as a setting bed for tiles.

The only problem is that plywood's expansion and contraction far outstrips that of ceramic tile, and that makes plywood a difficult bonding surface. Fortunately, the bonding problem is easily solved with the application of a load-bearing membrane system (made specifically for use with ceramic and stone tiles). There are numerous thinset mortars on the market that can be used to direct-bond tiles to plywood, but these are

Materials List: Project 1

Tile: 12-inch (nominal) vitreous, glazed floor tiles
Subfloor: nominal ¾-inch (²³/₃₂-inch) Exposure 1 plywood
Underlayment: nominal ¾-inch (²³/₃₂-inch) Exposure 1 plywood.
Fasteners: 1⅝-inch cement board screws.
Laminating glue: Titebond III
Membrane system: NobleSeal TS, Noble Company
Membrane sheet adhesive: NobleBond EXT, Noble Company
Membrane seam adhesive: NobleSealant 150, Noble Company
Method: TCNA F149, F150, and F160 for reference
Performance rating: Heavy Residential

Good Construction Practices

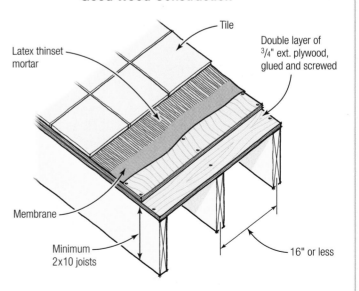

Poor Wood Construction

Tile installed directly over subflooring

Organic mastic or dryset thinset mortar

⅝" subfloor

Minimum 2x10 joists

Wide joist spacing (19.2" or 24" o.c.), springy subfloor

Good Wood Construction

Latex thinset mortar

Tile

Double layer of ¾" ext. plywood, glued and screwed

Membrane

Minimum 2x10 joists

16" or less

Figure 1-3. Because it is considerably stronger than the combination of plywood and backerboard, a double layer of plywood covered with a membrane system is the author's first choice for thinbed tile floors.

only useful on light-duty, dry-area installations. For medium- to heavy-duty service, especially where waterproofing is required, a double-layer plywood floor clad with a membrane is hard to beat. Figure 1-3 shows the cross-section of the plywood underlayment, the membrane, and the tile. The combination of double-layer ¾–inch plywood and membrane can be used for all ceramic tiles and many stone tiles. I designed this three-room project because it helps demonstrate so many fundamentals about tiling a wood-frame floor, not the least of which is the diagonal-and-border layout that is as old as Pythagoras. This basic layout can be used to give any floor a feeling of balance, interest, and elegance. It is the main method I use for installing square, rectangular, ogee, and other shapes of floor tiles because the border can conceal most problems created by a baseboard that does not meet the accepted standards for straight, square, and true.

Preparing the Subfloor

This installation method is a stronger version of TCNA Methods F149, F150, and F160, by virtue of thicker sheets of plywood as well as the addition of the membrane system. The subfloor needs to be flat and level and prepared as for any other tile installation. The joints of the second layer of plywood—the underlayment layer—should offset the subflooring joints as described below.

Notice, too, that construction calls for a movement joint in the underlayment layer around the floor perimeter. Normally, a movement joint is required between adjoining rooms, but because the entire floor is covered with the membrane, I felt safe omitting them on the two room-to-room thresholds of this rather small, interior floor.

Selecting the Installation Materials

There are many types of membranes available for tiling, with varying levels of performance. Where strength is an issue and maximum protection is desired, I prefer a system I have used since the 1980s called NobleSeal TS (noblecompany.com). NobleSeal TS offers both crack isolation and waterproofing, so it is perfect for this application.

This sheet membrane can be installed using a latex thinset mortar or a special contact-type adhesive supplied by the manufacturer. I prefer to use the contact adhesive because I can begin installing tiles immediately after the membrane sheet is laminated to the floor without having to worry about disturbing the laminating thinset mortar.

> *Trade Tip:* Many installers are comfortable setting tiles over sheet membranes freshly laminated with thinset mortar. However, to get the smoothest finish with this type of installation, I prefer to wait until the laminating thinset has cured and hardened before installing the tile or otherwise disturbing the membrane.

Installing the Underlayment

For best results, the ¾-inch underlayment should be

Figure 1-4. To achieve maximum strength and smoothness, 95% to 100% of the entire surface must be covered with ANSI Type 1 or 2 wood glue. At the perimeter of the floor, to avoid squeeze-over into the movement joint slot, the author keeps the glue about ½ inch away from the wall.

Figure 1-5. A standup screw gun with quick-loading, 22-screw clips is substantially faster than shooting individual screws, plus it is much easier on the knees.

fully laminated to the subflooring with an ANSI Type 1 or 2 wood glue spread uniformly over 100% of the subfloor surface with a $3/32$-inch U-notch trowel (Figure 1-4). For this project, I used Titebond III, a water-resistant ANSI Type 1 glue. You will get best results by offsetting the underlayment joints so they lie midway between the subflooring joints (a minimum 12-inch offset is required). The face grain of the subflooring and underlayment should be oriented perpendicular to the direction of the joists. As required by industry standards, there should be $1/8$-inch gaps between the subflooring (T&G or straight sided) and underlayment panels.

Spreading adhesive. Before spreading any glue, I do a quick layout and snap chalk lines on the subfloor (glue usually will not obliterate chalk lines). I spread only enough glue for one sheet of plywood, drop the plywood sheet into position, and secure it with $1\frac{5}{8}$-inch coated cementboard screws, spaced every 6 inches around the perimeter and every 8 inches within the field of each sheet, starting at one panel edge and working across to the other. (Working two ends toward the center of the panel can cause the underlayment to buckle in the middle.) The screws should penetrate the subflooring only, not the joists.

As with other repetitive fastening tasks that are an essential part of any backerboard or plywood installation, I use a stand-up, magazine-loading backerboard screw system called Quick Drive (Simpson Strong-Tie) and do in minutes what takes hours with an ordinary screw gun (Figure 1-5). Apart from pure speed, a stand-up screw gun keeps me off my knees. For greater efficiency, I install whole plywood sheets first, and then, starting with the largest and working down to the smallest, fill in the remaining voids.

Perimeter gap. A point to remember is that, with the exception of thresholds, the outer inch or so around the perimeter of a floor never has to support much weight since it is shielded by baseboard trim. When cutting plywood or backerboards to size around the perimeter, it's unwise to close-fit the pieces where there is a baseboard or other hard, restraining surface. Much more important than a tight fit at such locations is providing enough space for a movement joint.

Figure 1-6. The plywood underlayment is partially installed. Note that glue was spread a few inches beyond the footprint of the plywood sheets. As subsequent boards are secured, any exposed glue not covered within five minutes or so should be removed with a scraper and damp sponge.

Figure 1-7. For maximum waterproofing protection, the author installs factory-made accessories like this outside/dam corner patch and laminates them with the system's contact cement.

Figure 1-8. As soon as the contact cement for the sheet membrane is tacky, the author quickly applies beads of compatible sealant to the joint where the sheet membrane joins the trowel-applied membrane used on the shower floor. The same sealant is used to join all seams in the sheet membrane.

Across thresholds between rooms, a movement-joint gap is usually required, but the membrane used on this floor eliminates the need for an underlayment joint at this location.

For residential work, the minimum movement joint between the underlayment and tile layers and any restraining surfaces is ⅛ inch (¼ inch is recommended). When installing plywood underlayment, if the gap between the underlayment and any restraining walls is 1 inch or less, and I know the gap will be covered by baseboard, I don't worry about gaps at the perimeter of the underlayment layer. I am not very concerned about tile breakage here since the outer 1 inch of the floor will be covered by trim and does not carry any weight. On the other hand, if the plywood, backerboard, or tile touches an abutting surface (no movement joint), problems with cracked joints and loose or tented tiles are likely to occur.

Screw and glue. The floor is partially covered with wood glue, and the notched trowel, glue bottle, and screw gun are nearby. Notice that glue is spread a few inches beyond the perimeter of the underlayment sheets (Figure 1-6). Once the first plywood sheet is properly aligned and secured with screws, the remaining whole and cut panels are glued and screwed, leaving a ⅛-inch gap between sheets and a minimum

¼-inch gap around the perimeter of the floor.

After a quick check to see that no fastener heads protrude above the surface of the underlayment and once the floor is vacuumed clean, I snap a few more layout lines to guide the placement of the sheet membrane. Then I begin spreading the membrane system's contact cement.

Installing the Sheet Membrane System

When working with this sheet membrane, the first step is to plot enough layout lines to guide the membrane sections. (The sheet membrane I use is available in 5-foot-wide by 100-foot-long rolls.) The next step is to install any accessory pieces that might be needed, such as the outside/dam corner patch that is shown in Figure 1-7.

When attaching the membrane with thinset mortar, repositioning the sheet is not very difficult because the thinset remains plastic for up to an hour, depending on the brand. When laminating the sheet with the system's contact-type cement, however, repositioning after initial contact is almost impossible without destroying the sheet. For this reason, I used a technique, explained in full in Chapter 5, that ensures

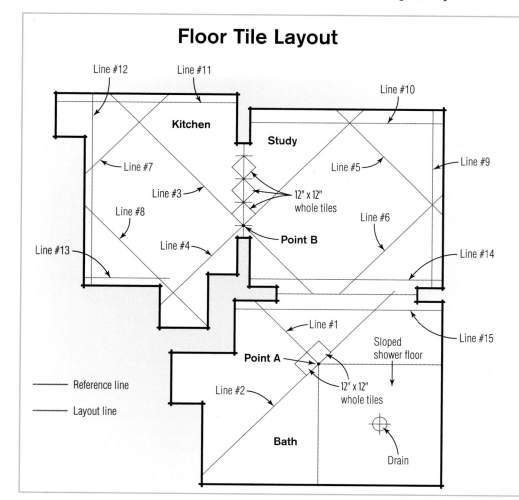

Floor Tile Layout

Line #12 Line #11

Line #10

Kitchen

Study

Line #7

Line #5

Line #9

Line #3

12" x 12" whole tiles

Line #8

Line #6

Line #13

Line #4

Point B

Line #14

Line #1

Sloped shower floor

Line #15

Point A

12" x 12" whole tiles

Line #2

—— Reference line

—— Layout line

Bath

Drain

Figure 1-9. The bathroom layout focused on the shower corner (Point A) and required only two lines (#1 and #2). To lay out the other two rooms, the author started by dry fitting three tiles along the centerline of the threshold separating the rooms, then extended lines #3 and #4 from Point B. A double tile border (lines #14 and #15) makes a smooth transition between the two spaces.

each sheet will go where I want it to.

This particular sheet has 2-inch-wide seams that are made watertight with the addition of two 1/8-inch beads of compatible sealant (not silicone, which releases from the sheet once it has cured). Two beads of the same sealant also are used (Figure 1-8) to join the sheet membrane to the trowel-applied membrane covering the sloped shower floor (the sealant is compatible with both membrane systems). On this floor, for maximum waterproofing protection, the mem-

Figure 1-10. On small installations, the author gets a better sense of the layout by dry-fitting tiles on the floor. This is much faster than producing a scale drawing or using math.

Figure1-11. The author plots layout lines between the field and border tiles on these long runs of baseboard. On shorter runs, he relies on a straightedge to align tiles.

brane laps up walls in the bathroom and up the toe kick in the kitchen, but it is installed without an upturn in the dry areas of the kitchen and the center room.

With the membrane installation complete, the tiles now have a structurally sound, stable, and waterproof base. A double layer of 3/4-inch exterior-grade plywood, glued and screwed, installed over 2x12 joists on 16-inch centers, and covered with this type of membrane should meet the demands of an L/720 installation, stiff enough for most stone tile installations. If you are installing a stone tile with special installation requirements beyond the L/360 tolerance for ceramic tile, you should consult the tile supplier or a structural engineer for a review and structural recommendations.

The membrane used in this project can be laminated to suitable surfaces with either latex thinset mortar or a compatible contact adhesive, but its installation should not begin until the tiles and installation materials are on site, acclimated, and ready to install over the completed sheet membrane. It is good practice to hold off on the installation of this or any other membrane until the tiles are ready to be installed.

Many careful membrane installations have been ruined when the surface of the freshly installed membrane was exposed to dust, overspray, and other contaminants or was used as a walkway before it could be covered with tiles. It is imperative that the surface of any membrane or setting bed material be preserved in

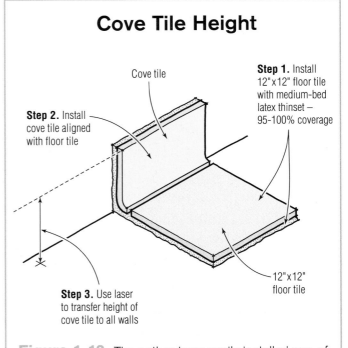

Cove Tile Height

Cove tile

Step 1. Install 12"x12" floor tile with medium-bed latex thinset – 95-100% coverage

Step 2. Install cove tile aligned with floor tile

Step 3. Use laser to transfer height of cove tile to all walls

12"x12" floor tile

Figure 1-12. The author temporarily installed one of the floor's 12x12 porcelain tiles close to the wall, and then set a cove tile to locate its proper height. With a laser, he transferred the cove-tile height to all walls.

its virgin state to allow for the strongest possible adhesive bond.

Tile Layout

The basic layout I used for this three-room floor—diagonal with a border—is as old as geometry and is one of the most useful design tools available to an installer (Figure 1-9). Regardless of the cost of the tiles, this method adds a measure of balance and elegance to any floor; and the border provides an effective, invisible way to mask out-of-square problems that are a part of every floor.

For this grouping of three small rooms, I began the layout by lining up full, half, and quarter diagonals along the floor and didn't bother with a straightedge or chalk line. Thus, each tile became an approximate unit of measure, with the objective of determining how many full diagonals it would take to fill the room and leave a border whose width, ideally, was slightly less than a whole tile. The starting point for this rough layout, and the final chalk-line layout, is the main focal point of the bathroom floor: the outside corner of the sloped shower area. My preference was to have the layout of the tiles flow, unbroken, from one room to the next. However, my initial layout revealed that the best layout would occur if I separated the bathroom from the other two rooms.

With two half diagonals and one quarter diagonal aligned with the shower floor tiles, the bathroom would have a 3- to 4-inch border around the floor. While not really close to a full tile, this more slender border is appropriate for a room this size. Extending the diagonal layout into the center room and kitchen, though, showed that a continuous layout would result in very unbalanced borders along most of the perimeter of these floors. Adjusting the layout one way or the other would only result in minor improvements to the border, but it would also wreck the symmetry at the shower floor.

Instead of a continuous layout, I decided to give the bathroom its own layout; to develop a continuous layout for the center room and the kitchen; and to create a simple, decorative transition between the two floor areas. The focus for the two-room layout would be the threshold between the two rooms (Figure 1-10). This leaves a somewhat uneven border around the kitchen, but I wanted the diagonal insert to be as symmetrical as possible as it flows from the center room to the kitchen.

The three rooms containing this layout are small enough to plot the final layout without a laser, using only a large folding square held against the shower floor tiles, a few straightedges, and a fine-line chalk box (Figure 1-11). The layout took about 30 minutes to finish. After dry fitting tiles showed me that a balanced layout for all three rooms was not possible, I plotted two different layouts: one for the bathroom alone and another for the remaining two rooms, a small kitchen and study. I used the corner of the shower as the focus of the bathroom layout (Point A in Figure 1-09) and the threshold between the two other rooms as their focus (Point B). Starting at Point A, I plotted fifteen layout lines to guide the full tiles, diagonal inserts, and the border tiles. With the layout grid in place, I computed the number of half and quar-

Figure 1-13. To make back buttering easier, the author uses a small wooden platform and a flat trowel to spread the mortar (left). For maximum adhesive contact, the author trowels a small amount of thinset on each corner of the tile (right).

ter diagonals needed for the three floors, plus the border trim for the transition between the two areas, and cut them on the wet saw (see Chapter 9 for more details on this layout).

Installing the Tiles

Before any floor tiles could be installed in the bathroom, the bathroom's cove tiles had to be installed. This floor's first tiling challenges were to ensure that

- each floor tile was fully supported with latex thinset mortar and had minimum 95% contact with the thinset

- the bathroom floor tiles were flush with the bordering curbless shower floor

- the border floor tiles were in plane with the cove tiles.

The height of the cove tiles, both inside and outside the shower area, was determined by setting a 12x12 floor tile in place and aligning a cove tile to the floor tile (Figure 1-12). To set the floor tile at the correct height, I first spread thinset mortar with a few different size notched trowels to determine which trowel would give the 12x12 tiles minimum 95% adhesive coverage. The test determined that after each floor tile was back buttered, a ¼x¾x¾-inch U-notch trowel would be required to apply the mortar to the floor. (I prefer to back butter most tiles for maximum adhesion.) With the cove tile aligned to the properly set

floor tile, I used a laser to transfer the cove tile height to the shower floor cove tiles and extended the line to all other affected walls.

Although the diagonals were cut on a wet saw, I saved time and energy by cutting each border tile (whose cut edge faces toward the wall) with a snap cutter. Back buttering takes time and can be a mess. To keep things orderly, I used a small wooden platform for back buttering, and to ensure that the tiles were completely supported, I also added an extra amount of mortar on each corner of the tile (Figure 1-13).

This results in mortar squeezing through the joints where four tiles meet (and another mess to clean), but this technique ensures 100% adhesive contact, which is the secret to long installation life and minimal maintenance. Regarding the mess sometimes generated by a tile installation, frequent and prompt application of a damp sponge and keeping tools, hands, and the job site clean are part of every installation and are required for good housekeeping.

Getting each tile fully bedded, submerging the lower third of each tile in adhesive mortar, and keeping the remaining two-thirds of the joint open for grouting is an art that requires patience and practice. And while practice may reduce some of the housekeeping required, achieving the correct level of adhesive contact still generates some mess. If the tile installation process is neat and tidy, without much need for the sponge, chances are there is not enough adhesive between the tiles and the setting bed.

Since spacers were not used for these tiles, cleanup was confined to sponging the surface of the tiles, keeping the top two-thirds of the grout joints clean,

Figure 1-14. The ¾-inch notched trowel applied enough mortar to handle small irregularities in the tile and setting bed. Aligning the adhesive ridges in one direction is one way to ensure good adhesion. Notice the detailing at the threshold between the two floors.

Figure 1-15. The author uses a flat trowel and pencil to mark cut lines on one of the border tiles. A ¼-inch (min.) movement joint must be located between the border tiles and the wall surface.

and keeping the movement joints clean down to the top of the membrane. The ¾-inch trowel deposited enough thinset mortar to provide an ample cushion to accommodate the irregularities in the tiles and the slight irregularities in the floor's height caused by seams in the membrane or slight glitches in the underlayment (Figure1-14). The result is a smooth tile surface with a minimum of lippage.

Wherever the floor tiles were covered with trim tiles, I made sure the movement joint between the floor tiles and wall was clean before installing the baseboard tiles. Where the perimeter of the floor would be trimmed with wood molding, the movement joint where the floor tile abuts the wall also had to be maintained (Figure 1-15). To cover the toe kick around the kitchen cabinets, tiles were snap cut, bedded in adhesive, and then shimmed temporarily with spacers.

After spending so much time on the underlayment and membrane installation portions of a project, I always look forward to seeing the finished project

Figure 1-16 Any multi-floor project requires the resolution of many details. Beginning in the bathroom, against the previously tiled curb-less shower (A), the project flows to the next concentrated detail zone, where the bathroom floor meets the center room (B). Symmetry at the threshold between the two rooms is almost perfect (C), but causes a compromise with the tiles bordering the countertop's toe kick (D). The final detail occurs at the opposite side of the countertop, where the border tiles expand toward an exit (E).

Figure 1-17. After removing most of the surface grout with one or two passes of a barely damp sponge, the author focuses on the joint itself—using a soft touch with the sponge (A) to give all joints a uniform appearance. Removing grout lumps and backfilling voids is part of this process. Next, to remove the diluted grout residues, he gives the surface a series of parallel wipes, each with a clean sponge (B). As soon as the surface of the tiles is dry, he uses a clean, soft cloth to buff off any remaining haze (C). The narrow margin trowel is used to loosen any grout that has strayed into the movement joint slots.

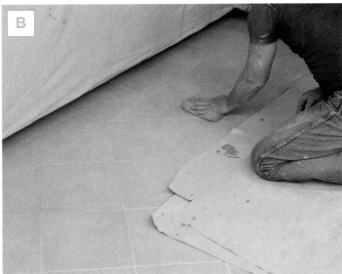

Figure 1-18. The author uses a margin trowel to pack the vertical joints at, and below, the toe kick. After sponge cleaning, the author will clean out the movement joint slots with a narrow margin trowel.

Figure 1-19. With a smooth tile and the face of the trowel held at a high angle, the grout trowel can remove most of the excess grout from a tile's surface.

emerge as the tiles are installed. Where the bathroom floor meets the shower (Figure 1-16A) was just the first of many details that were required to finish the project. The tile border where the bathroom meets the center room was the next major detail zone (Figure 1-16B), followed by the symmetrical threshold between the center room and kitchen (Figure 1-16C). The border tiles to the countertop's left side (Figure 1-16D) are a bit pinched, but at the right side where the floor ends, the border expands toward the exit door (Figure 1-16E).

Grouting the Tiles

All access to this floor was restricted after tiling, and all grout and movement joints were cleaned while the adhesive mortar was still soft. So, after the tiles had set for 48 hours, no other cleaning was required before grouting. Temperatures hovered between 65° and 75°F as I prepared the grout, a polymer grout that required only the addition of water for mixing. While the grout slaked, I moved a bucket of fresh water, a sponge, a grout trowel, a couple of margin trowels, and my kneeling pad onto the floor and removed the wedges shimming the base tiles.

After re-mixing the grout, I began forcing it into the joints. When properly mixed, this grout has a consistency that differs from regular cement grouts in that it has a cohesive, taffy-like workability. As usual, I forced the grout into the joints from several different attack angles and held the rubber trowel at a low angle to increase the compaction. Then I used the edge of the trowel to scrape off the excess.

Because of the size of the tiles and the room, I packed all the bathroom joints with grout before starting the initial cleaning. I don't go to extraordinary lengths to keep grout out of movement joints; I am more concerned about having all portions of each grout joint as dense and as fully compacted as possible. Cleaning excess out of movement joints was not a big deal and would be taken care of later, after the grout had a chance to set up and begin to harden. I focused on cleaning the surface of the tiles, and in less than 20 minutes, the bathroom tiles had been grouted and cleaned (Figure 1-17).

The center room took about the same time to grout and clean, and like the bathroom floor, all the joints were filled with grout before I stopped for cleaning. The kitchen floor, the largest of the three, was grouted and cleaned in two stages (Figure 1-18). I could have spread and cleaned the entire kitchen area in one step, but with temperatures rising, I did not want to risk having grout residue crust over the tiles (Figure 1-19). Including mixing the grout and stashing the tools, the three floors took about two hours to grout. I then left the installation to rest for a couple of days before filling the movement joints with sealant.

Filling the Movement Joints

This floor project was designed to demonstrate as many installation and finishing details as possible. For

Figure 1-20. A movement joint is required here because the shower and bath floor tiles have different setting beds.

Figure 1-21. The author modifies a standard caulking tube with a long neck to reach into tight areas.

this most critical part of the installation, there are five different movement joints:

1. the perimeter joints between the edges of the floor tiles and the abutting wall surfaces

2. the joints between the cove and the floor tiles

3. the joints between the floor tiles and the baseboard tiles

4. the joints between the floor tiles and the wood molding, and

5. the joint between the bath floor and the shower floor tiles due to a change in the setting bed materials (Figure 1-20).

To simplify the task of installing caulk or sealant in toe-kick areas, I fitted a standard tube with a long-neck extension (Figure 1-21).

Floor Project 2:
Stone Mosaic Sheets Over Wood Construction (With Electrical Resistance Mat)

This installation was part of a remodel of a lightly used bathroom that featured a ceramic-tile tub surround, traditional vertical wood-plank wainscoting, and a floor covered with 1⅜-inch hexagonal marble mosaic tiles mounted on 12-inch-square sheets. The mosaic mounting fabric, a tough fiberglass blanket, was glued to the backs of the tiles with a load-bearing, waterproof epoxy so proper adhesion would not be a problem. (Mosaic tiles mounted on perforated paper backing often present an adhesion problem because the paper interferes with the adhesive bond between the tile and setting bed. Paper is also an excellent food source for mold.)

With the goal of symmetry on opposing sides of the floor, the homeowner and I discussed a number of issues affecting the layout: the condition of the existing walls; the importance of purchasing a tub whose front skirt was plumb, straight, and true; the addition of a tile-warming system; and the height of the floor in

relation to the height of the hallway plank flooring that runs past the bathroom's threshold. We paid special attention to the layout of the tiles against the tub and at the threshold.

Evaluating the Structure

The bathroom remodel was part of a whole-house renovation that included replacing old 4x6-inch joists spaced at 24-inch centers with 2x12s at 16 inches on-center. The original subfloor, which was made of 1⅛-inch exterior plywood, would be more than adequate for the mosaic tiles, but it was slightly off level by about a quarter inch from one side to the other. Normally this would be a problem on a floor this small, but since a self-leveling underlayment would be used in conjunction with the radiant heat mat, we did not have to go back to the carpenter for another fix.

Choosing an Installation Method

Although not an exact TCNA Method for this particular floor, TCNA Methods RH130-03 and RH140 are close enough and will guide the placement of the tile, the electrical resistance mat, and the self-leveling underlayment (SLU). The manufacturer of the mat used in this project allows the use of some SLUs to encapsulate the wires, but the brand you select must be specifically approved by its manufacturer for tile installations and electric radiant heating.

Since electrical work is beyond the scope of this book, this project will not cover the installation of the electrical components except to point out how the main power supply cable is routed across the floor. All electrical-resistance tile warming systems need a careful installation and electrical hookup. The electrical instructions supplied with the product depicted (from SunTouch) are easy to understand and follow. If you

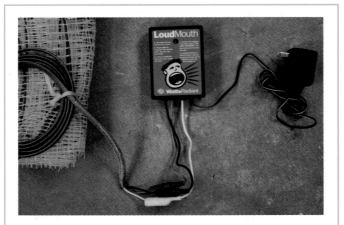

Figure 1-22. When installed properly, this device alerts the installer instantly if there is a breach in the insulation or break in the radiant heating wires.

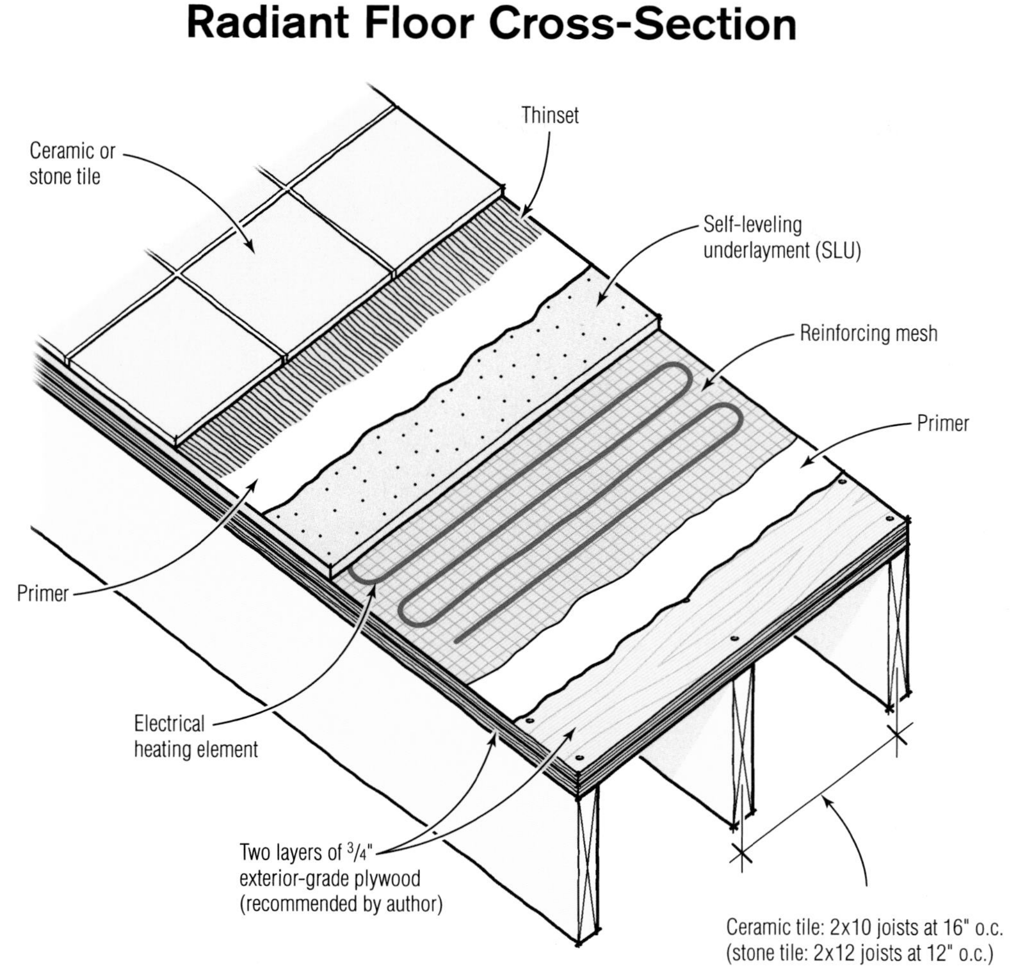

Radiant Floor Cross-Section

Ceramic or stone tile

Thinset

Self-leveling underlayment (SLU)

Reinforcing mesh

Primer

Primer

Electrical heating element

Two layers of 3/4" exterior-grade plywood (recommended by author)

Ceramic tile: 2x10 joists at 16" o.c.
(stone tile: 2x12 joists at 12" o.c.)

Figure 1-23. The author prefers to encapsulate electric heating wires with an SLU rated for radiant applications, rather than directly apply the tiles with thinset. This is especially true when working with tiles that are too small to bridge over at least two wires.

can measure electrical resistance, you can probably do the hookups required, although some local building codes require that hookup to the power supply be performed by an electrical contractor.

Whether or not you do the electrical work, I suggest you buy a device from the manufacturer, called LoudMouth, that will let you know immediately if a wire is cut or if insulation is breached (Figure 1-22). This tool helps workers recognize and locate wiring problems immediately and allows the tile installer to proceed with confidence.

Caution: An electrical-resistance floor warming system should never be wired to an existing circuit. Instead, it should be wired to a dedicated circuit breaker of a size recommended by the system manufacturer. Refer to the manufacturer's instructions regarding placement of heating wires in relation to wax rings, cabinets, perimeter walls, and permanent furniture and furnishings that cover the floor. Programmable controls are preferred and ensure more economical operating costs.

Materials list: Project 2

SLU: LevelQuik RS and primer, Custom Building Products (CBP)
SLU reinforcing: 2.5 lb. galvanized diamond lath
Floor warming system: Sun Touch, Watts Radiant
Tiles: 1 3/8-inch marble mosaics, back-mounted into 12-inch (nominal) sheets
Thinset mortar/tile bond coat: Porcelain Tile Fortified Mortar, CBP
Grout: Polyblend, CBP
Sealant: Polyblend, CBP
Sealer: TileLab, penetrating sealer, CBP
Subfloor: 1 1/8-inch exterior plywood existing over 2x12 joists at 16 inches on-center (2 layers 3/4-inch plywood preferred)
Method: TCNA RH130/140 for reference
Performance rating: Residential

Tile and the Installation Materials

After selecting tile for the project, the owners brought home samples for the tub walls and bathroom floor. The 3x6-inch glazed porcelain wall tiles met all our aesthetic and performance requirements, and the $1\frac{3}{8}$-inch marble mosaics would create the understated retro look the owners wanted for the floor. The wall tiles were ceramic and ready to install as is, but the floor tiles varied considerably in thickness, ranging from a little under $\frac{5}{16}$ inch to just over $\frac{3}{8}$ inch.

Since the floor tiles were honed and not polished, I decided to grind away any possible lippage *after* all the tiles were installed but *before* they were grouted. The electrical resistance mat would add approximately $\frac{5}{16}$ inch to the height of the floor. This layer would bring the finished tiles just slightly higher than the hallway floor. With the owner's requirement that the two floors be of equal height, there would be no room left for a membrane.

To compensate for the lack of a membrane, I would use a high-quality latex-modified thinset mortar, latex grout, a water-resistant SLU to encapsulate the wires, and a soft movement joint between the tile and tub to shield the plywood subfloor and underlayment from exposure to water. It was a judgment call for sure, but this bathroom would not be subject to heavy use, so I was comfortable not installing a waterproofing membrane (Figure 1-23).

Figure 1-24 With a cracked old tub removed and studs waiting to be shimmed plumb and straight, this old bathroom is ready for a make-over.

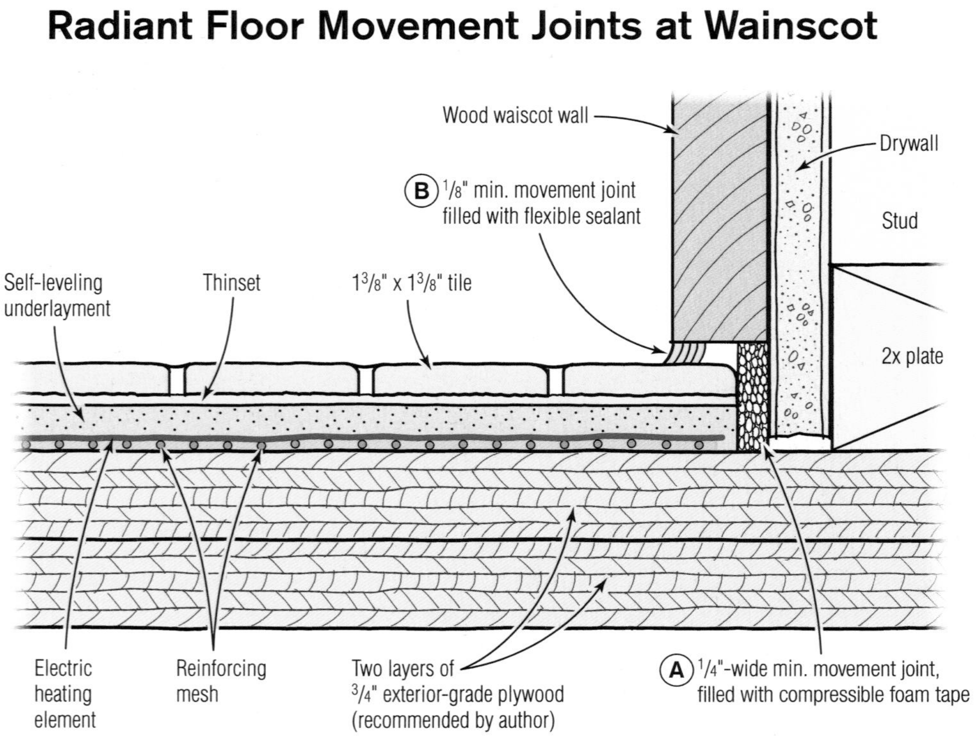

Radiant Floor Movement Joints at Wainscot

Wood waiscot wall

B $\frac{1}{8}$" min. movement joint filled with flexible sealant

Drywall

Stud

2x plate

Self-leveling underlayment

Thinset

$1\frac{3}{8}$" x $1\frac{3}{8}$" tile

Electric heating element

Reinforcing mesh

Two layers of $\frac{3}{4}$" exterior-grade plywood (recommended by author)

A $\frac{1}{4}$"-wide min. movement joint, filled with compressible foam tape

Figure 1-25. Movement joints are essential on a radiant tile floor. Here, as with all tile floor perimeters, two movement joints are required: one between the tiles and the abutting walls (A), and another between the floor tiles and the wall finish (B). Wall trim should never be buried below the surface of the finished floor.

When tiling over electrical-resistance heating systems, the tile size and wire spacing determine the complexity of the installation. With larger tile sizes and closer wire spacing, encapsulating the wires and setting the tiles can be done in one step by applying thinset mortar directly over the wires. Generally, if a tile can bridge at least two resistance wires, it can be installed by the one-step method.

Tiling with smaller tiles and wide wire spacing, however, is typically a two-step process in which the wires are first covered with an approved filler or SLU. It's possible to install small tiles over wires in one step, but the process is messier than usual, layout lines are obscured, and a lot of medium-bed thinset mortar is required to achieve 95% to 100% adhesive coverage. Also, installing tiles over a hard, flat base is much faster than bonding them directly over the wires. So on most electric radiant floors, I prefer to first encapsulate the wires, then install the tiles, regardless of their size.

Starting the Project

The project is located in a hall bathroom covered with tiles from the 1970s. The chilly floor was once covered with carpet, a practice that is neither practical nor sanitary. The remodeling would begin with stripping the bowed and uneven wall coverings and removing the floor tiles and old underlayment (Figure 1-24).

Had tiles 10 inches or larger been specified for this floor, I might have installed the tiles directly over the electrical resistance matting with a medium-bed, latex-modified thinset mortar. This would have saved the time and expense of encapsulating the matting with a self-leveling underlayment (SLU), but it also would have resulted in a much slower tile installation. At 10 inches or greater, a single tile can bridge over three or more resistance wires (as this system is wired), which helps to keep all the tiles on a smooth, even plane. Smaller tiles, however, especially those that can bridge only one wire, tend to tip to one side or the other and create excessive lippage and a very uneven surface finish.

If you are not familiar with installing tiles directly over electrical radiant heat systems or, like me, don't want the added mess and stress, you may want to install an SLU to ensure a smooth, flat finish, regardless of tile size. Another advantage of using an SLU is that encapsulating the wires significantly reduces damage caused by impact or abrasion to the wires, the primary cause of premature failure for this type of system. Yes, large tiles can be installed using the one-step method, but tile installation is much slower. In the long run, the relatively small amount of time and labor required for the SLU is more than offset by the time saved fussing with an extra-thick layer of thinset.

The movement joints for this floor are a bit unusual. Because of the overhanging wood planking used as wainscoting, the tiles stop well short of any restrain-

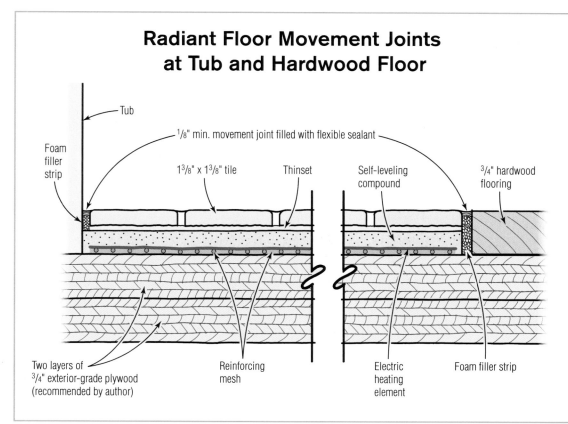

Radiant Floor Movement Joints at Tub and Hardwood Floor

Tub

Foam filler strip

1/8" min. movement joint filled with flexible sealant

1 3/8" x 1 3/8" tile   Thinset   Self-leveling compound   3/4" hardwood flooring

Two layers of 3/4" exterior-grade plywood (recommended by author)

Reinforcing mesh

Electric heating element

Foam filler strip

Figure 1-26. Joints where tiles meet other materials should be filled with flexible sealant—not hard grout—because of dissimilar movement in the materials. Opposing faces must be spotless and free of all dust, dirt, grease, oil, and soap residues prior to filling with sealant.

ing surfaces, and the tile movement joints for the floor tiles are obscured by the baseboard trim (Figure 1-25). At the tub and threshold, though, the tiles abut hard surfaces. At these two locations, I left $\frac{1}{8}$-inch joints, and when the grout had dried (about 72 hours at room temperature), I filled them with a resilient caulk color matched to the grout (Figure 1-26).

Preparing the Subfloor

Since the $1\frac{1}{8}$-inch plywood subfloor would be covered with a self-leveling underlayment (SLU), I plugged any holes, created dams to prevent the mix from flowing away from the floor, and vacuumed away the dust. This floor needed to be as low profile as possible, with no pinch points that might interfere with the heating wires, so I was especially scrupulous about getting all fastener heads flush or slightly below the surface of the subfloor.

Prepping the Self-Leveling Underlayment

After pounding down all the exposed nail heads and vacuuming the $1\frac{1}{8}$-inch-thick plywood underlayment/subfloor, I began the installation by applying a primer (supplied as a companion product by the SLU manufacturer) with a long-neck roller (Figure 1-27). This SLU has a high compressive strength—

about 2500 psi—but its bond strength is very low unless the primer is used. The primer soaks in and dries quickly, so other work can continue as long as no dust or dirt gets on the plywood. To keep it from being contaminated, the primer should not be installed until just before the SLU pour.

I prefer to use an SLU that requires the addition of a reinforcing mesh because expanded metal lath adds considerable tensile strength to the installation and helps reduce cracking in the setting bed and tile (Figure 1-28). The only downside of the galvanized diamond-lath reinforcing is that it would be sharp enough to damage the electrical-resistance matting if I was not careful. (I don't specify or use plastic lath because it lacks tensile strength.) Fortunately, this electrical-resistance matting is quite strong and can hold up to the usual job-site abuses. Nevertheless, I used the alarm device (see Figure 1-22, page 14) to keep the wires intact and keep me out of trouble. The galvanized mesh is held down primarily with $1\frac{1}{4}$-inch hot-dipped galvanized roofing nails.

Installing the Resistance Mat

The matting is ordered and delivered (or purchased from dealers' stocks) to fit a specific size, and the manufacturer's instructions guide its orientation and placement. When planning a tile-warming system, I follow three basic guidelines:

Figure 1-27. The companion primer prevents the plywood subfloor from sucking moisture from, and ruining, the SLU mix.

Figure 1-28. The author prefers to use SLU reinforced with galvanized, expanded metal mesh—instead of plastic—for its superior tensile strength.

- no resistance wires within 6 inches of a wall (a waste of heat)

- no wires closer to the toilet than 8 inches (don't want to melt that wax ring!)

Figure 1-29. The author unrolls the resistance heating mat (top). The orange fabric spaces the blue heating wire and allows the system to be attached to the floor. To simplify fastening, the author first stakes out the four corners of the mat with galvanized roofing nails, stretching the carrier fabric as each corner is nailed home (bottom). More nails, hot glue, and staples helped complete the installation.

- no wires where the floor will be covered with permanent furniture or furnishings (can cause hot spots or overheating)

Before leaving the factory, each mat is checked and marked for its electrical resistance, which must be verified on site before the matting can be installed. The resistance should also be re-checked before the SLU is poured, and again before the tiles go on, as recommended in the manufacturer's printed instructions.

> ***Caution:*** It is critically important to follow the manufacturer's instructions with all floor-warming products.

To help keep the heating wires (identified by the blue insulation) flat against the plywood, I drove roofing nails through the carrier netting (the orange material). Once the mat was unrolled and positioned, I began by staking the matting at four corners, stretching the material as I went and then securing the interior of the mat with more nails (Figure 1-29). Because of the additional height added by the resistance matting, I needed to keep this floor as flat as possible so the height of the finished tiles would be close to that of the wood strip flooring at the entrance to the bathroom. Nails, hot glue, and staples were used on this installation to help keep the mat and wiring in place. Double-sided tape can even be used to keep the mats flat, although too much tape can interfere with the adhesive bond between the tiles and the setting bed.

The matting must be positioned so that the shielded cable linking the resistance wires to the power supply

Figure 1-30. A groove in the subflooring is required so the fat power supply cable is clear of the plane of the tiles. Here, the author uses fast-setting hot glue to stake the cable until it is encased with SLU.

terminates as close to the junction box as possible. On this job, I pressed the thick cable into a channel I routed in the plywood underlayment to keep the cable below the level of the matting (Figure 1-30). A much smaller wire that connects a floor-level temperature sensor to the system thermostat was also run through this relief groove. The floor-mounted sensor (the black wire visible in the foreground of Figure 1-31B), which shipped as part of this system, provides more precise temperature control and more economical heating than eye-level, wall-mounted thermostats used with other systems.

With the floor prep done, I checked the tile warming mat with an ohm-meter one more time to ensure that the resistance was still within factory-set limits. When that checked out, I connected the three power supply wires to the warning device. Finally, the temperature sensor was threaded through the installation fabric to a point about mid-way across the floor.

Pouring the Self-Leveling Underlayment

This was a relatively complicated thinbed floor to assemble, but once the primer, reinforcing, and heat matting were securely in place, the $\frac{3}{8}$-inch-thick layer of SLU ties all the parts together and results in a simple, very flat surface that is easy to tile over. The SLU is relatively easy to install, but preparation to keep the heating mat as flat as possible is exacting (Figure 1-31).

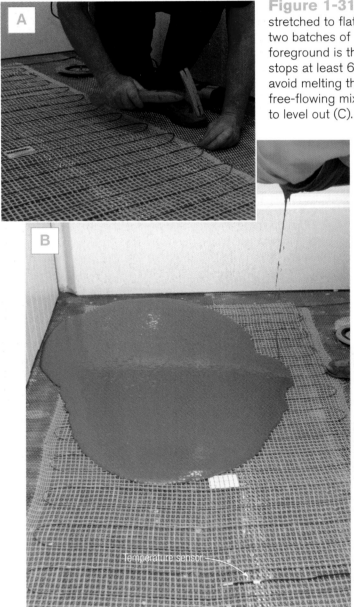

Figure 1-31. As each fastener is driven home, the carrier fabric is stretched to flatten its wavy surface (A). The author pours the first of two batches of SLU over the prepared subfloor. The black wire in the foreground is the temperature sensor (B). Notice that the heating mat stops at least 6 inches short of the wall, vanity, and toilet flange (to avoid melting the wax ring). Because the heating mat is a barrier to the free-flowing mix, it will require considerable troweling for the entire floor to level out (C).

Temperature sensor

Tile Layout, Cutting, and Staging

This floor has a design feature that requires some individual white tiles to be removed from the sheets and replaced with darker tiles. Because of this, and because cutting small tiles can be tedious and time consuming, I prefer to dry-fit all the sheets and cut mosaic tiles before mixing any thinset mortar (Figure 1-32). Because of the overhanging sidewalls, cut pieces are only required against the tub and where the tiles meet the threshold. I adjusted my layout to yield same-size cuts at these locations, removed the indicated white tiles, and sequentially marked the sheets for placement. With all the cuts made and ready to install, I flew through the task of installing the tiles without having to make frequent—and disruptive—trips to the tile saw.

First, I set up a sheet of tiles that had been marked for cutting. When dealing with small, porous stone tiles like these, I prefer to dry-cut when practical to minimize color variations when grouting. (Porous tiles that pick up moisture during wet-sawing can cause the grout and the wet tiles to dry to a different color.)

For safety and efficiency, small tiles need to be locked down tightly before they can be cut. Since the thickness of these tiles varies slightly, I placed a sheet of 1/8-inch-thick packing foam between the tiles and one of my trusty straightedges to help ensure uniform

Figure 1-32. For a small residential floor, the author prefers to dry-fit sheets of tile to ensure the designer's pattern will work. This results in a quicker installation.

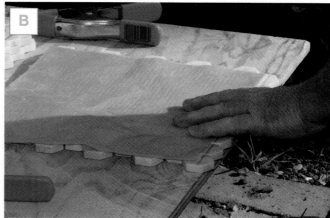

Figure 1-33. The author prepares a sheet of mosaic stones for cutting (A). A thin piece of foam used to pack the tile makes a handy gasket to help stabilize the sheet while it is being cut (B). Rather than hog-off the cuts in one pass, he takes several light passes (C), reducing heat and stress on the tile, the blade, and himself.

clamping of the tile sheet (Figure 1-33). A pair of spring clamps secured the straightedge.

When dry-cutting any type of tile, a lot of heat is generated. Much of this heat is carried away from the blade and the tile by the dust and chips. But if the cut is too deep, enough heat can build up to prematurely age the blade or cause thermal fracture-breaks in the tile. For this reason, I try not to hog off too much material. Instead, I bear down lightly and make several shallow passes. This helps extend the diamond blade's life and reduces chipping. To achieve a straighter cut, I position the straightedge carefully and use it as a rest for my hands.

Because the wall surfaces are so straight, and because we were careful to select a tub whose face was also very straight, this is one of the few installations I have done where no layout lines were used. In this case, the superb workmanship of the carpenter resulted in walls precise enough to serve as a reference point for aligning the tiles. Before removing the dry-fit sheets, I made a small registration mark on the tub so the first sheet was positioned in the exact spot needed to guide the remaining tile sheets.

After testing, I decided on a ¼x¼x¼-inch square-notch trowel to spread the thinset mortar. Nudging the first sheet into place, I tried to place it as accu-rately as possible to avoid needing to slide mosaic sheets around in wet thinset—an ideal way to clog the grout joints with unwanted adhesive and create a cleaning problem.

When I was satisfied with the positioning, I used a rubber grout trowel to press the sheet down into the adhesive layer (Figure 1-34). In the past, when install-ing tiles over thick mortar beds, I would use a hammer and a beating block, typically displacing a bit of mor-tar, to get the thicker tiles to sit even with the rest. On thinbed work over a hard setting bed, however, that technique would likely result in a few broken tiles.

Because all the tile sheets were prepared and all cuts were made before I spread any thinset, it took less than an hour to tile the entire floor. I paid a lot of attention to aligning neighboring sheets, but wasted no time attempting to set the tiles at an equal height, allowing a quick install. That meant there was more lippage than would ordinarily be acceptable. But as the remaining photos show, I used a much faster and more accurate technique—smoothing the tiles with a belt sander—that resulted in a perfectly smooth floor for these honed-finish mosaics. In Figure 1-35, all the sheets are in place, and all but a handful of the dark tiles have to be installed. Because the tiles would be ground flat before grouting (and thus lack the normal support

Figure 1-34. To ensure 100% adhesive coverage, the author uses a rubber grout trowel to press the mosaic sheet into the layer of latex thinset mortar.

Figure 1-35. The author places another dark marble mosaic to complete the design. This floor installed quickly because small differences in the height of the tiles were not an issue.

grout provides), I gave the floor a three-day wait to allow all the mosaic tiles to lock into the latex thinset.

Smoothing the Mosaic Surface

While the surface grinding of soft, unpolished stone tiles is thought to involve trade secrets, rare grinding compounds, and specialized equipment, it is rather easily accomplished with an ordinary belt sander and rough-grit carbide belts (50 to 80 grit for starters). Of course, experience goes a long way with this technique. But with a bit of experimenting—to avoid burnishing the tiles with too fine a grit or gouging them with too rough a grit for the density of the material—most installers new to the technique are surprised at how simple and effective the work is (Figure 1-36). The entire grinding process took about 50 minutes—less time than it would have taken to shim up the errant tiles with adhesive. Because of the fine dust created, it is important to wear appropriate respiratory protection during this and other cutting and grinding procedures.

Even though these relatively soft marble tiles will quickly wear down the rough-grit belts, the waste material does not clog the belt's remaining finer grits the way wood does. I use a belt until I feel the drag lessen and then replace the old belt with a new one. However, the old belts are not discarded yet. Instead, I re-use them for a second pass to remove scratches left by the first run of the sander. Often, this will leave a surface smooth enough for the honed look I prefer.

Once I am finished with the belt sander, I use a simple disc backing chucked into a 300-rpm drill, and about a half dozen 200-grit carbide stick-on sanding discs to smooth out the remaining scratches. The resulting surface is incredibly smooth and was a snap to grout after all the marble dust was vacuumed from between the tiles. The empty and rather wide movement joints at the sides of the floor are concealed by the overhanging wainscoting. The joints between the wainscoting and the tile floor and those where the tile floor abuts the apron of the tub and the threshold were filled with a latex caulk, color and texturematched to the grout.

This grinding treatment, using tools that any professional carpenter would have on hand, is fast and effective when used with soft stones, such as marble, in relatively small installations. The same basic techniques can also be used on any type of honed, nonpolished stone floor. When working harder, more difficult stones, however, specialized stone fabrication and finishing tools and equipment are essential—along with patience, training, practical experience with a variety of finishing techniques, an eye for detail, and strong hands with a craftsman's light touch. Fabricating and working stone tiles can be very satisfying work if you are equipped with the right tools and have a reasonable understanding of the patience, time, and special skills required.

I cannot over-emphasize the importance of testing an individual stone before committing to grinding, sanding, shaping, honing, or polishing an entire lot. Yes, there are many stone tiles that can be worked using woodworker-grade tools. With many normal and denser stones, however, cutting, shaping, and polishing equipment need to be stone-working grade to be efficient, effective, and able to withstand the rigors of fabricating stone.

Figure 1-36. The author uses a belt sander fitted with 80-grit belts to smooth the surface of these rather soft marble mosaics. To help the mosaic pieces withstand the sanding process, the thinset was allowed to harden for three days prior to sanding.

Floor Project 3:
Tiles Over a Wet-Area Concrete Slab

Although small in size, this residential bathroom floor demonstrates how to overcome a typical problem in tiling over concrete: how to apply tile to a cracked concrete slab using a crack-isolation membrane. The project specifications identified a crack in the slab, called for an isolation membrane, and required that the installation be waterproof. The building in which the bathroom is located serves as a recreation and billiards room and is located in a backyard that includes a swimming pool, an outdoor cooking area, seating areas, and gardens.

The building also houses my office, so I wanted the bathroom to be special. Clearly, this bathroom would get plenty of use, and get plenty wet, so I installed an integrated membrane system (combining crack isolation and waterproofing) to protect all areas of the bathroom to be tiled. In addition to the floor, the wainscoting would be tiled, and a thinbed stall shower would be built. The membrane system used on the floor would extend to the shower and lap up the walls to protect the wainscot area.

Evaluating the Slab

The slab on this floor was marked by cracks and surface patches caused by modifications to the plumbing system. The installation would begin by installing a membrane system that would mitigate cracks in the slab and provide a high level of waterproofing. The first step, though, was to take a straightedge to the floor to see if it was flat enough to meet the tile requirements. Using a 5-foot-long straightedge (Figure 1-37), I closely examined the floor in the shower and toilet areas. The floor beneath the shower and around the toilet had to be flat to within ¼ inch in 10 feet—a ⅛-inch maximum gap for the 5-foot straightedge I was using (¼ inch for a 10-foot straightedge).

In particular, I was looking for any parts of the floor that exceeded the industry tolerance or would cause water to be trapped or puddle. Unfortunately, the exam revealed a wavy surface whose high and low areas so greatly exceeded the tolerance—and would create significant problems if tiled over—that I decided to use a *bush-hammer* to remove the top ½ to ¾ inch of the slab and rebuild the bathroom floor portion of the room with a self-leveling compound made for use with tile. The shower floor needed to be sloped, and this was done with a mortar bed after the SLU was used to rehab the bath floor.

Another factor tipped the scale in favor of bush-hammering: The space had once been used as part of a manufacturing facility, and as such, the floor had probably been exposed to sealers, oil, solvents, paint residues, paint overspray, and other contaminants. Adding to the unevenness of the floor's surface was the fact that all of these materials would have to be

Figure 1-37. Depending on the size of the floor, the author uses either a 5- or 10-foot straightedge to assess its flatness. Any light coming through gaps under the straightedge indicates problem areas.

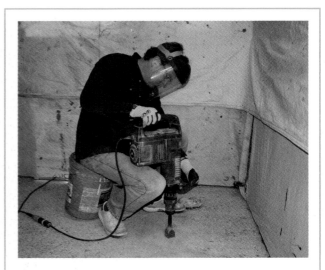

Figure 1-38. The bush-hammer shown here is appropriate for a typical reinforced residential slab. The larger bush-hammers used for commercial and industrial work can crack slabs up to 10 inches thick.

removed or they would significantly reduce bond strength.

Given these conditions, and the relatively small size of the floor, using a bush-hammer was the obvious approach. Removing the surface of the concrete with a bush-hammer and finishing the slab with a self-leveling compound are the tactics I use when dealing with concrete treated with curing compounds or any other coating or penetrant that acts as a bond breaker. For larger concrete floors, it may be more economical to use a shot blaster or other rehabbing equipment (for very large floors, Zamboni-like drive-around units are available).

Installation of the conventional clamping drain used on this thinbed shower is greatly simplified by a component flashing accessory. The installation of the pan liner, made using the same membrane covering the bathroom floor, was further simplified by the use of factory heat-formed inside and outside corners. To increase durability and eliminate potential swelling, the curb was made from reinforced, cast latex concrete (instead of wood). But before this could be formed and poured, the surface of the original concrete had to be rehabbed with the bush-hammer.

Choosing an Installation Method

A single method meeting the needs of this entire bathroom—the floor, wainscoting, and shower—does not exist. Instead, I relied on two individual TCA methods, one proprietary product, and best practices to tie all three together.

For the floor, I chose TCA Method F-122, which describes a waterproof floor with a membrane system installed between the tiles and the slab. The membrane I chose for the job (NobleSeal TS) can be applied to almost any horizontal or vertical surface, so this system will serve as the waterproofing bridge that ties the shower, the wainscoting, and the floor together and protects the entire surrounding structure. TCA Method W244, with the addition of a surface-applied waterproofing membrane, was used for the wainscot walls.

To provide a sloped base for the shower, I used a conventional clamping drain and a proprietary drain flashing called NobleFlex. Refer to Chapter 2, page 46, and Chapter 3, page 81, to see how the wainscot and shower stall were installed and tiled.

In addition to the membrane, the specifications called for latex to be used in all adhesive mortars and grouts and for a network of movement joints to be located at specific areas throughout the bathroom.

Tile and the Installation Materials

The first material required for this installation was a self-leveling underlayment (SLU) and its companion primer, followed by materials for the curb and shower floor. These included a sheet membrane adhered to the setting beds with a contact-type cement, latex-modified thinset mortar to install the tiles, latex grout, a sealer or impregnator, and, finally, several tubes of

Figure 1-39. A coat of spray paint helps the author gauge how much material has been removed and helps him preserve important areas like the edge of the circular depression cast for the shower drain.

Materials List: Project 3

Foam strip: $3/16$-inch x $1\,1/4$-inch x 30-foot PVC Foam, Ace Hardware

SLU: Level-Quik RS Primer, Custom Building Products (CBP)

Membrane system: NobleSealTS membrane, NobleFlex flashing, inside and dam corners, NobleSealant 150, NobleBond EXT, Noble Company

Tiles: 8x8-inch, glazed porcelain, porcelain accent tiles, Michelle Griffoul Studios (MGS); 12-inch nominal, sheet-mounted quartz rocks (Solistone)

Self-leveler: LevelQuik RS, LevelQuik Primer, Custom Building Products (CBP)

Sloped shower floor: CustomFloat, CBP

Thinset mortar: Porcelain Tile Fortified Mortar, CBP

Grout: Prism, CBP

Sealant: Polyblend, CBP

Sealer: TileLab, penetrating sealer, CBP

Subfloor: On-grade concrete slab

Method: TCNA F-122, W244

Performance rating: Heavy Residential

flexible sealant that are color and texture matched to the grout.

The glazed tile chosen for this wet-area installation was selected for its beauty, durability, and impermeability. In fact, my wife designed and made the porcelain wall tiles especially for this space by pressing bamboo stalks and leaves into the soft clay tiles before they were glazed and fired. For all of the shower floor and a portion of the bathroom floor, sheet-mounted quartz rocks (with impervious absorption properties) were used along with hand-molded 8-inch porcelain tiles that were hand glazed to complement the shower and wainscot wall tiles. The tiling materials I selected for this installation are impervious to moisture and provide a commercial level of abrasion resistance and durability I wanted for the bathroom.

Preparing the Concrete Slab

Preparing the slab for this floor tile project involved the following steps:

- installing a drain

- bush-hammering the surface of the slab

- prepping and pouring a self-leveling underlayment

- casting a reinforced concrete curb

- floating a sloped, bonded mortar bed for the shower floor, and

- covering all the surfaces with a membrane system

While a bush-hammer is not exactly a delicate instrument, in experienced hands it is capable of pro-

Figure 1-40. To avoid damaging embedded pipes, I stay away with the bush- hammer and, instead, finish sensitive areas with a hammer and chisel.

Figure 1-41. The temporary foam strip ensures that the perimeter movement joint extends from the top of the tile to the surface of the concrete slab (A). Thresholds need to be temporarily dammed with 2x4s or other scrap lumber in preparation for the SLU (B). Notice the bead of caulk to prevent seepage of the SLU. Here, the closet flange is sealed off with a few wraps of paper and tape (C).

Figure 1-42. On the rough bush-hammered concrete slab, the author uses a garden sprayer to apply a uniform coating of primer without leaving puddles. On smoother surfaces, a paint roller or brush would work.

Figure 1-43. The author uses a smart bucket to add water to the SLU mix. With only minutes of open time, preparation is critical to a successful pour. A trowel and other tools are nearby so the author can quickly distribute the mix evenly.

ducing fairly uniform results (Figure 1-38). The original surface of this slab—about 25-years old—required more time and energy to remove than did the repair patches, which were barely two months old. Although my intention was to renovate the entire top of the slab, for convenience I also wanted to retain some of the original slab. In particular, I wanted to retain a narrow ring of the section of concrete I had repaired around the shower drain. I had produced the circular indentation with a mold supplied with the NobleFlex flashing, and I wanted to use the rim of the indentation to guide the sloping of the shower floor.

Bush-hammering is hot, sweaty, dusty work, and sometimes vision is minimal. In this environment, to help determine what had been hammered and what had not, I gave the slab a light coat of contrasting paint (Figure 1-39). When enough material had been removed, a hammer and chisel took care of the close or delicate areas missed by the bush-hammer (Figure 1-40). Then the area was vacuumed clean.

In preparation for the self-leveling compound, a 1/4-inch-thick foam strip was temporarily fastened around the perimeter of the floor, and temporary dams were established at the thresholds and around the curb area. Next, holes, cracks, and seams were closed with caulk, tape, or stuffed with fiberglass insulation or other suitable material (Figure 1-41). Finally, the rough slab was thoroughly vacuumed and then sprayed with a primer to ready the slab for a topping of SLU. Both the SLU and its companion primer are made specifically for use with ceramic tile. On this rough surface, I used a garden sprayer to apply a uniform coat of the primer (Figure 1-42) rather than the usual brush or sponge. Puddles left by a brush or sponge take a long time to dry, and thick layers of primer turn into soft spots within the finished floor.

Placing the Self-Leveling Underlayment (SLU)

After the primer had dried (about 30 minutes, according to package directions), I prepared two sacks of SLU, using a 15-gallon plastic tub and the identical amount of water for each sack. I staged all the SLU tools and materials I needed close to the application site, since there would be only 8 to 10 minutes of working time before the SLU began to stiffen (Figure 1-43). I estimated the amount of material—about 5/8-inch thick—required to bring the floor up to the desired level (slightly higher than the original surface), plus some extra as a reserve to make fine adjustments to the height. Calculating how many sacks of mix are required is not difficult since only full sacks can be used. For most bathroom floors in the 40- to 80-square-foot range, I mix right in the room where the SLU is needed, and always use a "smart bucket" (see page 280) to deliver the correct amount of water for each sack of dry mix. Before mixing, I always double-check the batch numbers printed on, or taped to, each sack to ensure they are all the same. For this floor, I figured two sacks of SLU mix would be enough.

Using a smart bucket, I poured all the required liquid into the mixing tub and gradually added the powder while working out the lumps with a power mixer. As soon as the two sacks were mixed, I dumped about 30% of the contents of the tub onto one end of the bush-hammered slab, distributed it with a flat trowel, and quickly moved across the floor, alternately pouring and spreading. Most SLUs do a good job of seeking out a level plane on their own, but only when they receive a little human help right after they are poured. Otherwise, they may not have enough time to go level. The most important part of working with an SLU is to ensure that 100% of the floor is covered and wet with the mix. (When only a portion of a floor needs re-habbing, I use a featheredge compound instead of an SLU.)

As I jiggled the initial pour around the slab, the level of the SLU was lower than I wanted and still settling, so I poured the reserve amount on the floor and again used a flat trowel to distribute it. This took less than a minute for this floor, and after about 5 minutes, with the floor at the desired height and already looking flat, I barricaded the doors and let the SLU work its magic. Some brands may be ready for tile in as little as two

hours, but for this material, I waited overnight before trimming the perimeter foam strip flush with the new floor and beginning work on the concrete curb (see Chapter 3, page 82, for more on fabricating the shower curb).

Applying the Membrane

The only preparation needed for this membrane was to trim the foam tape used on the SLU pour flush with the top of the finished floor; sand away any upturned edges of the hardened SLU; and vacuum up any sanding debris, chips of hardened SLU, and dust. To achieve the properties of both waterproofing and crack isolation, the 5-foot-wide sheet membrane I used on this floor (NobleSeal TS) required a single waterproof seam made by overlapping the 5-foot wide membrane sheets by 2 inches. The manufacturer of the membrane provides 2-inch-wide bare seaming areas along both edges of the sheet for this purpose.

You can install this sheet membrane with latex thin-set mortar and close the seams with solvent, but to simplify and speed the installation, I used a companion exterior-grade contact-type cement (NobleBond EXT) rather than latex thinset mortar, and closed all seams with another system component, a compatible sealant called NobleSealant 150. The membrane was laid out so its perimeter would be marked by upturns

Figure 1-44. To speed the installation, the author installs pre-formed accessory pieces first. Here, he removes excess sealant from curb and inside corners with a clean rag soaked in naphtha.

Figure 1-45. The shower, wainscot, and floor are now protected with a continuous waterproofing/crack isolation system—all installed in a single effort prior to tiling.

at the walls and at the reinforced cast-concrete curb dividing the bathroom floor from the shower.

A quick sketch provided all the information I needed to cut and pre-fold the sheet sections. Before occupying myself with this task, however, I spread contact cement in those areas where factory-formed accessory pieces will go (Figure 1-44). The cement should only be spread on surfaces that are dry. After laminating the accessory pieces, I dry-fitted the sections of sheet membrane, made any adjustments (re-folding) as needed, and began installing the sections. To ensure a watertight installation, it is important to use the compatible sealant, instead of the contact cement, wherever the membrane is joined to itself or to an accessory piece. The sealant is also used where the sheet membrane terminates against a tub, shower receptor, or other fixture where a watertight seal is desired.

As with any other multi-plane membrane, the entire membrane should be installed in one continuous process before any tiles are installed (Figure 1-45). This bathroom's membrane system for the shower, wainscot, and floor is covered in Chapter 7. Although I am confident that my methods work, I never begin tiling a stall shower without a water test. I am also convinced that the best way to verify the watertightness of the shower stall pans I make is with a water test. After almost a hundred hours of testing, this thinbed hybrid pan remained filled. After completion of the

test, the plug was pulled, and when the test water drained, I towelled the floor dry and began tiling the shower floor with the mounted stones.

> ***Trade Tip:*** The industry standard water test is 24-hours. For first-floor tests over concrete, 24-hours is fine, but over wood construction, I test for a minimum 48-hours. For second story and higher installations, I test a minimum 72-hours.

The Tile Layout

The layout for this project is part of an overall layout that was developed for the bathroom floor, the wainscot walls, and the shower area. It started with a rough sketch of the room for planning the tiles and ordering materials (see Figure 1-9, page 7). The focus of the layout—and of this bathroom—is the set of 6x6 tiles covering the shower and wainscot walls. The location of this mural was fixed when its tiles were fired to porcelain.

If the bathroom floor were to be covered with 8x8 tiles only, a balanced layout would have meant cut tiles all around the perimeter. But since the rock pathway runs through the center of the floor, I used two separate layouts for the 8x8s that resulted in full tiles

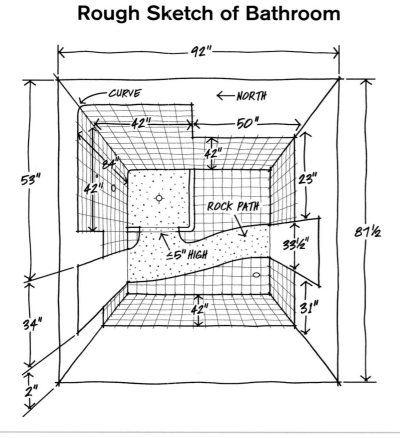

Rough Sketch of Bathroom

Figure 1-46. This sketch provides all the information needed for ordering materials and plotting layouts.

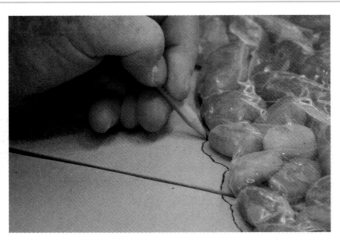

Figure 1-47. Prior to installing any tiles, the author scribes the 8x8 tiles surrounding the rock pathway (left). With the rock sheets removed, the author will make the irregular cuts on a wet saw. Whole and scrap tiles were used to support the face-mounted sheets while scribing (right).

all along the west and east sides. The 8x8 tiles were also used to cover the inner and outer faces of the curb. Narrow 3/4-inch-wide slivers were used to ease the tiles around the curb's curved sections. The tile manufacturer provided   specially molded quarter-round trim tiles for the curb edges.

> ***On the Job:*** I had planned to cut the rock sheets to fit the pathway, but a problem with the backing, uncovered during the tiling of the shower floor (see Chapter 3, page 96), forced me to remove the mesh backing from all the rocks that were needed and then re-mount them with adhesive plastic film (available from Mesh-Mount Paper, Fiberglass & Tape). I arranged the loose rocks, along with several fish-shaped porcelain tiles, to fit the pathway and then face-taped the entire pathway. Next, I cut the pathway tiles into five large sections that would simplify layout and installation.

Because the layout of the floor tiles is interrupted at the center, layout lines for the floor tiles (one on each side of the floor) were plotted parallel to the walls with a chalk line. The layout of this floor, with its rocky inlay, was done in two stages. First, I dry-fitted all the whole and cut 8x8s, and when all were positioned, I covered them with the sheets of face-taped rocks and fish. Second, after all the sheets were aligned, I drew a free-hand pencil line around the perimeter of the rocks to guide the cutting of the 8x8 tiles that surround it (Figure 1-47).

To suit the nature of the hand-molded tiles and the wildly irregular rocks, the cut line does not have to be made with absolute precision, but I did want to maintain a minimum 1/8-inch width for the grout joint between the tiles and rocks. When the entire rock inlay was scribed, I removed the mounted sheets and

Rock/Tile Transition

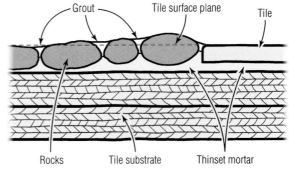

Figure 1-49. For the smoothest transition, the rocks must be set higher than the adjacent tiles. The entire underside of each rock must be supported with medium-bed thinset mortar.

began the process of cutting the 8x8s on a wet saw.

When all the cuts were made, I replaced the 8x8s on the floor and dry-fitted the rock sheets again. When I was satisfied that everything fit, I removed and staged the 8x8s, vacuumed the exposed area, and began preparing a batch of medium-bed latex thinset mortar. My plan was to install the 8x8s first, then the sheet-mounted rocks and fish tiles.

Installing the Tiles

Rounded stones present a bonding challenge, and fitting them against flat tiles can be a problem. After testing for adhesive contact, I decided to use a modified 1/4x1/2x1/4-inch U-notch trowel to spread thinset mortar for the sheets. The adhesive bed produced with a standard 1/4x1/2x1/4-inch U-notch trowel was too thin to

Figure 1-48. With all but a few cut 8x8s to install, the author removes the first of the mounted sheets (A), and spreads medium-bed thinset with the modified trowel (B). He adds more thinset where the rocks meet the 8x8 tiles (C), and sets the sheet into the fresh thinset (D).

provide the necessary adhesive contact required for the industry standard of 95% uniform coverage, so I modified a trowel of this size by grinding away every second and third tooth with a dry-cutting diamond blade.

For installing the 8x8 tiles, I used a conventional ¼x½x¼-inch U-notch trowel to apply mortar to the setting bed and a flat trowel to back butter each cut and whole 8x8. After the thinset mortar bonding the 8x8s hardened, I filled the movement joint between the 8x8 tiles and the abutting walls and curb with a high-quality, long-life sealant to keep moisture out of the movement joint.

As soon as all the 8x8s were installed (with the exception of a few very small cut pieces), I removed the first sheet of mounted rocks at the south end of the floor, spread thinset with the modified trowel, applied additional thinset with a grout bag to adjust the height of the

rocks bordering the 8x8s, and then carefully draped the first sheet into the thinset (Figure 1-48). To install large sheets of tile, I aligned one edge first—without pressing against the sheet—then lowered the rest of the sheet. When I was satisfied with its position, I pressed the rocks and decorative fish tiles firmly into the mortar.

For the smoothest transitions, the rocks neighboring the 8x8s had to sit slightly higher than the other rocks and the tiles (Figure 1-49). If the border rocks were too low, I peeled back the sheet, added more latex medium-bed thinset mortar with a grout bag, and replaced the sheet. As each sheet was installed, any remaining cut 8x8s were installed. When subsequent sheets were ready to set in mortar, I aligned the connecting edge first, then the rest of the sheet (Figure 1-50).

As each section was installed, I cleaned up excess mortar from the tops of the surrounding 8x8s, but there was

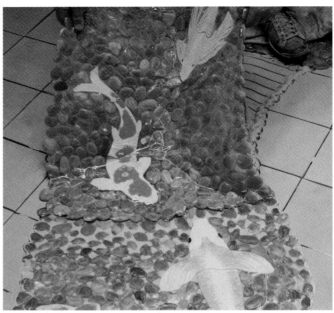

Figure 1-50. To help lift rocks sitting too low, the author adds more thinset mortar with a grout bag (left). As he sets each sheet into place, he aligns it to meet the previously installed sheet (right). Notice the mortar ooze between the rocks.

little I could do with the ooze between rocks until the mortar hardened—about 24 hours or more later. The first test of the mortar's bond strength occurred when the face film was removed. I did this slowly, at first, to avoid pulling rocks off the setting bed, but once I was confident the mortar had a good grip on the rocks, I stripped the film away and re-set any rocks or tiles that came loose with fresh thinset mortar. If more than one or two rocks pulled off per square foot of the floor, I stopped and gave the sheets another four hours (or whatever was required) for the mortar to harden. If few rocks were pulled off, as soon as the film was removed from a section, I immediately used a utility knife to slice through the excess thinset (Figure 1-51).

Because the rock sizes were so variable, and because the rocks were difficult to bond and required more than the usual amount of thinset needed for flat-backed tiles, the amount of ooze (the only practical indicator that the bottom of the stones is completely covered) was considerable and took about two hours to remove. Following the utility knife, I used a scrubbing pad to remove lingering traces of mortar, and then vacuumed away the dust and grit. Some of the rocks were supported by as much as $\frac{1}{2}$-inch of mortar. For this reason, I let the floor dry another day before applying grout.

Grouting the Tiles and Finishing the Installation

Two different grout colors were used for this floor: a lighter sanded grout for the 8x8s and a darker sanded grout for the rock inlay. The 8x8s were grouted first, requiring about half an hour to mix, pack, and clean up. The entire 8x8 portion of the floor was packed with grout before I began the cleaning process. After

Figure 1-51 Because the face film has to remain until the thinset sets up, the author must work quickly to remove excess thinset mortar with a utility knife once the film is removed.

removing the excess grout from the movement joints between the floor and wainscot tiles, the grout was left undisturbed for about three hours before I started on the rock inlay.

Finishing the rocks took more grout, labor, detailing, and patience than is normally required for square tiles, but I used the same basic grouting techniques I use for any tiles. One difference, though, required some sponge work to keep the darker grout from staining the hardened, lighter grout. I dampened the light grout with clean water just before grouting the rocks and wiped the dark grout from the light joints as quickly as possible (Figure 1-52) as work proceeded across the rock pathway. Another difference is how I held the grout trowel. Normally, after packing the

Figure 1-52. To prevent the dark grout from staining the lighter grout, the author dampens the surrounding 8x8 joints before spreading the darker grout over a section of rocks (left). After applying the dark grout, he quickly removes any dark grout sitting on the lighter colored 8x8 joints (right).

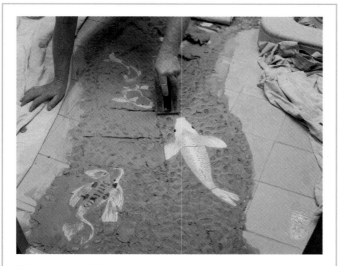

Figure 1-53. For greater efficiency when removing excess grout on rough surfaces, the author uses the narrow edge of the grout trowel.

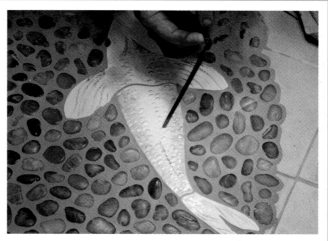

Figure 1-54. As each section of the inlay is finished, the author uses a narrow tuck pointer to remove any grout embedded in the textured surface of the porcelain fish.

grout, I use the wide edge of the trowel to remove excess grout, but the surface of the rocks offered plenty of resistance, so I used the narrow edge instead (Figure 1-53).

With thin grout joints and absorbent tiles, I cannot spread and pack too much grout before using the sponge to clean up. With very wide joints and impervious rocks, however, I grouted the entire rock pathway and waited about 20 minutes before cleanup. Sponge cleaning this rock inlay was done using the same techniques I ordinarily use, but the rounded surface of the rocks presented a challenge. Remove too much grout and the inlay would be covered with little water-catching "birdbaths." Remove too little and the finished grout would begin flaking. The trick was to remove just

enough grout so the rocks wouldn't trap water, but leave enough that the finished grout retained its strength (as illustrated in Figure 3-101, page 100). To complete the grout cleaning, I used a 1/4-inch tuck pointer to carve out grout that was embedded in the textured surface of the porcelain fish tiles (Figure 1-54).

It took about an hour to pack and clean the rock inlay, and after a 20-minute wait, I used a 1/4-inch tuck-pointer to clean out the movement joint between the inlay and the rocks covering the face of the curb. Then I allowed the installation to rest for 72 hours for the grout to cure. After 72 hours, I filled the movement joints with a flexible sealant that is color and texture matched to the grout. When the sealant had cured, I treated the tiles, rocks, and grout with a quality sealer.

NOTES

Chapter 2
HOW TO INSTALL WALL TILES

At first, it might seem that tiling walls is no different than tiling floors. But, while both share many of the same requirements (surface prep, layout, adhesion, flat and smooth, etc.), the two are very dissimilar. Gravity helps simplify a floor tile installation, but it can be a formidable obstacle on wall installations—especially if the tiles are installed with a diagonal layout. Gravity makes spreading tile adhesive or grout on a wall more difficult. And, unlike floor tiles that sit still until the adhesive hardens and cures, wall tiles sometimes have to be immobilized with spacers, shims, or other means while the adhesive is setting up.

In the U.S., most wall tiles, with the exception of backsplashes, are found in the bathroom. Wet-area installations are the focus of this chapter. If you can handle the complexities of a wet installation, you should have no trouble completing a dry-area install. The projects in this chapter are the most basic wall installations: a tub surround and a shower built around a pre-formed and finished shower receptor. More information about wall tiling can be found in the three projects described in Chapter 3.

A fundamental step in successful wall tile installations is establishing a secure, level base from which the tiling can proceed. This base will support the weight of upper courses until the adhesive mortar sets up and locks all the tiles permanently to the setting bed. Ideally, a shower receptor or bathtub should be leveled as part of its installation (Figure 2-1). Its rim serves as the base for setting the wall tile. If a rim is out of level and cannot be repositioned, I temporarily secure a level straightedge to support the second and higher courses of tiles. I remove the straightedge when the thinset mortar has set up, then I cut and install the first row.

Tiles with built-in spacing lugs are able to hang without sagging, but others may require supplemental spacers, shims, or other supports (string and rope are still used by some installers for spacing tiles). The ability to hang on the wall without slipping depends on the weight of the tile and the type of adhesive used. To achieve the greatest marketing impact, some thinset manufacturers like to demonstrate this property by hanging the largest tiles possible. However, tile size has less to do with hanging than the weight per square inch of the tile. If a tile adhesive will allow a 1-square-inch tile to hang, the same adhesive should just as easily support a 36x36-inch tile as long as the weight per square inch is the same.

Structural Support

Weight is an important factor with all tile installations, whether on floors, walls, countertops, or ceilings. On walls, it may appear that the weight is concentrated along the bottom edge of the wall—and, unfortunately, on many installations it is. The weight of any properly built and finished tile wall, however, should be evenly supported by the studs or masonry on which it is built. It is possible in some cases to tile over 24-inch stud spacing, but overall, there is only one industry standard: 16-inch centers. There are several membranes that claim they can protect tiles

Figure 2-1. Fixtures, such as bathtubs and this shower receptor, should be leveled as part of their installation, so that tiles do not have to be cut or trimmed to fit. To maintain a flat, plumb setting-bed surface, the mounting flange of a receptor must be flush with the face of the studs. Notice the notch in the stud and the flush placement of the horizontal blocking above the receptor.

installed over 24-inch stud spacing, but tiling over stud spacing greater than 16 inches on-center is not recommended, especially for glass tile installations.

For stud walls, wood framing or well-braced 20-gauge steel studs can be used, provided the minimum stud depth is not less than $3\frac{1}{2}$-inches. Like floor installations, tiles mounted on masonry or concrete construction have a more stable setting bed than tiles installed over stud construction. The height and width of a wall tile installation deserves careful consideration because of the need for movement joints about every 10 feet vertically and every 12 feet horizontally.

When installed directly to the wall structure, tiles of practically any weight can be used. Tile weight becomes an issue, however, when a surface-applied membrane is installed: All the weight of the tiles, adhesive, and grout hangs on the membrane before it is transferred to the wall structure. Verify that the membrane system you plan to use can support the weight of the tiles you want to install. In addition to the weight of the tile, a thinbed installation can weigh from $\frac{1}{2}$ to 2 pounds per square foot without a membrane, and another $\frac{1}{2}$ to $1\frac{1}{2}$ pounds per square foot with a membrane.

Flat and Plumb

The structure not only has to be strong enough to support the tiles and other installation materials, it also has to be plumb enough so tile cuts are straight and not uneven or tapered. The industry standard for plumb and flat calls for no variations more than $\frac{1}{4}$ inch in 10 feet or $\frac{1}{16}$ inch in 1 foot. This is a minimum standard that is OK for tiles smaller than 10 inches (in length), but for a more professional appearance or when installing larger tiles, I maintain a setting bed surface that is true to within $\frac{1}{8}$ inch in 10 feet or better.

To prevent tile edges from casting shadows, a tighter tolerance for both structural and finish materials is a must, especially when installing wall tiles that will be illuminated with wall-washer accent lighting or cove-type lighting, or that will be exposed to side lighting from surrounding doors and windows. Similar problems are common on exterior wall tile installations where exposure to direct sunlight can produce unwanted shadows if the transition from one tile surface to another is not smooth.

A mortar bed is both a setting bed and a means of

Inside Corner Fastening

A recurring problem with all types of tile backerboards involves fastening at inside corners. Stud detailing that may be OK for lighter weight gypsum-board walls can create fastening problems for tile backerboards and may have trouble carrying the additional load and transferring it to the studs (Figure 2-2). Toe-nailing can cause damage to backerboards that undermines the load path

to the corner stud. Whether or not installation instructions have minimum setback distances for edge fasteners, most tile backerboards require full-face attachment (minimum $1\frac{1}{2}$ inches) to all studs; fasteners installed closer to the edge than recommended lead to board, membrane, and tile failures.

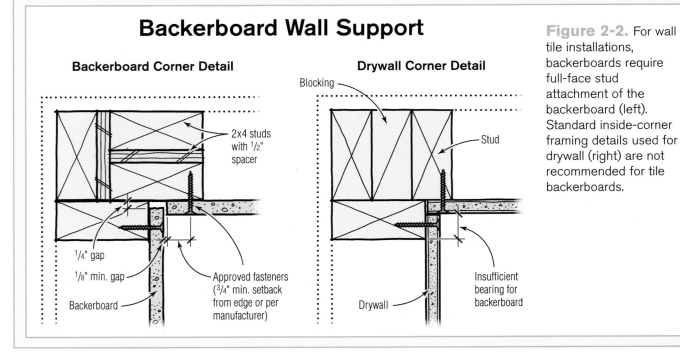

Backerboard Wall Support

Backerboard Corner Detail

2x4 studs with $\frac{1}{2}$" spacer

$\frac{1}{4}$" gap

$\frac{1}{8}$" min. gap

Backerboard

Approved fasteners ($\frac{3}{4}$" min. setback from edge or per manufacturer)

Drywall Corner Detail

Blocking

Stud

Drywall

Insufficient bearing for backerboard

Figure 2-2. For wall tile installations, backerboards require full-face stud attachment of the backerboard (left). Standard inside-corner framing details used for drywall (right) are not recommended for tile backerboards.

truing out-of-plumb walls (and other surfaces), so uneven subsurfaces for mortar-bed installers— within reason—are acceptable. But since no such adjustments are possible with hard backerboards, the accuracy of the tile installation depends almost completely on the smoothness and accuracy of the framing or masonry base. Whatever surface tolerance is desired for thinbed wall work must also be applied to the construction of the stud (or masonry) wall supporting the tiles.

According to industry standards, you cannot use thinset mortar to make surface corrections for any surface that does not meet the ¼-inch-in-10-foot tolerance. While it is possible to make minor corrections of ⅛ inch or so by varying the thinset thickness, any more is not recommended or advised, since thinset mortar is an adhesive, not a filler. Thinset's strength quickly diminishes when its cross section exceeds ¼ inch.

If minor corrections have to be made over any wall surface that does not meet the industry minimums, the surface should be restored first. Ideally, you should check the framing before installing backerboards and make corrections or adjustments as needed (Figure

Figure 2-3. Since this badly out-of-plumb wall could not be removed and rebuilt, the remodeling contractor used furring strips and shims to create a smooth, even base for tile.

2-3). For masonry or concrete walls, high spots should be ground flat, and an approved patching compound should be used to fill in low spots before membrane or tiles are installed.

On remodeling or repair jobs where it is not possible or practical to make structural corrections, I don't install tile. On new construction or additions, however, the builder should understand the need for accuracy in tile areas and build to the desired tolerance. If the setting bed surface for your wall installation is out-of-plumb masonry or concrete, it may be necessary to contract with a plaster contractor to float a corrective, bonded mortar bed. If the out-of-plumb wall is wood- or steel-stud construction, refer to Chapter 8.

Waterproofing

When vitreous tiles are installed with a quality latex thinset mortar, and the grout joints are filled with properly proportioned and compacted grout, moisture has little chance of entering an installation. However, for best results under normal or heavy exposure to water or steam, I recommend adding a surface-applied membrane.

This approach protects the setting bed from exposure to moisture, and the membrane makes it much easier to detail critical areas, such as where tile meets a tub or precast shower floor (Figure 2-4). Also, a membrane is the only practical way to waterproof a steam shower. Detailed methods for sheet and trowel-applied systems are explained in Chapter 5.

Adhesive Coverage

Wall tiles do not support the heavy loads that floor tiles do. However, wall tiles still require adequate adhesive coverage to prevent the intrusion of water or moisture, which can allow mildew and mold to flourish and cause freeze/thaw damage in exterior applications. Good adhesion is also a personal safety factor when installing tiles on interior wall surfaces and is an important public safety issue when tiling exterior or high interior walls (more than 8 feet). For dry areas, 80% adhesive coverage is the industry standard, but I prefer to follow the 95% wet-area standard for all wall tiling in either dry or wet areas (interior and exterior applications).

When purchasing thinset mortar for wall use, select a brand that has good hang (initial grip) to help reduce or eliminate slippage. I normally install wall tiles from the bottom up, using shims, wedges, and— under unusual conditions—a straightedge (as a ledge) to start the tiles level.

When working with lightweight tiles, however, I can save considerable time by using a strong thinset and starting from the top and working down. This method works well only when there is no sagging and should only be attempted by installers with some experience. Note: All the wall projects in this Chapter were done from the bottom up.

Movement Joints

Cracked joints are a widespread problem where wall tiles meet at inside corners and where tiles meet a tub or shower receptor, because most installations do not include movement joints (Figure 2-5). Walls are not walked on, but they still flex and move. I may criticize some industry standards as being too minimal or ineffective, but for movement joints, the standard could not be more correct: All tile installations require movement joints! Membranes, especially those that provide waterproofing protection, need special detailing at movement joints. This prevents damage to membrane materials where they cross a structural movement zone and allows membranes to be joined successfully to non-tile materials, such as a bath tub or precast shower receptor.

Tile Selection

Dry areas. Above the first or second course, wall tiles do not have to endure foot traffic and, thus, no harsh cleaning or aggressive maintenance routines. So, above the first or second course, a less durable surface is required than on floors, allowing a much wider selection of tile materials. In fact, for dry-area installations, practically anything can be (and has been) used as tiling material.

Wet areas. In wet or exterior areas, however, the selection is somewhat reduced because porous materials are not recommended. In wet areas, I recommend only impervious or vitreous ceramic tiles or other tile materials that have similar non-absorbent properties. For wet-area applications, I also avoid installing tiles with crackled or crazed glazes because, in spite of frequent applications of a high-quality sealer or impregnator, these tiles may still admit moisture, discolor, harbor mildew, and create ongoing maintenance problems.

Textured and stone tiles. Other tiles that should not be used on wet-area walls are any with a rough surface texture. Yes, there are some gorgeous textured ceramic and stone tiles available, but tiles with a rough surface are difficult to clean and maintain. They can be just as problematic in wet areas as tiles that are highly absorbent.

In addition, many stone tiles require frequent applications of a sealer to maintain their impermeability or to facilitate cleaning of their textured surfaces. In my opinion, tiles that need this level of maintenance are a mistake in a wet area.

When installing stone tiles in a wet environment, ask the stone supplier for examples of installations where the stone you want has been used under similar

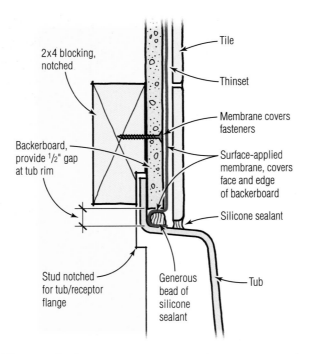

Figure 2-4. Surface-applied membranes are simpler to install than traditional waterproofing methods and provide much better moisture protection. The membrane tucked into a ½-inch gap between the board and shower receptor can absorb any movement and provides generous purchase for the silicone sealant. The studs and blocking are notched to allow the flange to sit flush.

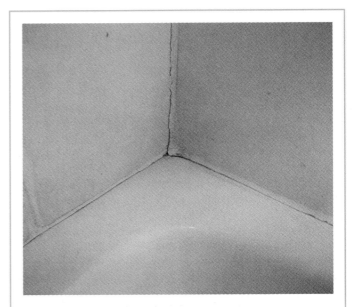

Figure 2-5. Cracks in the corner and along the shower receptor occurred due to normal building movement acting against joints filled with hard grout. Unless the grout is removed and replaced with a flexible sealant, these cracks will wick moisture into the setting bed.

conditions. Your selection should not require frequent application of a sealer: Once or twice a year should be enough under normal use. Many stones have a long history of use around water, but others can be a problem when exposed to moisture. If such verifiable documentation is not available, select another stone.

Grouting and Finishing

Walls are supposed to shed water, but if the grout is porous, water running down the face of a wall is more likely to be absorbed sideways into the joints. This can occur when grout is swiped over the joints rather than being packed into them according to industry standards. Unsanded grout is used for joints less than ⅛-inch wide and has a smooth surface texture after cleaning. Sanded grout, on the other hand, when cleaned properly during installation, has a very abrasive surface similar to that of sandpaper. Grout manu-

facturers are very specific about the quality of sand mixed in with packaged grout. Sand for grout purposes has sharp corners and edges (not rounded and smooth) to increase its compressive and cohesive strength.

The process of cleaning sanded grout is very similar to the process of exposing the aggregate in concrete work, only instead of smoothly rounded stones, sharp sand edges are exposed. The glaze of some wall tiles can be harmed by sanded grout, which can also cause problems with the high-polish finish of some stone tiles, so choose both tiles and grout carefully. For best results, all sanded grout joints in wet areas should be struck with a smoothing tool, called a striker, using a process most commonly associated with brick masons. This produces a surface whose smooth texture is easier to clean and maintain. For more information about this process, refer to Chapter 6.

Wall Project 1:
Shower Walls with a Precast Receptor

In this section, precast shower receptors include sloped shower floor units made from plastic, fiberglass, composite materials, cast iron, terrazzo, and stone. Typically, these units are used in place of a tile floor and, after installation, are inherently waterproof and do not require a water test before their surrounding walls are covered with tile.

Depending on the type you select, precast shower floors vary considerably in weight, performance, and installation. All, however, have similar installation requirements that include building subfloor surfaces and surrounding walls that meet or exceed industry standards, making a watertight connection between the unit and drain pipe, and providing firm support for the unit.

This project focuses on basic installation concepts for most receptors: how to waterproof backerboards installed above them and how to establish a flexible, waterproof joint between the walls and the receptor.

Flanged and Unflanged Receptors

All varieties of shower receptors can be divided into two basic types: Those that have perimeter flanges and those that do not. The presence of a perimeter flange is no guarantee of a trouble-free installation with regard to waterproofing. In fact, the metal flanges of some units are too thin, inadequately protected or coated, and prone to rapid rust through. As shown in Figure 2-1 (page 35), the face of all flanged units need to be installed flush with the face of the studs so that the flange does not interfere with the proper orientation of the backerboards.

Figure 2-6. Two-by-four blocking provides support for the shower receptor as well as for the lower edges of the tile backerboards.

Structure and Layout

The market is full of 3x3-foot precast shower receptors with drains, weighing in at less than fifty pounds. However, large, carved stone units weighing more than 500 pounds are also widely available. Regardless of the project budget, the structure must be able to support the anticipated dead and live loads. Generally, lightweight plastic, composite, and fiberglass units do not require any special construction considerations, as long as they are not installed in the middle of a large-span floor.

As a rule of thumb, if a precast pan weighs so much

that two people are required to handle and install it safely and properly, the project designer should ensure that no parts of the structure in the shower area will measurably deflect under anticipated loads: This applies to both wood and concrete construction. For best results, floor, wall, and ceiling surfaces in the shower area should be built level, plumb, and flat to within ⅛ inch in 10 feet when installing tiles less than 10 inches, 1/16 inch in 10 feet when tiles 12 inches or greater are used.

All backerboards require solid blocking between studs at all horizontal joints and a good fit against surrounding walls. The blocking around the receptor flange typically also serves as blocking for the bottom edge of the tile backerboards (Figure 2-6). Flat-laid 2x4s are installed between studs to support board edges. To achieve the tightest possible fit against the wall studs, I apply the same technique I use when installing receptors, bathtubs, ready-to-tile shower pans, and similar applications: Shoot fasteners only in the upper plate of the right wall so the lower plate can be pulled back a few inches out of the way (Figure 2-7). This is enough to allow for easy insertion of the receptor and—once the wall is repositioned and refastened—provide a tight fit with no gaps between the receptor and the walls.

Bedding the Receptor

A strong subfloor can still allow the receptor itself to deflect if there are gaps between the subfloor and the bottom of the receptor. Small gaps (less than ⅛ inch) can crack and destroy terrazzo and stone units and make them leak. Gaps under flexible units cause movement in associated plumbing connections, resulting in loose or broken connections and unwanted noises caused by parts rubbing against one another. Perfectly flat subfloors and receptors are virtually impossible to achieve. The solution? Apply a layer of bedding plaster or mortar between the two. When enough mortar is used to support the entire underside of a molded plastic receptor, that unit becomes more solid underfoot and less noisy once the mortar hardens.

To install this unit, I dryfitted the receptor over a level subfloor to ensure the pipe stub was at the correct height and checked the fit against the surrounding studs. After observing a good fit of the unit against the left side, with some gaps on the right, I decided to move the right wall out of the way, as shown in Figure 2-7. First I cut through all the nails holding the right wall to the subfloor, plus a few more along the lower portion where it meets the back wall. Then I pulled the wall an inch or so away from the receptor opening. I used one screw to temporarily hold the wall out of the way while I installed the receptor over the bedding mortar.

With the receptor held firmly against the two walls still fastened in place, I positioned a short 2x4 snug against the face of the receptor and the subfloor and temporarily fixed it in place with a couple of screws. This provided a positive stop and a dam for the bedding mortar. With the stop in place, I lifted the receptor and propped it out of the way (Figure 2-8) and dampened the subfloor to prevent the plywood from wicking moisture from the bedding mortar.

Next, I mixed enough bedding mortar to lift the bottom of the receptor about an inch above the subfloor and distributed the mortar over the receptor footprint. With this done, I gently lowered the receptor over the

Figure 2-7. By cutting through the right side wall's lower fasteners and temporarily moving it a few inches away, the author has a much easier job of installing the receptor and achieving a snug fit.

Materials List: Wall Project 1

Precast shower floor: Fiberglass flanged receptor
Bedding plaster: General-purpose bedding mortar
Membrane system: Custom 9240, Custom Building Products (CBP)
Tiles: 6x6-inch non-vitreous tiles (Note: used for demonstration purposes only—not recommended for use in wet areas)
Thinset mortar: Porcelain Tile Fortified Thin-Set Mortar, CBP
Grout: Polyblend, CBP
Sealant: Polyblend, CBP
Method: B412

mortar and pressed it firmly until the unit hit bottom (Figure 2-9). With the receptor in place, I checked the perimeter with a small level, pressed the unit against the back and left walls, and secured those flanges with screws. Then I removed the temporary screw holding the right wall, pressed the wall firmly against the receptor flange, and re-fastened the wall (Figure 2-10). Finally, I ran screws through the right side flange and then allowed the bedding mortar to set up hard overnight.

Preparing for Membrane and Tile

Because the studs were notched the thickness of the flange, the cement backerboards sat plumb and flat instead of flaring out. Flat and plumb are essential to good looks, but to ensure the installation remains watertight, it is important that there is a movement joint between the receptor and the backerboards. To simplify this task, I spaced the boards ½ inch above the receptor with shims until they were secured with screws (Figure 2-11). I used shims to maintain a ¹⁄₁₆- to ⅛-inch gap between boards (Figure 2-12) and a ½-inch minimum gap at all inside corners. To improve the installation and performance of the membrane, I cut all boards with power shears to produce smooth, straight edges; cut tight curves with a jig saw fitted with a carbide blade; and drilled small holes with dia-

Figure 2-8. The right wall has been pulled back a few inches and the receptor has been propped out of the way. To ensure that the receptor will install snug against the back wall, the author relies on a short 2x4 stopping block (just above the kneeling pad) that he screwed in place while dry fitting the receptor. The floor beneath the receptor will be ready for the bedding mortar once it is dampened.

Figure 2-9. After distributing the mortar into a donut-shaped ring, the author lowers the receptor into the mortar (A). The 2x4 stopping block at the front of the receptor ensures accurate, trouble-free positioning (B). To ensure that the receptor is properly seated, the author spends a few moments walking on the receptor floor to help spread the mortar (C).

mond core bits. (See Chapter 8 for more information about tile backerboards).

After all boards were installed, I applied the same latex thinset used to install the tiles to fill over fastener heads, fill seams, and smooth the transitions between the drywall and backerboards. I smoothed the thinset with a trowel and allowed it to harden and dry (Figure 2-13).

At this point, it was a good idea to mask off the receptor. To prepare for the membrane, I scraped, sanded, and ground any excess materials; vacuumed the surface; and gave the backerboards a thorough soaking with fresh water. This increased bond strength and reduced the amount of moisture suctioned from the membrane liquid into the board.

Installing the Membrane

The membrane I selected for this project is a trowel-applied type with both waterproofing and crack-isolation properties. The finished membrane is composed of overlapping sections of reinforcing fabric embedded in layers of specialized latex. The corner and junction details are particularly important because the membrane will be tucked inside the movement joint opening rather than making the traditional 90-degree bend. The result is a membrane with a stress-free corner that can move and provide excellent waterproofing protection. Where the backerboards meet the receptor, the membrane fabric laps in to seal off the lower edge of the board rather than terminating where it meets the receptor ledge.

Figure 2-10. The author presses the wall back against the receptor (above) and re-secures the wall with long construction screws (right).

Figure 2-11. Backerboards are positioned ¹/₂ inch above the receptor (or tub) to allow space for the movement joint between tile and receptor. The author uses shims to maintain the space until boards are secured with screws.

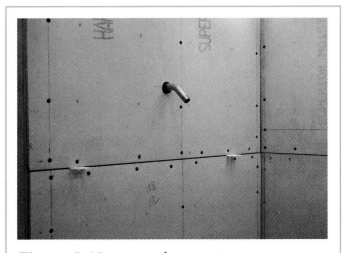

Figure 2-12. Uniform ¹/₁₆-inch shims establish gaps between boards. The author uses a core bit to make a neat access hole at the showerhead. A ¹/₂-inch gap at inside corners allows plenty of room for the membrane to make a gradual, low-stress corner.

I began by masking the receptor, projecting a single horizontal laser line indicating the top of the shower area and two vertical lines indicating the end of the tile walls. I used the laser lines to pencil in a layout to guide in cutting and placing the membrane's fabric and liquid components. I began by installing 6-inch-wide flashing where the walls meet the receptor and in the shower's two vertical corners and used full-width fabric to cover the entire shower area (Figure 2-14). Once I was certain that all portions of the fabric were fully bedded and laminated, I let the installation harden and cure.

Joining Finished Membrane to Receptor

The typical approach to sealing backerboard to a receptor or similar fixture is to butt the edge of a sheet membrane to the fixture and cover the edge with sealant, as shown in Figure 7-10 (page 197). However, this is an ineffective way to join the receptor to the membrane-covered backerboards. To provide a larger contact area in this project, the terminal edges of membrane sheets were folded over the backerboard edges where they meet the receptor. A bead of sealant can elongate more than the edge of a sheet or reinforcing fabric, so there is less strain on the membrane at this movement junction.

The same basic concepts can also be used with sheet membrane systems. Lapping the membrane around the edge of the setting bed and filling the joint between the lower edge of the covered board and the top of the receptor with a compatible sealant ensures effective waterproofing of the surface and the elimination of wicking through the edge of the backerboard (or mortar bed, masonry, etc.) into the structure. The same treatment is carried through at the inside cor-

Figure 2-14. To coax the fabric around the bottom edge of the backerboard and into the joint at the receptor, the author uses a sash brush soaked with the liquid (top). The extra fabric tucked into this recessed corner reduces the stress at this critical movement joint (bottom).

Figure 2-13. In preparation for the membrane, the author uses the tile-setting thinset to fill over fastener depressions and board seams.

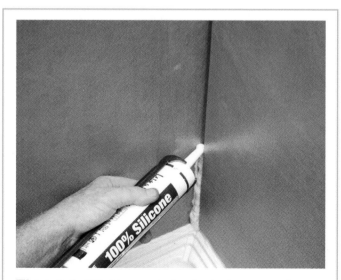

Figure 2-15. The semi-circular tuck-in gives the membrane the flexibility to absorb movement, while the soft silicone fills the voids that can harbor mildew and mold.

Figure 2-16. This latex thinset mortar has excellent grab, but to ensure that each tile is immobilized, the author uses shims and spacers and keeps them in place until the thinset mortar has set up hard. Here, he uses a ¼-inch tuck pointer to remove excess thinset mortar (left). Shims, spacers, small nails, and prop sticks are useful for positioning tiles and fixtures until the adhesive sets (right).

ners, where the reinforcing fabric makes a wide bend instead of a sharp fold (Figure 2-15).

The compatible sealant needs time to cure properly—up to 72 hours under cold conditions. However, since long grout joints remain open until all materials have cured properly and grouting is delayed, tiles can be installed immediately over this type of joint. With any type of membrane system, however, water testing or immediate installation of tile may not be possible; check the membrane manufacturer's instructions for details.

Movement Joints

The gaps in the backerboards at the corners, the extra membrane tucked into the resulting opening, and its filling of sealant make up a movement joint in the cor-

ners of the setting bed and where the tile meets the tub or receptor. This movement zone must be continued through the tile layer, with tile joints aligned over the corner joints and filled with a flexible filling instead of hard grout. For this reason, I began the first course of tiles with ⅛-inch shims and used spacers or shims (or both) to maintain ⅛-inch minimum corner joints (Figure 2-16). The tile-to-receptor and corner movement joint must also continue through the tilework.

In corners of wet-area installations, movement joint slots on the first plane of tiles must be filled before the installation of the second plane of tiles.

Movement joints around plumbing and other tile penetrations allow normal movement, provide good waterproofing, and allow plumbers reasonable access for tools, repairs, or replacements.

Wall Project 2:
Preparing and Finishing a Tub Surround

Without shower equipment, bathtubs are usually trimmed with a single row of tiles. When the tub also serves as the shower area, though, tub walls need to be waterproofed, and a durable waterproof connection must be made between the tub and the tiled walls that enclose it. This is difficult to achieve with traditional waterproofing methods that include placing the waterproofing materials behind the setting bed. Even when done well, these methods are often ineffective.

With current methods and materials, however, waterproofing a tub surround is simple, effective, and durable. A tub surround has many similarities with a shower

receptor, but it has its own structural requirements. This project covers the installation of the tile backerboards and membrane system only, and it points out where movement joints are required for this popular installation.

The Structure

Bathtubs and other plumbing fixtures with similar wall configurations (pre-formed shower receptors, for example) require additional structural detailing (Figure 2-17), which includes:

- providing blocking between studs for support and attachment of fixtures, and to support all

backerboard and drywall edges

- providing full-face fastening for all tile backerboards

- ensuring that the structure below a tub is able to comfortably support the tub plus the weight of the water and all occupants

- providing extra studs in areas where partitions or enclosures might be installed (Figure 2-18)

- notching the studs so the raised lip around the tub's rim is within the plane of the studs (Figure 2-19)

- shimming with metal shims—not wood! (Figure 2-20)

Cast-iron tubs have a rather rounded hump where the lip of the tub meets the wall (it can interfere with the backerboards or tile), while stamped metal and synthetic tubs have a raised flange that can get in the way of tile backerboards unless the studs are notched.

If a tub flange or other mount cannot be let into the studs to clear the backerboard, a portion of the rear of the backerboard can be notched or beveled so that the board clears the flange. For this example, I used a 4-inch diamond blade mounted in an angle grinder and cut away the minimum required for a good fit—no less than 60 degrees. Before installing the board, I trowelled thinset mortar over the bevel (Figure 2-21) to help support the weakened edge of the board. After it began to harden, excess thinset in the movement

joint slot between the walls and the tub was removed with a ¼-inch margin trowel.

Installation Method and Details

This project follows the general guidelines of TCA B412, with one exception: The membrane will be installed on the surface of the backerboards rather than between the boards and the studs. I began by penciling in a layout of the tile. Then I cut and fastened the backerboards, leaving ¹⁄₁₆- to ⅛-inch joints between boards and a ½-inch joint between the boards and the tub and between the boards at inside vertical corners (Figure 2-22).

After installation, I left corner joints open, but filled board-to-board joints with latex thinset mortar and

Figure 2-18. Extra studs, shown on the left, are required to supply solid anchorage and support for enclosures.

Figure 2-17. The tub-surround framing has been set up for 3x5-foot cement backerboards. The flat-installed 2x4s provide the backerboard edges with 1¹⁄₂ inches of support. Five end-grain-cut 2x4s provide excellent, consistent support for the tub lip even if the 2x4s become wet and swell.

Figure 2-19. These studs have been notched to allow the tub's raised lip to sit slightly behind the plane of the 2x4 studs and out of the way of the backerboards.

allowed it to harden before installing the membrane system. As in most other wet-area residential installations, the tile had to be laid out so that trim tiles covered the joints between gypsum drywall and the tile backerboards.

It is good practice to pre-drill and countersink narrow sections of backerboard in order to avoid breakage and edge cracks (Figure 2-23). This method is also useful when dealing with the young-growth wood commonly used in modern framing lumber. The lumber's soft, annular rings provide little bite for backerboard screws designed to grind their own countersink. For most projects nowadays, including this one, I pre-drill and countersink all boards prior to fastening.

The key to my waterproofing strategy was to allow each plane of tile to move independently without stressing neighboring planes. For this project, I used a liquid-applied system with a gel and reinforcing fabric. I began by making a cut list and started stacking sections of straight and folded reinforcing fabric in the

order I need them (Figure 2-24). In this project, flashing was used to lap around corners. Wherever possible, I cut sections oversize to incorporate a minimum 2-inch-wide overlap. Instead of terminating the membrane at board edges (the top of a tub, for example), I ran the reinforcing fabric and liquid, paste, or gel around backerboard edges and into movement joint openings. After the membrane had cured, I filled the resulting gaps with sealant for optimal protection against mold.

Installing the Membrane

When all the fabric sections were prepared, I masked off the tub surface and started to flash the inside corners first, creating corners with double layers of reinforcing fabric. After flashing the corners with 6-inch-wide flashing, I started installing the larger sections of fabric (Figure 2-25). I began by covering sections of backerboard with uniform layers of the gel, embedding and smoothing the reinforcing fabric into the gel as I proceeded across the surface. The fabric was cut long enough to lap around corners and dip into the corner voids, with enough left over for a minimum 2-inch overlap to connect to neighboring sections of fabric. Seams were located outside movement joint areas.

Where the fabric meets the top of the tub, there should be enough fabric to fold around to cover the bottom edge of the backerboard and tuck into the movement joint slot (Figure 2-26). Often, short folds are difficult to maintain, and folded sections covering the lower edge of a backerboard often separate from the edge. When this happened, and it was obvious that enough gel had been applied, I resisted the urge to do anything. Instead, I let the two opposing surfaces become tacky before attempting to re-laminate

Materials List: Wall Project 2

Backerboard: 1/2-inch HardiBacker, James Hardie
Membrane system: B-6000 gel, non-woven polyester reinforcing mat, Bonsal American, www.bonsalamerican.com
Method: TCA B412, with membrane on setting bed surface.

Figure 2-20. When wood shims are used to shim a cast iron tub, the wood eventually crushes and the tub rocks. To prevent that, the author uses stainless-steel shims about 1 1/2 to 2 inches wide by 6 inches long, ranging from 1/64 to 1/8 inch thick (purchased from a scrap dealer).

Figure 2-21. Half-inch cement backerboards can be cut on an angle to help clear a raised tub flange. The author butters the angled edge of the board with latex thinset to fill the gap and support the weakened edge.

them. If the problem is a lack of gel or paste, re-application must take place as soon as possible before the fabric can be re-embedded.

At the inside corners, after painting the inside of the corner board joint with gel and smoothing the fabric over the surface of the board, I used a stiff paint brush to tuck the fabric into the opening at the corner. Instead of a flat 90-degree turn at the surface of the boards, looping the reinforcing fabric into the corner opening and then embedding it with gel or paste reduced the stress placed on the membrane at this critical, always-moving location. The looped corners

Figure 2-22. The author stacks shims to align the backerboard and maintain a $^1/_2$-inch-minimum gap where it meets the tub (left). He installs the predrilled sheets with square-drive backerboard screws (right). Gaps between boards are maintained by temporary nails lightly nailed into studs.

Figure 2-23. To prevent splitting, the author pre-drills and countersinks narrow sections of cement backerboards.

Figure 2-24. To save time during the installation of the membrane, the author precuts all fabric sections needed for the tub area.

of the membrane ensured complete waterproofing, but to prevent water from collecting there, the voids were filled with silicone (or a compatible) sealant.

At the legs extending down the face of the tub (Figure 2-27), the membrane should bridge between the walls and floor, and the movement joint between the tiles and tub should also extend to the floor. The entire surface receiving tile was covered with membrane and allowed to cure overnight. Before the tiles were installed, though, the board-to-tub and corner joints were filled with a compatible sealant (Figure 2-28). For sheet systems, this can happen immediately; for liquid-applied membranes, application of the sealant should not be done until the membrane materials have cured. The sealant must be given time to cure as well.

Finishing the Installation

Once the membrane had cured, tiles were installed. For this project, I have only installed the tiles necessary to identify the locations of movement joints required on a tub surround installation (Figure 2-29).

Figure 2-25. The author installs 6-inch-wide flashing over the inside corners of the tub surround (left) and then embeds larger sheets of fabric, providing two layers of reinforcing fabric in the movement joint areas (right).

Figure 2-26. There should be enough fabric to fold over the lower edge of the backerboard and to tuck a loop into the movement joint slot. Here, the author embeds the last of this fabric section on the back wall.

Figure 2-27. The author positions a section of reinforcing fabric that bridges the walls and floor. To spread liquid in tight areas, the author uses a stiff paint brush.

Tiling Baseboards, Toe Kicks, and Risers

Tiles can be used in many places around the house. They serve well wherever performance and good looks are required. Baseboard trim, toe kicks, and stair risers are three places where tiles can play an important role. Unlike other wall applications, however, tiles in these three areas need to be tough and durable enough to bear foot traffic. And because they must withstand considerable impact, they need a careful installation, too.

Performance ratings. Performance ratings in each of these three locations can range from Residential to Heavy Duty, depending on the setting and usage. While specific industry standards do not exist for these locations, it is important to understand how the installation will be used. For example, a residential bathroom with a single row of baseboard tiles can use the existing drywall (covered with a waterproofing membrane) as the substrate. In a gas station rest room, however, a gypsum substrate for a row of baseboard tiles would not last very long because of hard, continuous use as well as harsh daily cleaning routines. In the commercial bathroom, cement backerboards will hold up much better than gypsum board.

Substrates. A lot of toe kicks get tiled at the bottom of bathroom and kitchen cabinets and other cabinetwork. However, the dimensional lumber (and sometimes particleboard) that is typically used to make the kickboard is a very poor setting bed for tile. If you are planning to tile the kick, make sure the cabinetmaker uses ¾-inch exterior plywood for the kick. In residential work, this is strong enough for a direct application of tile, but for best waterproofing practices, first lap the floor waterproofing up and over the kickboard —then tile. Another option in a dry area is to cover the plywood with a layer of backerboard and then begin to tile.

Movement joints. For baseboard trim and toe kicks, movement joints are relatively simple. Figure 1-2 (Chapter 1, page 2) shows a variety of baseboard styles with their required movement joints. Notice, in particular, that floor-to-baseboard junctions actually require two movement joints when both the floor and baseboard are covered with tile.

Tile Baseboards

In my opinion, nothing sets one tile floor apart from the rest better than cove tile. The smooth curve looks beautiful and makes the floor a lot simpler to clean

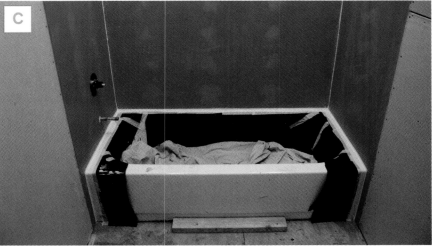

Figure 2-28. While the sealant is still soft, the author uses a margin trowel to shape the joint and scrape away excess material (A). To keep water out of the framing, he fills gaps around plumbing with silicone (B). Sealing around all plumbing, including the shower head, is essential with steam showers. This surface-applied membrane system,, with high-flexibility movement joints, will provide years of service and performance (C).

and maintain. However, a cove tile floor takes extra time and effort to get right, so this section will begin with a much simpler baseboard treatment: a single row of tiles. One-row baseboard installations are usually finished with bullnose trim tiles. Not all tiles have companion trim pieces, but some manufacturers offer tiles with one glazed edge just for this use. When field tiles are used for the baseboard, the square edge may be covered with a strip of wood.

Once the floor tiles were installed and the thinset had set up hard, I began installing the baseboard tiles with the same latex thinset used to install the floor tiles. Rather than attempt to notch thinset on the narrow baseboard strip, however, I used a ¼x½x¼-inch U-notch trowel to back butter the tiles and, with a margin trowel, spread a thin layer of thinset mortar over the setting (Figure 2-30).

When placing the tiles, I rested them temporarily on shims or spacers until about 6 lineal feet had been covered. Then I bridged the top edge of the tiles with a long straightedge and fine tuned the alignment with shims. Generally, I grout the baseboard tiles when I grout the floor tiles and install caulk or sealant in the

movement joints when the grout has cured and dried. When time and materials allow, I prefer to finish in this order:

1. install tiles on wall

2. paint or wallpaper remainder of wall and allow to dry

3. mask paint or wallpaper

4. grout tiles

For this method to work, any paints and coatings must be fully cured and hardened off. It will not work with some wallpaper types, such as flocked papers.

Cove Tiles

Cove tiles have always been one of my favorite trim shapes, but unfortunately, fewer and fewer companies are making cove tiles. As a result, I often pair cove tiles from one manufacturer with floor or countertop tiles from another. As discussed above, a cove tile installa-

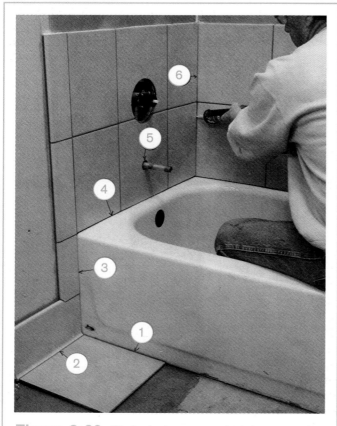

Figure 2-29. Six typical movement joints required for a tiled tub surround: between the tub and floor tiles (1), between floor and cove tiles (2), between tub and trim tiles (3), between tub and field tiles (4), to fill the voids between plumbing fixtures and the tile opening (5), and between neighboring walls (6).

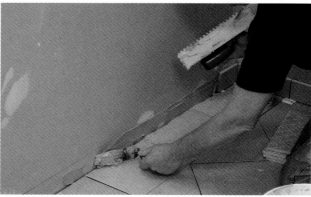

Figure 2-30. The author uses the flat side of the trowel to key the thinset into the back of the narrow baseboard tile, then uses the trowel's notched side to deposit an even amount of mortar (top). For convenience in this tight area, he applies a thin coat of mortar with a margin trowel (bottom).

tion is a complicated one, but when properly done, it rewards the user with a beautiful look and easy maintenance. When installed incorrectly, however, cove tiles look bad and perform terribly, especially when they are positioned atop the floor tiles (Figure 2-31). For more information on installing cove tiles, see Chapter 3, page 63.

Stairs

Tiling the treads and risers of a staircase is one of the most tedious and detail-oriented tile installations you can complete because of all the movement joints required between the treads and risers. If you are planning a tread/riser installation, refer to S151 in the TCA Handbook for all the details. Residential tiled-riser installations with wood, carpet, or resilient treads are quite common and do not require the myriad of details required for jobs with tile on both the tread and riser.

The two most important aspects of a project with tiled risers are movement joints between the treads and risers and full support for the tiles. Wood, steel, and concrete staircases all move considerably from the weight of people walking up and down. They move even more when used by young people, who often regard stairways as adventure trails. (Remember when your older brother dared you to jump down seven steps to the landing?)

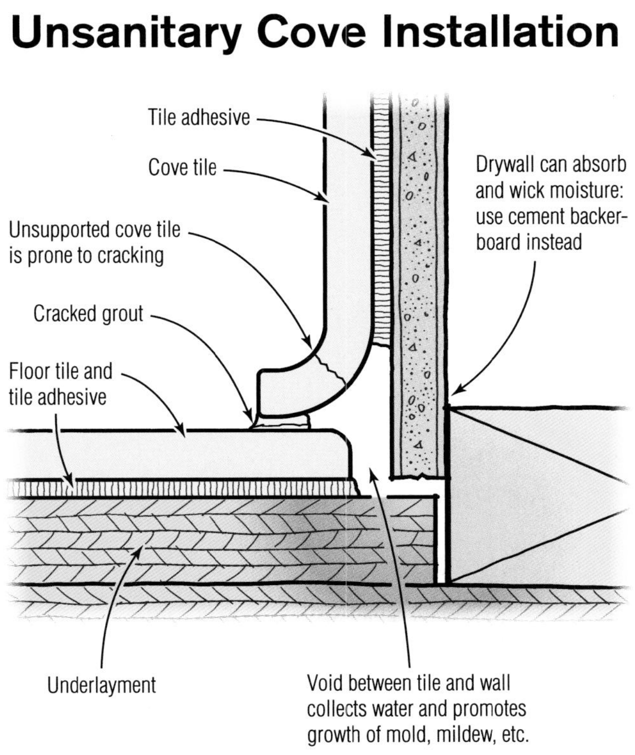

Unsanitary Cove Installation

- Tile adhesive
- Cove tile
- Unsupported cove tile is prone to cracking
- Cracked grout
- Floor tile and tile adhesive
- Underlayment
- Drywall can absorb and wick moisture: use cement backerboard instead
- Void between tile and wall collects water and promotes growth of mold, mildew, etc.

Figure 2-31. Far from improving an installation, cove tiles set atop floor tiles actually create a cleaning, maintenance, and hygiene problem.

When tiling the riser on a cast concrete stairway (interior or exterior), the risers should be medium-rough bush-hammered and cured a minimum 28 days before tiles are directly installed. For tiling the risers on a steel stairway (interior only), tack-weld reinforcing mesh to the risers and hire a plasterer or mason to float individual mortar beds for each riser. An alternative for steel stairways involves bolting sections of ¾-inch exterior plywood to the riser and covering the plywood with a crack isolation/waterproofing membrane. The risers on interior wood staircases also can be tiled, but the riser substrate (if it is dimensional lumber) should be covered with plywood and a crack isolation membrane for best results.

Stair movement joints. A small network of movement joints is needed to frame each tiled riser to prevent tiles from shearing off the surface. For stairs with tiled risers and carpeted treads, movement joints can be quite simple (Figure 2-32). The carpet at the top and bottom of the riser provides horizontal "movement joints," and ⅛-inch (min.) vertical joints on either side of the riser are filled with a resilient caulk, thus providing movement joints on all four sides of the riser. With an all-tile staircase, the riser tiles must also be isolated from the tread tiles above and below with resilient-filled movement joints. Whether movement is allowed via carpeting or resilient-filled joints, movement joints are an essential part of every riser installation.

Tiling a Fireplace or Stove Surround

Masonry fireplaces covered with ceramic tile have been part of residential construction for hundreds of years, and the development of low-cost fireplace inserts have made tile even more popular. Ceramic and natural stone tiles are also excellent materials to decorate areas around wood-burning stoves. Tiling walls around fireplaces and wood-burning stoves is similar to tiling any other wall surface, but you will need to take a few special precautions when working with a metal-box fireplace or the walls surrounding a wood stove.

Tile and Installation Materials

Most ceramic tiles, unless they have a crackled or very delicate glaze, can be used around fireplaces and wood stoves. Most natural stone tiles also can be used, but some stones may not be suitable for use around hot surfaces (ask the tile dealer which tiles are best and which to avoid). Agglomerated or resin-matrix stone tiles should never be used in these areas, and some resin-based tiles may actually be flammable.

Fireplaces and wood stove applications are one of the few areas where I won't use latex or polymer-modified thinset mortars and grouts. For these jobs, I prefer dry-set thinset mortars and grouts (which need to be damp cured) because they contain nothing that could be volatile in a hot environment. Also, I never use membranes for high-heat installations because those materials can soften and cause grout cracking and loose tiles.

There are few restrictions when tiling over poured concrete or laid-up masonry fireplaces, especially when you consider that ceramic tiles are created in a fire much hotter than you would find within a fireplace. With masonry or concrete construction and the right tile, it is even possible to tile the firebox. But with metal-box insert fireplaces, direct application of tile to any part of the fireplace insert is prohibited unless specifically approved by the manufacturer (some units have extra-strength zones where tile can be applied). Consequently, for insert-type metal fireplaces, the tiles can only be applied to surrounding drywall, and in some building jurisdictions, the drywall in such areas must be replaced with cement backerboards.

Masonry Fireplaces

Uncracked masonry or concrete fireplace surfaces need typical surface prep: clean, flat, and plumb. If the fireplace has been designed and built to receive tile, most likely its outer surface is made from blocks rather than bricks, in which case, the surface should be smooth enough for tiles. If the fireplace is brick, the tile install is usually part of a remodeling project that should include rehabbing the bricks by deep dry cleaning (usually sandblasting) followed by the application of a bonded mortar bed or approved patching material. If your project requires such a mortar bed, contract with an installer to float the bed. Installers lacking mortar-bed skills, however, can handle the installation of approved patching materials provided the fireplace surface is flat and plumb to an appropriate tolerance.

Most important, though, is cleanliness. Old fireplaces, however well-maintained, are generally covered with soot that acts as a bond breaker. Old masonry or concrete surfaces should be sand or shotblasted to reveal a fresh, uncontaminated surface and to eliminate all traces of bond-breaking soot that can also discolor grout. With masonry fireplaces, I prefer to use bullnose trim on the face around the opening, with a row of tiles trimming the throat (Figure 2-33).

With metal-box insert fireplaces, often the most pressing problem is how to deal with the junction where the tiles meet the metal box. This is a real problem in some applications because the drywall literally ends without touching the box. On such installations, I make certain the project specs call for the face of the firebox to be inset about $1/16$ inch from the plane of the drywall; this allows me to run the tiles slightly

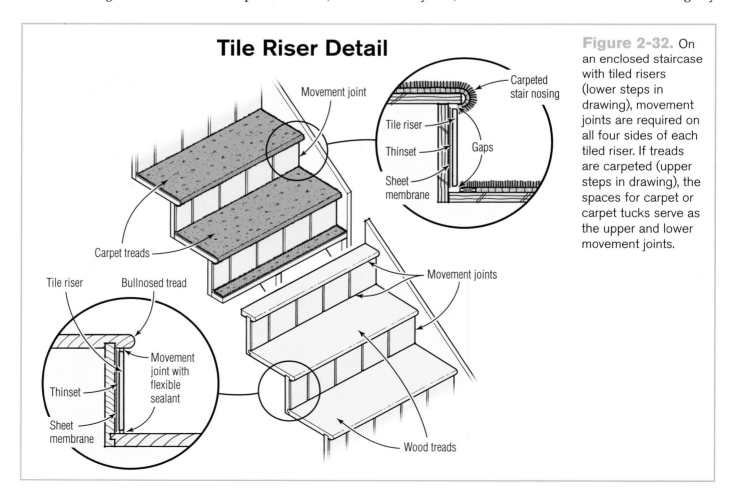

Tile Riser Detail

Movement joint

Carpeted stair nosing

Tile riser

Thinset

Gaps

Sheet membrane

Carpet treads

Movement joints

Tile riser

Bullnosed tread

Movement joint with flexible sealant

Thinset

Sheet membrane

Wood treads

Figure 2-32. On an enclosed staircase with tiled risers (lower steps in drawing), movement joints are required on all four sides of each tiled riser. If treads are carpeted (upper steps in drawing), the spaces for carpet or carpet tucks serve as the upper and lower movement joints.

beyond, and conceal the edge of, the firebox. To keep tiles in place until the adhesive hardens, I use shims, spacers, and a bridge made from scrap wood. Where the backing is interrupted, the tiles should overhang no more than $1/16$ inch. (When installing the grout, a margin trowel slipped behind the lip of the overhanging tile will prevent squeeze through of the soft grout.) In spite of the necessary gap, it is important that all the tiles receive full support. Tiles hanging off in space, especially in a rough fireplace environment, are bound to break. It's not a matter of if, but when!

Wood Stove Wall Shields

Ceramic or natural stone tiles provide an attractive way to protect against sparks and heat, but special construction details may be required in your local building jurisdiction. In this case, special construction means mounting the surround tiles on a non-flammable surface and far enough away from existing wall surfaces to create an air space between the gypsum walls and the tile surround. Whether or not your local building code requires a stand-off installation, called wall shields, for stoves and heaters, it is a good idea to assume that the laws of physics will apply to your installation and to use this method rather than worry about fire safety. Not all tile backers can be used around heat (foam or pressed cellulose, for example), and this type of installation is not referenced in most product literature. To my knowledge, only three

cement backerboards have been approved by UL Labs for this purpose: Durock (USG Corp.), Util-A-Crete (FinPan), and WonderBoard (Custom Building Products).

Building a Wall Shield

The easiest method available for building a wall shield assembly—sometimes called a standoff—involves the use of a material called hat channel, which is used to space and mount building panels approximately $7/8$ inch away from the structure. The hat channel is screwed into wood or metal studs (through existing drywall), and backerboards are fastened to the hat channel with backerboard metal stud screws. The wall shield should extend no less than 8 inches beyond the top and side profiles of the stove or heater and no less than 8 inches on either side of the flue pipe. The shield wall should extend to within 2 or 3 inches of the ceiling. To allow for the free flow of air behind the assembly, the lower edge of the shield wall should be a minimum of 2 inches from the top of the floor on which the stove or heater sits. Hat channel may be found at many drywall and general building supply outlets. If the stove surround is part of new construction or remodeling, the project specs should include extra studs so that the ends of the overlying backerboards are supported. A standoff can also be framed with 2x4 or 2x6 lumber, covered with $3/4$-inch plywood and skinned with cement backerboards.

CAUTION: Fireplace Tile Hazards

To avoid tile or installation failures:
- never install tiles over a cracked fireplace surface
- never install a crack-isolation membrane over a cracked fireplace surface

A cracked floor may be an inconvenience, but a cracked fireplace can emit fumes and carbon monoxide. It is a fire hazard that should be repaired—not covered over with tile. When working with metal-box insert fireplaces:
- never penetrate any portion of the box with fasteners
- never attempt to cover a metal firebox with tile or backerboard

First, the metal surfaces are too flimsy for tile. Second, penetrating any part of the box (unless approved by the unit's manufacturer) may allow fumes and carbon monoxide to escape into the living area or create a fire hazard.

Fireplace Opening

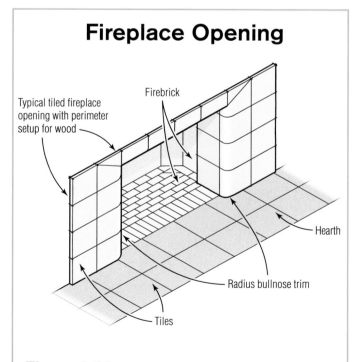

Figure 2-33. The author prefers trimming fireplace openings with radius bullnose trim, when such trim is available.

NOTES

Chapter 3
THIN-BED SHOWER STALLS

Tiled shower stalls are specialized applications combining floor and wall (and sometimes ceiling) techniques into a single installation.

Mortar beds are no longer required to construct all-tile shower stalls. Ready-to-tile shower bases and thin-bed components, including low-profile drains, slip-on curb and jamb sections, and pre-formed niches, are all widely available from tile distributors and some building supply outlets. When combined with tile backerboards and either sheet or trowel-applied waterproofing, these components give anyone with moderate building skills the tools to build beautiful and durable shower stalls. There are three basic ways to build an all-tile, thin-bed shower stall:

- with a modular shower base

- from individual components

- by flashing a conventional, thick-bed, clamping ring drain

Handicapped-accessible shower stalls, made without curbs, can also be built using thin-bed materials and techniques. The fourth project in this chapter explains how to build an easy-access shower that is as functional as it is beautiful.

Modular Shower Base

The first and easiest method is to use a pre-formed, modular shower base that includes an integral sloped floor, curb, upturned walls, and drain (Figure 3-1). The modular base is installed over a leveling bed of thinset mortar with multiple beads of sealant and connected to a waste line. You must provide a flat, level floor; plumb stud walls; backerboards; and a membrane system to protect the walls and tie into the modular base.

Tiles are applied directly to the base unit, but local building codes may require standard 24-hour water testing for some brands of ready-to-tile shower pans before tiling can begin. Water testing for the UL-listed base (TileRedi, www.tileredi.com) featured in Project 1

Figure 3-1. This molded, UL-listed shower base is connected to the waste line via its drain hub. The curb and upturned walls allow for immediate water testing, if required by code.

Figure 3-2. The bonding flange drain and sloped floor sections are part of a packaged kit (Schluter-Kerdi-Shower-Kit) that includes a load-bearing curb, sheet membrane, flashing, and pre-formed dam and inside corners.

was not required by my local code. While modular shower bases are relatively simple to install, you are limited to the sizes and shapes that are available.

Component System

The second way to build a thin-bed, all-tile shower is with individual components. Project 2 uses a variety of components, including a low-profile drain, pre-cast sloped floor sections, and liquid-applied membrane.

Some of the components I used in Project 2 came packaged as a kit (Figure 3-2) (Schluter-Kerdi-Shower-Kit, Schluter Systems, www.schluter.com), but individual components are available. Because this system addresses the entire shower—not just the pan—it is less complex than a modular base, and it allows for more flexibility in size, shape, and design. Handicap access ramps, pre-cast curb sections, thinset mortar, and flexible sealant also are available as part of the overall system.

Drain Flashing Method

Even though the third way to build a thin-bed shower stall requires some dry-pack mortar, I have included it in this section because the trowel work needed to produce a sloped shower floor is relatively simple. Also, in many areas a traditional clamping ring drain is the only method approved by the local code for use in shower areas. Perhaps an even better reason for including this type of installation is that, unlike expanded foam or composite pans, a mortar-bed shower floor can support very heavy loads.

A specially made CPE drain flashing (Figure 3-3)

Figure 3-3. This heat-molded NobleFlex CPE drain flashing eliminates the problem of connecting a surface-applied membrane system to a clamping ring drain.

(NobleFlex, Noble Company, www.noblecompany.com) solves the problem of how to connect a thin-bed membrane to a conventional clamping ring drain and is featured in Shower Stall Project 3.

This product can also provide an economical solution to repairs and renovation work. The flashing allows an installer to provide a level of waterproofing protection that is simply not possible with traditional materials and methods. It can eliminate the major problems inherent in a traditional shower pan—absorption and wicking—and it also requires fewer tools and skills than does a traditional pan.

Shower Stall Project 1:
Installing a Modular Shower Base

A traditional all-tile shower is one of the most challenging residential tile installations, but advances in materials and technology have put tile shower stalls within the reach of anyone who is patient, handy with tools, and ready for a challenge.

This project covers the installation of the shower base, backerboards, and alcove, followed by the membrane and tile, and focuses on the details required to ensure a waterproof and non-waterlogging setting bed for tiles installed in very wet areas.

The molded base used for this project significantly reduces the complexity of building a traditional shower stall, and the use of a molded inset alcove makes customizing the shower relatively easy when all the parts are joined by a waterproofing/crack isolation membrane. The shower base can be used with any

nominal $7/16$-inch-thick backerboard. For this project, I used $7/16$-inch fiber-cement backerboards installed with corrosion-resistant screws, all covered with a membrane (Figure 3-4).

Normally, I prefer to follow manufacturer's instructions, but the instructions found on this product's Web site were incomplete. The instructions did not account for the joint between the unit and the backerboard walls, and the kit did not include enough epoxy adhesive to install tiles as directed. For these reasons, I made a few changes in the way this ready-to-tile unit was prepped, installed, and tiled.

Some of these changes run counter to the manufacturer's instructions, and all add more time to an installation. In my opinion, however, they are more consistent with tile industry standards, and they yield a more durable and leak-proof installation. In spite of some easily fixed shortcomings, I like this ready-to-tile unit and am impressed with its water-tight qualities. The resulting shower, the first shower project in this book and part of a demonstration bathroom, is a beautiful example of what can be done using only thin-bed methods and materials.

Installing the Shower Base

The stud walls should be prepared as for a traditional stall shower, including 2x10 blocking between studs for securing the upturned walls and the lower edge of the companion backerboards.

Figure 3-5 shows how this pan is supported with beads of sealant applied to the reinforcing ribs cast into the bottom of the unit. Notice, too, the 2-inch ABS pipe that has been stubbed to the proper length (flush to the subfloor for this unit) and beveled about ¼-inch for easy insertion into the base connection. It is essential both to remove the drain screen to gain access to the inside of the drain housing and to dry-fit the base unit to the stub—at least once—prior to installation.

When finally installing the base unit, you may need to simultaneously bed the unit in thinset mortar and join the pipe stub to the unit's drain housing with a pipe solvent. Dry-fitting uncovers problems that would slow the installation and possibly ruin the pipe connection. When installing this type of modular shower pan, I am less concerned with the slower drying sealant below the unit than I am with the PVC solvent, which dries hard within a minute and is difficult to correct if contact is delayed or if the pipe and coupling are misaligned and the installation aborted

midway. If you have access to the base unit from below, the installation is much simpler, since the plumbing hook up can be done as a separate step.

With modular shower pans, it is important to construct a tight-fitting opening so the pan's upturned walls—and the tiles—are fully supported. However, a snug fit can slow installation (regardless of your tiling skills) and even damage the unit. Many otherwise careful installations show either some damage to the

Materials List: Shower Stall Project 1

Shower base kit: 48x48-inch Tile Ready shower pan, Tile Redi, www.tileredi.com
Membrane system: Custom 9240, Custom Building Products (CBP)
Tiles: 12x12 porcelain tiles, 6x12 cove, 3x12 surface trim, StonePeak Ceramics, www.stonepeakceramics.com
Thinset mortar: MegaLite medium-bed latex thinset mortar, (CBP)
Grout: Prism, CBP
Sealant: Polyblend, CBP
Sealer: TileLab, penetrating sealer, CBP
Method: A variation of TCNA B422
Subfloor/Underlayment: ¾-inch plywood over ¾-inch plywood (exterior grade)
Performance rating: Moderate Residential

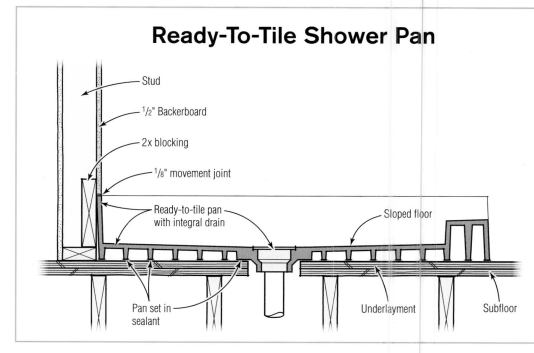

Ready-To-Tile Shower Pan

- Stud
- ½" Backerboard
- 2x blocking
- ⅛" movement joint
- Ready-to-tile pan with integral drain
- Sloped floor
- Pan set in sealant
- Underlayment
- Subfloor

Figure 3-4. The upturned walls of the shower base are continued by cement backerboard separated from the base by a ⅛-inch movement joint. The joint is filled with the liquid component of the membrane used on the backerboard.

base unit or air gaps between the base unit and the surrounding framing. Figure 3-6, however, reveals a trade secret that ensures a tight fit, a quick installation, and zero damage to the base unit.

The process I use to install modular units like this ready-to-tile pan, as well as shower receptors and bathtubs, involves identifying which side wall is most square to the back wall and temporarily repositioning the opposite sidewall to allow plenty of room for inserting the base unit. To ensure that I could move the wall out of the way and reposition it in the right location, I marked the position of the left wall, cut

through the fasteners holding the wall, pulled the wall back, and staked it temporarily with a duplex head nail (Figure 3-6). The wall only needs to be pulled back about an inch from the line, then pushed back into position after the pan unit is installed.

I dry-fit the base unit for level and square and used

Shower Base Prep

Not all modular shower bases are the same. Tiles and tile membranes can be installed directly over the dense polyurethane unit displayed in this project, but only after the proper prep work. Other ready-to-tile units must be prepped and installed according to the individual manufacturer's instructions. As delivered from the factory, the slick surface of this base requires a few minutes of roughing up with 50- to 80-grit sandpaper. For convenience, and because the heads of the attachment screws were slightly below the surface, this was done after the unit was installed. One factor that made installation of this pan simple was the self-leveling underlayment used on this bathroom floor.

Figure 3-5. The author shoots beads of sealant on the unit's lower ribs just before installing the pan. The drain pipe has been stubbed to the correct height and beveled for easy insertion into the drain hub.

Figure 3-6. The author marks the position of the wall with a pen (A). Using a reciprocal saw (B), he cuts through enough fasteners to allow the lower portion of the wall to be repositioned. He then pulls back the wall and temporarily stakes it out of the way to allow for easy installation of the base (C).

shims, as necessary, to make certain the unit was level in all directions. That done, I flipped the lightweight pan unit up, applied beads of sealant to the bottom ridges, and applied pipe cement to the drain stub and the drain housing. Then I lowered the unit, carefully aligning and seating the drain, and butted the unit against the two square walls (Figure 3-7).

I walked around the unit, inspecting it from all sides to make sure that it was in full contact with the floor and that the back and right upturned walls of the unit were in contact with their anchor walls. Next, I pushed the left wall back into place until it was in full contact with the left side of the unit. I secured the wall with fasteners and began securing the top inch of the pan's upturned walls with 1⅝-inch, non-corrosive backerboard screws (Figure 3-8). This method eliminates any gaps between the base unit and surrounding walls and provides a solid foundation for the tiles. (Note: This unit's instructions did not call for any fasteners.)

The base unit is virtually impervious to moisture and requires no membrane, but successful tile bonding requires the use of epoxy mortar that is included in the shower base kit. The base unit and its upturned walls are relatively strong, but their bonding surface can be fragile until covered with tile. To avoid contaminating the floor of the unit, and to preserve the bite of its abraded surface, I protected it with a piece of clean plastic film, covered by a tarp folded over into a thick pad, with a layer of heavy cardboard on top. To avoid damaging the curb, I covered it, too, with layers of tarps. Once the base was secured with a screw at

every stud and one between each pair of studs into the blocking, I began installing the backerboards.

Installing the Backerboard Walls

The base unit was designed to be used with any ⁷⁄₁₆-inch backerboards. For this project, I used nominal ½-inch (⁷⁄₁₆-inch actual) fiber-cement boards. The boards are unaffected by exposure to water. Like other setting bed materials, however, they will absorb water and, when sufficiently saturated, can wick water into upper portions of the board. To guard against that, I filled the joints between the pan and backerboards

Figure 3-7. After dry-fitting the pan and applying sealant to its bottom ribs and pipe cement to the drain stub and drain housing, the author carefully lowers the pan into position, checking to make sure the drain pipe stub is bonded to the drain housing. Then he pushes the unit snug against the back and right walls.

Figure 3-8. After pushing the left wall back against the pan, the author re-secures the wall with construction screws (top). Next he secures the pan's upturned walls with corrosion-resistant backerboard screws positioned an inch below the top of the pan (bottom).

and those between board joints with the latex paste used for the membrane (Figure 3-9).

The base unit does not absorb water and needs no further protection, but the backerboards need to be waterproofed and installed to ensure a leakproof connection between the boards and the base unit. Because the pan unit and the backerboards are different materials with different properties, I eliminated all concerns about waterproofing and crack isolation by installing a membrane that extends from the floor of the shower to the top of the walls.

To reduce foot traffic, I made one trip onto the shower floor to make a list of all backerboard dimensions needed for the shower and returned only after all the boards were cut, drilled (if required), and ready to install. Outside the shower, I staged a screw gun, 1⅝-inch backerboard screws, and a squeeze bottle of waterproofing gel for sealing the board seams. I used power snips to cut this type of board to length and width and wet-cutting diamond core bits to make holes. Additional tools included dry-cutting diamond blades, carbide jig saw blades, and other carbide and diamond cutting tools to produce smooth cuts whose edges can be easily waterproofed.

When all the boards were cut, I dry-fitted them and then staged them close to the shower curb, placing them in the order they would be installed. I began by shooting a fat ¼-inch bead of waterproofing paste on the top edge of the shower base unit's upturned back wall and shot a similar bead along the lower edge of the board cut to fit the back wall. The lower edge of the backerboard should be no less than ⅛ inch and no more than ¼ inch away from the top edge of the shower base unit. You have to work carefully and use shims to avoid squeezing the paste out of the board joints! Board manufacturer's instructions call for fasteners every 6 inches around the perimeter of the board and every 8 inches over studs within the field of the board. After each board was secured with fasteners, I backfilled any voids and used a sponge to remove any excess paste that had bled out of the joints (Figure 3-9).

Detailing the Pony Wall

Backerboards were used to cover four sides of the pony wall, but to provide extra stability for this open-topped wall, it was first skinned with a layer of ½-inch plywood, screwed and glued to each side. To prevent standing water anywhere along the top of the finished pony wall, one of the plywood reinforcing sheets was positioned to provide slope for the top backerboard (Figure 3-10). After the backerboards were screw-fastened to the pony wall, I used a patching compound to fill in the gaps at the top of the pony wall and at other locations that needed filling.

Parging the Pan With Epoxy

The idea of installing tiles on four walls of the pan, plus the floor and curb, with a single, small batch of epoxy

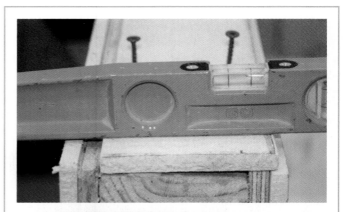

Figure 3-10. To prevent water from accumulating around the glass installed on this pony wall, its top surface must be sloped toward the shower drain (top). When finished, the patching mortar (bottom) helps create a smooth, void-free surface for the membrane.

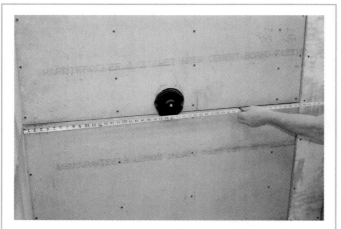

Figure 3-9. The junction between the upturned walls of the shower pan and the backerboards is filled with orange-colored waterproof membrane paste, the same material used to seal seams between the upper and lower backerboards.

sounded like a prescription for disaster. So instead, I decided to use the epoxy supplied by the pan manufacturer to parge the surface of the pan and then let it dry and cure (Figure 3-11). After curing, the sandy surface of the epoxy would provide plenty of tooth to grab the latex thinset I would use to install the tiles. As it turned out, there was just enough epoxy to cover the pan with a very thin layer—not a tablespoon more and certainly not enough to properly install tiles!

Installing the Membrane

The membrane for this project, a trowel-applied membrane with a companion polyester reinforcing fabric, has two functions: waterproofing for the shower walls and crack isolation protection where the backerboards meet the pan's upturned walls. The manufacturer of this pan did not specify fasteners for the upturned walls or a movement joint where they meet the backerboards. That was the reason I decided to install a combination membrane over the pan/backerboard junctions. The epoxy coating would ensure that the membrane stays attached. A trowel or airless sprayer can be used to apply some brands of waterproofing paste, but for this project, I used a small diameter paint roller and a stiff paintbrush to apply the paste and smooth out the reinforcing fabric.

> Note: The reinforced membrane used in this shower area was installed on the wainscot and bathroom floor areas at the same time (see Chapter 2, Project 1, page 39, for details).

Figure 3-11. To ensure the latex-based membrane will stick to the pan, the author flat trowels the entire surface of the pan with the epoxy mortar provided by the manufacturer. After curing, the epoxy will provide an excellent bonding surface for the membrane.

Tiling the Shower—Walls First

The sloped floor on this unit is strong, and the setting bed surface is well protected as described above, so I could install the 12-inch wall tiles first without worrying about hurting the floor surface.

The process of transferring the rough layout from my notebook to the walls was quick because of the size of the tiles and was made even quicker with the help of a laser designed for wall work. In a few minutes, I was able to begin tiling. I used the layout to establish sizing for the first and second courses of tile (cove tile plus a 1-inch liner), made cut pieces on a wet saw for the entire first and second courses, and began spreading latex thinset mortar on the lower back wall with a ¼ x ½ x ¼ U-notch trowel. Once the cove and liner tiles were installed and spaced or shimmed, I spread more latex thinset and began installing the whole tiles. To help contain the freshly installed tiles and keep them stacked true, I sometimes plumbed a straightedge to ensure the tiles would not slide out of position (Figure 3-12). With the first two courses leveled and the straightedge guide in place, the remainder of the wall went up quickly (Figure 3-13). Once the back wall was finished, I removed any side spacers or shims occupying or obscuring the movement joint slot on the left and right hand sides. I filled these joints with silicone just before tiling the side walls (Figure 3-14).

As part of this project, I wanted to demonstrate the use of a ready-to-tile alcove, so before tiling the left wall, I laid out a suitable location for the alcove and installed the unit after the walls had been waterproofed (see "Installing the Alcove," page 63.)

Figure 3-12. This straightedge, once it is plumbed and held in place with screws, will prevent the fresh tiles from slipping sideways.

With 12-inch tiles, a lot of ground can be covered quickly, but tiling the alcove took time to make good cuts and good fits. Before tiling inside the box, though, I installed as many full tiles around the alcove as possible. Because of the alcove's placement, the section separating the top recess from the bottom recess did not make for an ideal layout, but it did give me an opportunity to demonstrate how to prevent L-shaped cuts from cracking at the inside corner. I typically place a galvanized finish nail in a thick layer of medium-bed thinset to reinforce this type of L-cut tile (a layer of regular thinset mortar would be too thin to hide the nail and not force the tile out of plane) (Figure 3-16).

Manufactured alcoves such as this one are inherently waterproof and should not leak if they are installed properly—especially if the alcove is covered with a membrane. The trick is not to have any voids behind the tiles that could trap water and harbor mold or mildew. Another thing that helps is to slope the floors of the alcove so they drain (¼ inch per foot is the standard). Nevertheless, for complete protection, I covered the alcove surfaces with membrane.

To tile the inside of the alcove, I used surface bullnose tiles, first cutting each tile to its proper width, then aligning it with the openings to mark its length.

To get accurate cuts along the bottom and top of the side pieces, I used a bevel gauge to record the slope angles and mark the tile for cutting (Figure 3-17). I installed the tiles in the following order:

1. floor

2. back

3. roof

4. side

Note, too, that the roof is sloped to drain toward the shower—not the back of the box.

After all the walls were finished, I used more surface bullnose to trim the top and sides of the shower walls. To keep the 3x12-inch surface bullnose pieces aligned, I used spacers and a piece of tape to hold the tiles until the adhesive hardened (Figure 3-18). Oddly enough, although the tile manufacturer makes a broad line of trim, down angles to finish off outside corners in 3x12 surface bullnose were not available, so I mitered bullnose sections, did some extra cutting, and inserted a decorative flair to finish the corners (Figure 3-19).

Figure 3-13. Once the foundation courses are aligned, the rest of the wall installs rather quickly.

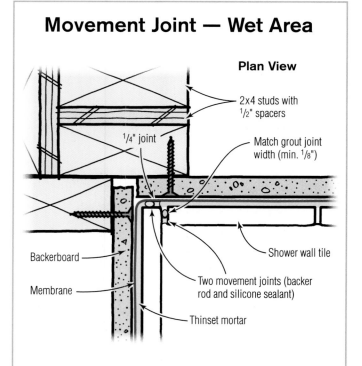

Movement Joint — Wet Area

Plan View

2x4 studs with ½" spacers

¼" joint

Match grout joint width (min. ⅛")

Backerboard

Membrane

Shower wall tile

Two movement joints (backer rod and silicone sealant)

Thinset mortar

Figure 3-14. There are actually two movement joints per inside corner of the shower: one for the first wall tiled and another for the second. Both are essential if the installation is to avoid damage by normal structural movement.

Installing the Alcove

Building a leakproof, custom inset soap dish with traditional mortar-bed methods requires planning, skill, and close attention to details. Modular units like the companion alcove used in this project require skill and attention to details but with significantly less labor.

The walls on this project were built with 16-inch-on-center studs and the alcove instructions called for horizontal blocking, a requirement that also applied to backerboard edges. The alcove is designed to fit within one of the wall's 14$\frac{1}{2}$-inch stud cavities, so its position is fixed from side to side. The ultimate positioning of this alcove was a compromise, like most installations.

To lay out the opening, I placed the alcove against the backerboard, determined its position with a tape measure, and traced around its perimeter, making allowances for a minimum $\frac{1}{8}$-inch, gel-filled joint between the alcove and surrounding board. The installation of the niche was an afterthought and was based on the position of the studs and existing blocking, plus the layout of the tiles.

To cut and fabricate the hole in the backerboard, I used a jig saw fitted with a bi-metal blade. To keep the wall surface as flat as possible, I slit through the existing membrane and removed about 1 inch from around the perimeter of the opening. Next, I added blocking to the top of the opening to help support the alcove, ran sealant over the exposed studs and blocking, and pressed the alcove in place (Figure 3-15).

I filled the resulting joint with more sealant, shot backerboard screws around the mounting flange, and allowed the sealant to dry before covering the alcove with membrane.

Figure 3-15. After aligning the alcove and tracing its outline on the wall, the author uses a jigsaw to cut the opening (A). To keep the installation as flat as possible, he makes a shallow slit through the membrane and removes about 1-inch from around the opening (B). After adding top blocking and shooting sealant around the framed opening, he presses the alcove into place (C). Sealant and screws will secure it, and once the sealant has dried, the alcove will be covered with membrane.

With all the wall tiles installed, I turned my attention to the top of the pony wall and the top of the curb.

Detailing the Tops of the Pony Wall and Curb

A slope of ¼ inch per foot is required on shower seats, the floors of inset soap dishes, and the tops of pony walls and curbs. To get the right slope, I used the tiles set on the faces of these features to help guide the floating of the patching mortar used to fill these areas. The adhesive behind these tiles should be hard so the tiles don't get pulled off the setting bed while the patching mortar is being worked.

Using the curb as an example, the first step is to give the curb top a thin coating of thinset mortar (this will

Figure 3-16. To keep the L-shaped cut from cracking, the author places a 3½-inch galvanized finishing nail into the thinset mortar (left). A thick layer of medium-bed thinset mortar allows the tile to sit flat over the galvanized nail (right).

Figure 3-17. The author marks the length of the alcove side tile (left) and uses a carpenter's bevel gauge to ensure that the slope angle of the cuts are correct (right).

bond the patching mortar to the curb top). For this tight area, I used a sponge to apply the mortar. Next, I troweled on the patching mortar and used a flat trowel, held tight against the curb tiles, to finish the mortar flat (Figure3-20). I try to keep the patching mortar on this type of sloped top less than ¾ inch thick; if thicker, corrosion-resistant reinforcing will be required to strengthen the mud.

The patching mortar dried in less than an hour, but with other work to do on this project, I let the patching mud set up overnight before tiling.

Floating the curb top is fun work, so to balance things out, make sure you take the time to clean all traces of mortar off the screed tiles! To avoid discoloring the grout, make sure the entire top edges of the screed tiles are completely free of patching or bonding mortar.

Figure 3-18. To keep the bullnose tiles from sliding sideways, the author secures the trims with a piece of tape. Note the site-made substitute for a down angle, a piece not available from the manufacturer.

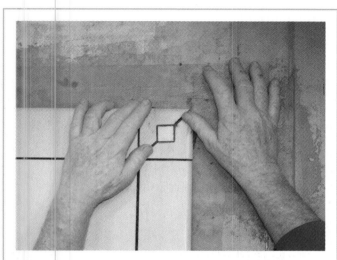

Figure 3-19. To substitute for a down angle, the author miters two pieces of bullnose.

Figure 3-20. The author uses a sponge to spread a thin layer of latex thinset on the top of the curb (A) to serve as a bonding adhesive for the patching mortar. With the facing tiles sitting proud of the curb top by ⅜- to ⅝-inch, not much patching mortar is required for this slope (B). Using the facing tiles as screeds, little skill is required to produce a perfect top. Here, the author glides the flat trowel over the mortar in one last finishing pass (C).

Tiling the Modular Shower Floor

This floor is one of the simplest of all the floor installation projects because the tiles will be adhered directly to the surface of the base unit with a latex thinset mortar, without a membrane—just the epoxy coating. As you will see from the photos of the finished bathroom, this shower floor was a delight to install because simply by following the ANSI standards for finish work (balanced cuts, no cuts less than half-size, etc., ANSI A108, 4.3), the resulting floor layout is a little mathematical gem—tiles balanced and simply, but elegantly, detailed.

To ensure the smoothest conical shape to the slope of this shower floor, I spent about 15 minutes using a palm sander to smooth out lumps and trowel marks in the epoxy coating (Figure 3-21). This project began with cutting the 12-inch tiles into nominal 3-inch tiles (see "Finishing Cut Tiles," next page). Twelve-inch tile stock is also used to cut a transition border between the smaller floor tiles and the cove tiles (Figure 3-22). Sloped floors require smaller tiles that are better able to conform to the ideal conical shape without excess lippage—no more than the thickness of a dime.

The trick to producing the smoothest tile finish is to use a bit more thinset than is needed to lift all the tiles high enough so the tiles can be "beat in"—gently!—

with a rubber grout trowel. To help accomplish that, and to ensure maximum adhesion, all the floor tiles were back buttered and set over a bed of adhesive spread with a $\frac{1}{4}$x$\frac{1}{2}$x$\frac{1}{4}$-inch U-notch trowel.

Installing the Shower Floor Tiles

Layout for this shower floor is simple and straightforward (Figure 3-24). It is anchored off the center of the drain, which has been adjusted to sit slightly below the tiles around it. Using only whole tiles, half diagonals, and quarter diagonals, I covered the back half of the floor and filled the gap between the diagonal section and the cove tiles with border strips aligned with the joints on the wall tiles (Figure 3-25). In non-cove tile installations, the lower edge of the wall tiles should be positioned to allow the floor tiles to pass beneath the surface plane of the wall tiles but remain at least $\frac{1}{8}$ inch away from any hard wall surface.

Before moving my position, I double-checked tiles on the back half of the floor, as I would not be able to reach them easily later. First, I checked the alignment of the tiles in all directions. Then I checked to ensure that at least 70% of every grout joint and 100% of every movement joint was free of any thinset residue and that all tile surfaces were clean. Once satisfied with these details, I moved outside the shower base to tile the remaining sloped floor area.

Figure 3-21. To smooth out trowel marks, the author uses a palm sander fitted with 80-grit paper and follows that with the vacuum to remove bond-breaking dust.

Figure 3-22. The liners, floor tiles, diagonals, and borders were all cut from 12-inch tiles.

Usually, white thinset is used to install white tiles so that excess adhesive bleeding through the grout joints won't be so noticeable. Bleed through is caused by adhesive ridges, which are only essential for depositing a uniform amount of adhesive; they are not critical to bonding. In fact, most of the adhesive that squeezes up into the grout joints is wasted adhesive that must be removed.

To reduce bleed through, first, spread the thinset mortar with the smooth edge of the trowel to key it into the setting bed. Next, add more thinset. Then use the notched edge to lay down uniform ridges. With that

Finishing Cut Tiles

The 3-inch tiles used on the shower floor are cut from 12-inch tiles on the wet saw, preserving as many factory edges as possible. To ensure a smooth tile-to-tile transition at cut edges, I dry-ground bevels on a bench-top belt sander, trying to mimic the shape, curvature, or bevel of the original as closely as possible. With these tiles, I beveled each cut edge about 1/16 inch with 80-grit belts (Figure 3-23). Then I smoothed each corner to remove the sharp point made during the beveling process.

I use this cutting and edge-profiling method for natural stone and color-through porcelain tiles only. With all other tiles, unless the glaze color matches the color of the bisque, I use only light edge sanding, just enough to break the sharpness of the wet saw's cut. Note: All porcelain, impervious, and vitreous tiles cut on a wet saw should be thoroughly dried before making contact with any adhesive.

Figure 3-23. To mimic the original factory edge, the author uses a bench sander fitted with 80-grit carbide belts to lightly bevel all cut edges.

Figure 3-24. For this floor, the author proves his math with a layout of the actual tiles lined up against straightedges (left). The finished layout, plotted with a pencil and straightedge, focuses on the joint between the diagonal and border tiles, while two other lines cut the floor into four sections (above).

done, clean off the trowel and use the flat edge to gently flatten the ridges (Figure 3-26). I selected the ½-inch-deep trowel to deposit a lot of adhesive, but with ridges higher than the thickness of the tiles, flattening the ridges was essential. This was especially important because to maximize adhesion, each of the tiles on this floor had been back buttered as well (Figure 3-27).

The second half of the floor was done in the same order as the first: fill in with the 3-inch tiles, then measure, cut, and install the border tiles. The last step on this floor was to mark and cut the four tiles surrounding the drain. These cuts should be pretty because they will be directly under the eyes of anyone using the shower. To ensure a good cut line, I used a compass to mark the tiles (Figure 3-28) and used a wet saw to make the cuts and create a slight bevel on the curved edge.

Tiling the Tops of the Curb and Pony Wall

Both the curb and pony wall tops required trim on their inner and outer edges. To do this, 3x12 surface bullnose tiles were cut to the right width, with a grout joint running parallel to the top of the curb or pony wall. To break up the monotonous grout joint running through the center, I borrowed an element from the

floor—a diagonal tile—and inlaid one where four surface bullnose tiles come together.

The first step, though, was to cut the tiles to size. To do this, I cut one side of trim tiles, dry-fitted them, and then measured the opposite side and cut the trim for that. When all the trim tiles were cut, I laid a diagonal over the intersection of four tiles, marked the cut lines, and sent the tiles back to the wet saw. I didn't knock down the adhesive ridges for this part of the project, but I did take care to keep the tile edges clean (Figure 3-29). The diagonal inserts can match or contrast, and they add a spark to an otherwise plain surface (Figure 3-30).

Other Details

The left side of the shower was finished with surface bullnose tiles. The joint between the bullnose and cove tiles is a modified miter that I think looks more tailored than a full miter (Figure 3-31). Figure 3-32 shows the accent tiles inlaid into the pony wall and curb tops. The end of the pony wall required a lot of cuts to make everything fit. The down angles trimming the front corners were cut from bullnose stock. The second bullnose edge was rough profiled with a dry-cutting diamond blade and finished on the belt sander.

Figure 3-25. Border tiles create a smooth transition between the floor and wall tiles.

Figure 3-26. To keep thinset from clogging the grout joints, the author uses the flat edge of the trowel to gently flatten the adhesive ridges.

Grouting the Modular Shower Stall

Tiles installed over waterproofing membranes need a bit more drying and curing time, since moisture in the adhesive is not readily absorbed into the setting bed and can only evaporate through open grout joints. I waited

Figure 3-29. To eliminate adhesive bleed through, the author cleans the edges of the curb tiles with a damp sponge.

Figure 3-27. Because porcelain is difficult to bond, the author back butters every tile on the floor.

Figure 3-28. A compass assures a smooth cut line for the tiles located around the drain.

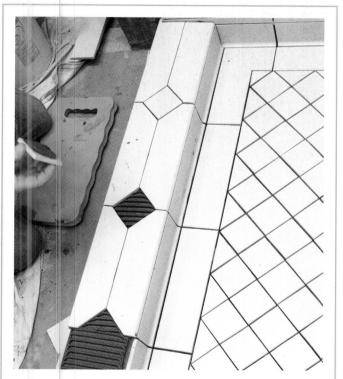

Figure 3-30. Instead of a boring straight line, the curb becomes more interesting with these diagonal inserts.

Figure 3-31. The abbreviated miter between the cove and bullnose tiles looks more trim and stylish than a full miter.

48 hours before starting to grout and began the process by inspecting all the joints, cleaning out any remaining adhesive residues clogging the top two-thirds of the joints, and making sure all the tile surfaces were clean.

The porcelain tiles used in this modular shower stall grout up quickly due to crisp tile edges, but like the relatively impervious setting beds, the tiles absorb virtually no moisture and, therefore, require more time for hardening and proper curing. With the ambient temperature approaching 90°F., I grouted one wall at a time before stopping to sponge clean. To ensure the grout was packed into the lower cove tile joints, I held the edge of the trowel—instead of its handle—for more leverage (Figure 3-33).

For tiles this size, I concentrate on individual joints and use the grout trowel to compress the grout—not just fill the joints. I use a minimum amount of water and remove any lingering cement haze within an hour after cleaning. As with any installation, movement joints need to remain open throughout the installation, so I use a ¼-inch tuck pointer to easily slice through grout that has long lost its plasticity, turning it into crumbled lumps that are easily removed. After a 72 hour wait, these grout crumbs can be vacuumed away and the joint filled with a resilient caulk.

Figure 3-32. This entire bathroom was tiled using only 12-inch field tiles, 6x12-inch cove tiles, 3x12-inch bullnose, and a few other trim pieces. The down angles trimming the front top of the pony wall were rough formed with a diamond blade and smooth finished on a tabletop belt sander.

Figure 3-33. For more leverage in tight areas, the author grips the blade of the trowel rather than its handle.

Shower Stall Project 2:
Installing a Thin-Bed Component System

This shower is part of a three-room floor project that uses a component drain and two interlocking sloped floor sections to create a curbless, waterproof shower. I included this project because installers need more and more options for handicap applications, as well as for customers who want a curbless shower.

The walls of the shower are covered with 24-inch porcelain tiles that, among other things, significantly reduce the number of grout joints. The shower floor is another diagonal-with-border layout, with tiles cut from full-size tiles into $3\frac{3}{4}$-inch (nominal) squares to match the dimensions of the square drain screen, diagonals, and half diagonals, as well as the border tiles. Normally, the border around a shower floor abuts the restraining walls and curb, but in this curbless design, the border tiles are used as a transition between the shower and bathroom floors (Figure 3-34).

I designed this project to demonstrate a number of materials and concepts that the thin-bed installer can use to increase efficiency and ensure quality waterproofing protection. There are two products in particular that help improve the performance of this shower. The first is a load-bearing, water-resistant sloped floor manufactured in two sections, and the second is a companion shower drain designed specifically for thin-bed shower floors.

Prepping the Shower Stall

The stud walls for this 4x4-foot shower were built to provide full-face attachment for all the backerboard edges (Figure 3-35). As is commonly built for handicap access, such stud walls may also require extra framing for grab bars, seats, hoists, and other equipment. Specs for these features should come from the product manufacturer or a qualified structural engineer.

Because the goal was to make this shower flush with the bathroom floor tiles, the floor required special consideration. Normally, when this system is installed using component curb sections (Figure 3-36), the curb hides the fact that the thickness of the sloped sections raises the shower floor tiles about $1\frac{1}{2}$ inches higher than the tiles installed on the other side of the curb (the bathroom floor tiles). The wood subfloor shown in this project was lowered in the shower area to accommodate the perimeter thickness of the sloped floor sections, $1\frac{1}{2}$ inches for this 4-foot size. For concrete slab floors, the best approach is to position the bonding flange drain so that the slope of the concrete in the shower area meets tile industry standards: a smooth and uniform $\frac{1}{4}$ inch per foot (Figure 3-37).

The sloped floor sections and bonding flange drain were installed using the manufacturer's recommended

dryset thinset mortar prior to installation of the backerboard walls. To prevent damaging the soft floor sections while I worked on the walls, I covered them with a scrap piece of $\frac{1}{2}$-inch drywall.

The wall setting bed for this project is made from $\frac{1}{2}$-inch-thick cement backerboards. On these hard boards, I prefer to pre-drill and pre-countersink screw holes. After recording dimensional information of the location and spacing of the studs, I saved some fabrication time by stacking three sheets of backerboard (the number of boards required on each wall), laying out fastener locations on the top board, and pre-drilling the fastener holes simultaneously (Figure 3-38).

After all the boards were cut and drilled, I installed them with a $\frac{3}{8}$-inch gap between the boards and the top of the sloped floor and a $\frac{1}{2}$-inch gap at the inside vertical corner. Finally, I filled the backerboard seams with latex thinset, covered them with polyester joint tape, and filled the screw heads to produce a surface flat enough for the waterproofing membrane.

Figure 3-34. Because no mortar beds are required, construction of this 4x4-foot curbless shower is as simple as it gets.

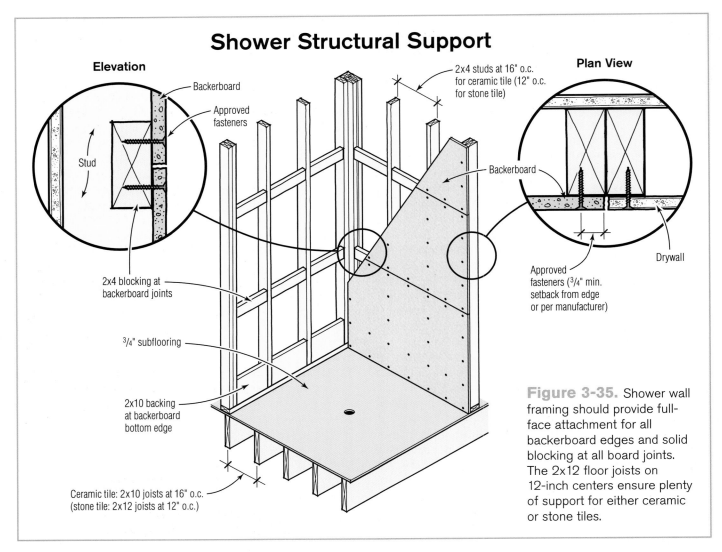

Shower Structural Support

Elevation

Backerboard

Approved fasteners

Stud

2x4 studs at 16" o.c. for ceramic tile (12" o.c. for stone tile)

Plan View

Backerboard

Drywall

2x4 blocking at backerboard joints

Approved fasteners (³/₄" min. setback from edge or per manufacturer)

³/₄" subflooring

2x10 backing at backerboard bottom edge

Figure 3-35. Shower wall framing should provide full-face attachment for all backerboard edges and solid blocking at all board joints. The 2x12 floor joists on 12-inch centers ensure plenty of support for either ceramic or stone tiles.

Ceramic tile: 2x10 joists at 16" o.c. (stone tile: 2x12 joists at 12" o.c.)

Curb Detail

Slope: ¹/₄" per foot

Preformed curb

Preformed sloped floor section

Bathroom floor

Figure 3-36. On the curbed installation, the curb masks the dissimilar heights of the shower and bath floors.

Shower Drain in Concrete Slab

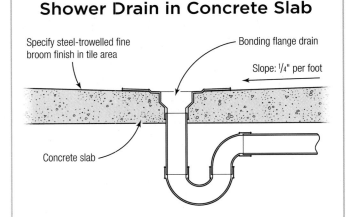

Specify steel-trowelled fine broom finish in tile area

Bonding flange drain

Slope: ¹/₄" per foot

Concrete slab

Figure 3-37. To increase the compressive strength of the sloped floor when a bonding flange drain is specified, the author eliminates the lightweight, sloped floor sections and specifies that concrete in the shower area be sloped and given a fine-broom finish, as required by tile industry standards.

Installing the Membrane

The membrane system for this project is based on a latex gel and 36-inch-wide reinforcing fabric. Because of the thick consistency of the gel, I preferred to spread it with a $1/8$-inch V-notch trowel instead of a roller or brush. I used a brush to work the fabric into the inside corner (Figure 3-39), and then applied a top coat with a small diameter paint roller.

To complete the floor portion of the membrane, I cut fabric to fit the area, spread more gel, positioned the fabric over the uniform layer of gel, then troweled the fabric flat. To ensure complete waterproofing, the membrane extended about 6 inches beyond the footprint of the shower. (In Chapter 1, Project 2, this extension is joined to a sheet membrane used on the adjoining bathroom floor.) The membrane also laps up the side wall for the one-row cove base that will be installed after the shower is finished (Figure 3-40). For more information about installing membrane systems, refer to Chapter 5.

Figure 3-38. To save time, the author stacks and clamps all the boards needed for one shower wall, lays out screw locations on the top board, and pre-drills holes in all boards simultaneously.

Materials List: Shower Stall Project 2

Shower drain: Kerdi Bonding Flange drain, Schluter Systems

Shower base kit: 48x48 Kerdi sloped floor sections, Schluter Systems

Backerboards: $1/2$-inch Durock, USG

Membrane system: B-6000 gel plus fabric, Bonsal American

Tiles: 24x24 porcelain tiles, 6x12 cove, 3x12 surface trim, Stonepeak, www.stonepeakceramics.com

Thinset mortar: MegaLite, Custom Building Products (CBP)

Grout: Prism, CBP

Sealant: Polyblend, CBP

Sealer: TileLab penetrating sealer, CBP

Method: a variation of TCNA B422

Subfloor: Depressed wood framing

Performance rating: Light to Moderate

Figure 3-39. To apply the gel in a consistent thickness, the author uses a $1/8$-inch V-notch trowel (above). He then works the fabric into the corner with a stiff brush (right).

Tile Layout

To lay out the walls, I used a laser and straightedge to provide reference lines for the tiles. For each wall, I drew a horizontal line for the joint between the cove and field tiles, another for the joint between the second and third course of field tiles, a vertical line splitting each wall, and two more for the joints between the field and bullnose tiles (Figure 3-41). When this project was framed, both walls were plumb to within $\frac{1}{16}$ inch in 8 feet where they met at the inside vertical corner. This tolerance was maintained throughout the installation of the backerboards and the membrane, so no cuts or trimming was required for any of the 24-inch field tiles

Companion cove tiles for the 24-inch tiles measure 6x12 inches, while the surface bullnose trim measures 3x12. To create a framework around the 24-inch tiles, I decided to cut the cove tiles down to 3x12 and miter the surface trim where it meets with the bullnose-topped cove tiles (Figure 3-42). The cove tiles installed in the shower area serve two purposes: foundation course for the wall tiles and framework for the floor tiles. The curved edge of the cove tiles determines the perimeter of the floor tiles.

The floor tiles for the shower floor were cut down from 24-inch tiles into squares matching the dimensions of the square drain screen. By dry-fitting the small squares, diagonals, and half diagonals, I could quickly determine if the layout of the tiles would work and if the width of the border tiles was reasonable (Figure 3-43).Quarter diagonals play a key role when installing a checkerboard-patterned floor, but for this project (and if the proportions were OK), the insert corners could have been finished with two half diagonals instead. See Chapter 11 for more information on diagonal-and-border layouts.

Figure 3-40. The author begins to spread gel on the sloped floor. Notice the generous lap-overs from the walls to floor and the pencil line to mark the first area to be covered (top). He uses a margin trowel to flatten the fabric where it laps up the wall (bottom).

Figure 3-41. Four vertical and one horizontal layout line provide plenty of reference for the 24-inch tiles.

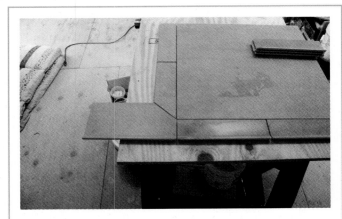

Figure 3-42. To create a smooth junction, full-size cove tiles were cut to match the width of the bullnose trim, which was mitered to the cove tile.

Installing the Tiles

Cove tiles play a critical role in the installation of the wall tiles. On this job, they needed to be installed with far more adhesive than is usually required for a 12-inch-long tile because the 24-inch tiles have special adhesion requirements and need a far thicker adhesive layer than smaller tiles would.

I began the process by hard troweling a thin layer of latex thinset mortar in the cove tile zone. Next, I back buttered one of the pre-cut, full-length cove tiles; positioned it with a carpenter's square; and made light adjustments—no more than required to bring the tile into square (Figure 3-44). Next, I used a scale held against the wall to see if the face of the tile was in plane with the wall and made any light adjustments required to bring it into this plane. I re-checked the tile again, this time pressing the cove tile inward a bit at each check until the tile was in its final height, level, and square. Each cove tile was subject to the same routine until a group of cove tiles was set. Then I used a straightedge to ensure all the curved edges were aligned (Figure 3-45).

Because a factory-made inside corner was not used (this would have required a completely coved vertical corner), for the inside corner I profiled the inside cove tile with the outline of its neighbor (Figure 3-46). With all the shower's cove tiles set, I re-checked for level before moving to the hefty, 16-pound field tiles (Figure 3-47).

Before installing any more tiles, though, I used a dry-cutting diamond blade to rough cut and finish the tiles around the mixing valve and shower head openings so those tiles would be ready when needed. Installing the field tiles began with spreading a layer of latex thinset over the membrane surface with a ¼x¾x¾ U-notch trowel. For this installation, I only

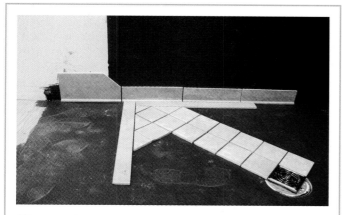

Figure 3-43. To quickly assess a projected layout in such a small area, the author places rows of border tiles (cut from scraps) and cove tiles, and positions whole, half- and quarter-diagonals around the drain.

Figure 3-44. To install the cove tiles, the author hard trowels a layer of adhesive onto the setting bed wall (A). Placing the first cove tile in the right position requires checking several axes. Here, the author checks if the face of the cove tile is square to the opposing wall (B). Then he compares the edge of the tile with the outer edge of the ruler to see if the face of the cove tile is parallel with the face of the wall (C).

Figure 3-45. When a group of cove tiles has been set, the author uses a straightedge to ensure that the front edges of the cove tiles are aligned and in plane. Unlike the usual soft tile spacers that easily deflect under weight, these calibrated framing spacers are used, temporarily, to support the weight of the heavy 24-inch tiles until they are under the grip of hardened thinset mortar.

Figure 3-46. This profile cut will allow the corner movement joint to move from the floor of the shower to the top.

Figure 3-47. By leveling the small cove tiles with hard shims, a more stable foundation is created. This allows the more cumbersome 24-inch tiles to be installed with less fuss.

spread enough mortar for one tile at a time, positioned two spacers, cleaned up any mess (Figure 3-48), quickly back buttered a tile (with a flat trowel), and pressed it home.

On-site testing determined that the ¾-inch U-notch trowel was needed to apply thinset mortar to both the setting bed and the backs of the tiles to achieve the desired 100% coverage. To simplify this task, I set up a work table close to the shower to support tiles while back buttering, which was a four-step process on this project. The first was to hard trowel a thin layer of medium-bed latex thinset mortar over the membrane. The second was to apply a buildup layer of thinset with the notched side of the trowel. The third step called for a hard-troweled thin coat of thinset on the tile back, and the fourth was to build up the thinset layer on the tile back with the trowel's notched side. The thinset ridges should run in one direction only (Figure 3-49). As soon as this was done, I pressed the tile into the setting bed and checked its alignment.

If a tile was sitting above or below plane and required the addition or removal of thinset mortar, I used a

Figure 3-48. The first step in bonding the 24-inch tiles to the membrane is to hard trowel a thin layer of medium-bed latex thinset mortar over the membrane and then build up the thinset layer with a deep U-notch trowel (top). As soon as the thinset is spread, the author positions two spacers, cleans off the excess thinset, and back butters the next tile (bottom).

margin trowel as a lever and a wooden wedge as a holder to gradually pull the top of the tile away from the wall so I could adjust the mortar on either the tile back or the setting bed (Figure 3-50). As each tile was installed, I checked its alignment before adding another tile. For tiles this size, I had to exert considerable force to ensure that each tile was properly bedded in mortar.

Installing the Surface Bullnose Trim

Once all the field tiles were set, stable, and clean, I started setting the trim tiles, working from bottom to top. The trim tiles required a fat cushion of medium-bed thinset mortar to sit flush with the field tiles, as well as spacers and tape to keep them aligned until the mortar hardened (Figure 3-51).

The tape, spacers, and wedges remained in place for about 48-hours after the remainder of the trims were installed, or until the thinset mortar had hardened and begun to cure.

Figure 3-49. The third step to a superior bond is to hard trowel a thin layer of thinset mortar onto the tile back (top). The fourth step is to apply a buildup layer with the notched side of the trowel. Notice that the adhesive ridges are one-directional (bottom).

Installing the Shower Floor Tiles

The layout of the shower floor tiles is controlled by the location of the square drain screen. For small installations, I like to dry-fit whole, half-, and quarter-diagonal tiles, along with spacers, to help plot accu-

Figure 3-50. Even a small amount of adhesion can create a powerful grip. To help reduce stress on the tile he is removing, the author uses a margin trowel to lever the tile and a wooden wedge to stabilize it (A). Instead of completely removing this tile, he hinges it away from the wall, adds more mortar so the tile will be in plane, then hinges the tile back onto the setting bed (B). For tiles this large, it is important to check the alignment of each before adding another tile to the wall (C).

rate layout lines and to provide dimensions for cutting the border tiles. With that done, I applied thinset mortar to the adjustable-height drain housing and the housing's lower shell (Figure 3-52) and set the housing with the drain screen about ¾-inch above the sloped floor. Once the drain was surrounded by tiles, I pressed the drain screen down until its top was just slightly below the plane of the floor tiles.

Then, with a ¼x¾x¾ U-notch trowel, I spread the

back corner of the floor with thinset mortar and flattened the adhesive ridges so the grout joints of these small tiles would not get too clogged with adhesive. I used a flat trowel to backfill any voids beneath the cove tiles, a ½-inch-wide margin trowel to scrape excess thinset out of the movement joint, and a 2-inch-wide margin trowel to back butter border tiles (Figure 3-53).

All the tiles on this floor were back buttered before installing to provide an ample cushion between the

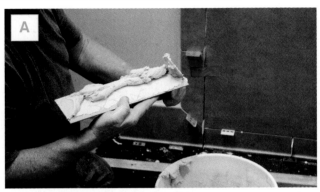

Figure 3-51. To sit flush with the field tiles and achieve a good bond, the trim tiles require fat back buttering (A). Sitting on a fat bed of mortar, the trim tiles need to be stabilized with tape and spacers (B). With one side of the shower trimmed (C), the author will complete the other side and allow the shower to rest for 48-hours for the thinset mortar to harden and start to cure.

Figure 3-52. The conical shape of the floor distorts straight-line measurements. For small areas, such as this shower floor, the author often dry-fits to provide accurate layouts as well as dimensions for border tiles (A). With the floor cleaned with fresh water to improve adhesion and with the proprietary drain ready to be installed, only a minimum of layout lines are needed (B). Next, the author butters the drain housing with thinset mortar (C). The housing's lower shell has also been buttered with thinset.

cone-shaped floor and the flat tiles. As soon as the back corner was framed with border tiles, I set one quarter diagonal in the corner and aimed a row of whole tiles toward the drain screen (Figure 3-54).

Installing a sloped floor requires more adhesive than is required for a flat floor, and this resulted in some bleed-through into the grout joints (Figure 3-55). This created another cleaning task, but it was also the sign that the tiles were in 100% contact with the adhesive, with no voids in the thinset mortar that might cause problems. The second half of the floor was covered with tile, final alignments were made, and then the entire shower was allowed to rest for 48 hours before grouting.

Grouting the Installation

Before grouting, I went over all the grout and movement joints, cut through any stray globs of thinset

Figure 3-53. Flattening the adhesive ridges on the floor reduces bleed through into the grout joints (A). The entire lower portion of the cove tiles must be supported. Here, the author uses a flat trowel to backfill voids left by the spacers (B). Next, floor tiling begins in the corner with two border tiles (C).

Figure 3-54. Working from the back corner out, the author lines up a row of tiles with the drain housing. After adding spacers, the areas to each side will be covered with tiles.

Figure 3-55. Although a nuisance to clean, these clogged grout joints are also a sign that the tiles are fully bedded in a void-free layer of thinset mortar.

mortar, and used a vacuum to remove all the crumbs that might mar the appearance of the grout. The wall tile and trim joints were filled with grout first, followed by the floor tiles.

After mixing the grout and allowing time for slaking, I remixed the grout, loaded my hawk with some of the mix (Figure 3-56), and used the hawk to load a rubber grout trowel. Since the joint between the trim tiles and the surrounding drywall is the widest, that got packed and filled first to give its extra cross section enough time to set up. The stiff rubber blade of this trowel was useful for compacting the grout into a sloping surface along the top joint; this accelerates drainage at the drywall interface and prevents puddling (Figure 3-57).

When the trim tiles were filled, I began packing the cove tile joints, working upward until all the wall joints were filled. With tiles this size, the joint spaces are very obvious, and an installer has to apply the grout differently than with smaller tiles. Instead of applying grout everywhere, grout is focused on the joints only (Figure 3-58). Because there are significantly fewer joints to fill, grouting the first wall took only minutes, so instead of sponge cleaning, I decided to grout the second wall. After the joints in that wall were filled, I used a margin trowel to shape and smooth the trim tile/drywall joints and a sponge to clean the tile surface.

When the walls were clean, I snowplowed the damp grout crumbs away from the shower floor and began to pack fresh grout into the floor joints. After filling all the joints, I let the floor sit for about 30 minutes before sponge cleaning (Figure 3-59). After the tiles had been cleaned, I took care of other housekeeping chores, then returned to the shower approximately 30 minutes later to clear out unwanted grout residue from the bath floor tile joints (they would be grouted a different color) and the movement joints. The movement joints would be filled with sealant after the grout had cured.

Figure 3-56. For repetitive grouting tasks, like filling the joints between the trim tiles and the drywall, the author uses a hawk to help load the grout trowel.

Figure 3-57. The top grout joint between the trim tiles and the drywall should be sloped to shed water quickly.

Figure 3-58. With such large tiles, the author focuses the trowel primarily on the grout joints instead of smearing grout across the whole surface.

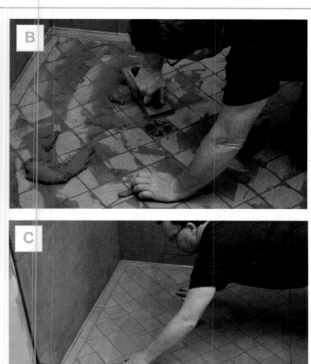

Figure 3-59. Damp grout crumbs that have lost their plasticity should be removed (A). Packing joints with this material will result in weak joints. Instead, use fresh grout, which has a stout consistency that allows the grout trowel to pack the joint—not just fill it (B). Sponge cleaning starts in about 30 minutes (C). The crisp edges of the tiles make finishing the grout relatively simple.

Shower Stall Project 3:
Drain Flashing Method

This shower stall project is located in a multi-use bathroom that serves a backyard pool and recreation area. The bathroom also is located next to my office, so I wanted it to be special (Figure 3-60). This project shows how to use a traditional clamping-type drain with a sloped thin-bed shower floor. I selected this project because it shows a variety of techniques and details I use for working with various irregular and ornamental tiles (Figure 3-60).

The focus of the prep work for this shower was a heat-formed drain flashing (NobleFlex) that allows a clamping-type drain, normally used for a shower pan and overlying mortar bed, to be used with a surface-applied membrane instead (Figure 3-61). The flashing is part of a system that I used to waterproof and crack-isolate the shower, wainscot, and bathroom floors. It is suited for new construction and remodeling (Figure 3-62).

The project began after the plumber had removed some of the original concrete floor and installed a clamping drain at the desired height. When this was done, I removed the top half of the drain and its bolts and used a mold provided by the flashing manufacturer to shape the concrete I floated to support the

drain. After the concrete cured, the drain flashing was installed, followed by the membrane over all areas in the bathroom receiving tile and stone.

> *Note:* The tiles used for this shower-stall project extend into the wainscot walls as well as the bathroom floor surrounding the shower. The bathroom floor may be found in Project 3 in Chapter 1, and the wainscot walls can be found in Project 2 in Chapter 2.

Surface Prep for the Shower

This bathroom is part of a remodeling project that required removal of portions of the concrete slab floor in order to make changes in the plumbing. Before the tile or membrane work could begin, though, more work was needed for the 20-year-old slab. During its lifetime, the slab was exposed to a variety of solvents, paints, coatings and other bond-breaking contaminants. In Chapter 1, Project 3, I used a bush hammer to remove the top $\frac{1}{2}$ to $\frac{3}{4}$ inch of concrete from the slab and a self-leveling underlayment (SLU) to finish the flat bathroom floor. Just before the SLU pour, I installed a formed, reinforced concrete shower curb.

Fabricating the Shower Curb

There are numerous ways to build a shower curb. With wood, the curb can begin as a stack of three or four 2x4s laid flat atop each other, two 2x6s shouldered togethe. Or as I discovered while removing an old shower, it can begin as a a solid 4x8 chunk of redwood. Whatever is used, it (or they) must be securely fastened to the rest of the structure, followed by covering the wood with a setting bed, which must be water-

Shower Stall Floor Plan

Figure 3-60. This porcelain tile and stone shower was built using thinbed materials and methods resulting in a durable, high-strength installation with low water absorption and low maintenance.

Materials List: Shower Stall Project 3

Mortar bed: CustomFloat, Custom Building Products

Shower drain flashing: NobleFlex, Noble Company

Weep hole protector: Weep Hole Protector, Noble Company

Backerboards: 1/2-inch Durock, USG

Membrane system: NobleSeal TS, Noble Company

Tiles: 8x8 porcelain (bathroom floor), 6x6 porcelain (shower walls) Michelle Griffoul Studios, 12-inch nominal, sheet-mounted quartz rocks (bath and shower floors) (Solistone)

Thinset mortar: MegaLite, Custom Building Products (CBP)

Mortar for slope and vertical cove feature: Custom Float, CBP

Grout: Prism, CBP

Sealant: Polyblend, CBP

Sealer: Miracle 511, Miracle Sealants and Abrasives

Method: a variation of TCNA TR420

Subfloor: Concrete slab

Performance rating: Heavy Residential

Figure 3-61. This flashing was developed to link a traditional thick-bed drain to thinbed installations.

proofed before tiling can begin.

The untiled top of the curb—regardless of its construction—must be sloped at least ¼ inch per foot toward the drain (Figure 3-63). This slope also applies to any other horizontal surface within the shower stall: shower floor, shower bench, woman's shaving ledge, toiletry shelf, etc. For thin-bed work over a wood curb, it is possible to cut the curb material to a sloped or beveled edge, but if cement backerboards are being used, the inner, top, and outer faces of the curb core have to be covered with ⅝-inch (minimum) exterior grade plywood first. There are numerous light-

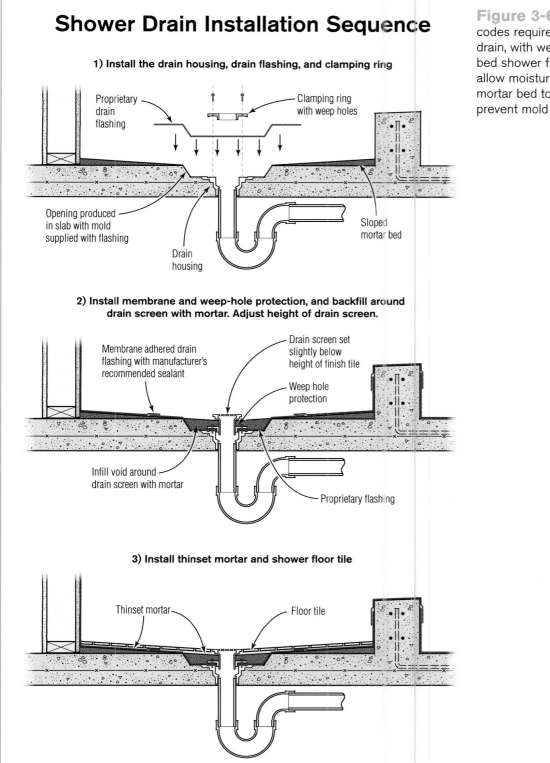

Shower Drain Installation Sequence

1) Install the drain housing, drain flashing, and clamping ring

Proprietary drain flashing

Clamping ring with weep holes

Opening produced in slab with mold supplied with flashing

Drain housing

Sloped mortar bed

2) Install membrane and weep-hole protection, and backfill around drain screen with mortar. Adjust height of drain screen.

Membrane adhered drain flashing with manufacturer's recommended sealant

Drain screen set slightly below height of finish tile

Weep hole protection

Infill void around drain screen with mortar

Proprietary flashing

3) Install thinset mortar and shower floor tile

Thinset mortar

Floor tile

Figure 3-62. Most building codes require a clamping shower drain, with weep holes, in a mortar-bed shower floor. The weep holes allow moisture absorbed by the mortar bed to drain away, helping to prevent mold and mildew.

weight, slip-on curb components that can be used, but in my opinion, most are for light-duty work only, thus are not covered here.

For this project, I formed a reinforced, latex concrete curb and constructed the casting forms to incorporate the sloped top into the casting—this saves time and materials and also produces a curb with incredible strength and resistance to water.

To begin, I laid out the location of the curb and built forms from scrap 2x4s and ¾-inch plywood for a 6-inch-high, 3½-inch-thick curb. I beveled the tops of the forms to produce a 1½-inch-per-foot slope that easily exceeds the industry minimum of ¼ inch per foot. The inner walls of the forms were quite stiff, but the outside walls flexed a bit. I used a combination of straightedges to provide plenty of support so the forms would not bulge, deflect, or lift (Figures 3-64). The con-

crete reinforcing is made from ½-inch rebar and 9-gauge galvanized rod wired together, coated with a corrosion-resistant industrial paint, and epoxied into ⅝-inch holes drilled into the slab. Where the reinforcing terminates against the stud walls, its ends are secured by corrosion-resistant fasteners and straps.

When I was ready to pour, I soaked the form boards with water (never use form oils!), applied a layer of latex thinset mortar to the rough concrete floor to help bond the new concrete, and laid in the concrete. I rodded the freshly poured concrete to ensure good settling and compaction and over-filled the forms a bit so that later, when the concrete had begun to set up (15 to 20 minutes), I could trowel the sloped top (Figure 3-65). At the very last minute, I also slid in a piece of membrane to help round the outside corner of the curb. The membrane was strong and long

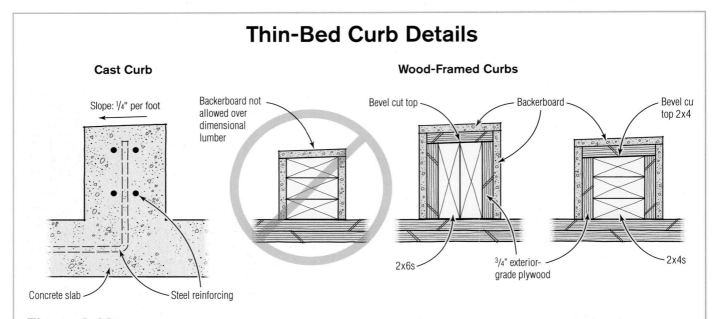

Thin-Bed Curb Details

Cast Curb   **Wood-Framed Curbs**

Slope: ¼" per foot

Backerboard not allowed over dimensional lumber

Bevel cut top

Backerboard

Bevel cut top 2x4

2x6s

¾" exterior-grade plywood

2x4s

Concrete slab   Steel reinforcing

Figure 3-63. Curbs can be made from a wide range of materials, but all must be securely attached to the structure and have sloped tops for tiling.

Figure 3-64. The tops of the forms are beveled to permit easy sloping of the concrete curb. Straightedges, clamped together and extending to the opposing walls, keep the forms straight and true (left). Anchors for the reinforcing cage are inserted into holes in the slab filled with epoxy (inset). Galvanized conduit clamps secure the cage ends. The pink disc was used to form the dished concrete shown in Figure 3-62.

Figure 3-65. To strengthen the bond between curb and slab, the author uses a stiff brush to apply a layer of latex thinset mortar to the surface of the bush-hammered concrete (A). To ensure a void-free pour, he rods the fresh concrete with a 1/2-inch tuck pointer. A short length of membrane is used to simply form the rounded corner (B). Slightly over-filling the forms with concrete ensures that the top of the curb will be void free. The beveled form makes troweling the slope of the curb simple (C).

Figure 3-66. The author uses a 1/8-inch V-notch trowel to spread a thin, even layer of latex thinset over the prepared concrete slab. This will bond the new mortar bed to the existing concrete slab.

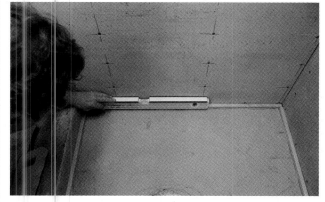

Figure 3-67. The author rips wood float strips to guide the outer edges of the sloped mortar bed. After wetting the strips to minimize warping, he butters their lower edges with latex thinset mortar to help stabilize and level them (top). He positions the float strips to produce a smooth, level perimeter—and an even, conical slope to the drain (bottom).

Figure 3-68. Because the distance from the perimeter of the floor to the drain constantly changes, the author uses the wood float to gradually pare down the excess mortar and always keeps it pointed toward the drain.

enough that the weight of the concrete would keep it from moving or sagging.

When this was done, I let the concrete sit in the forms to cure and harden. At 3½ inches, this curb took about 7 to 10 days to damp cure, but I stripped the forms a couple days after the pour and kept the curb moist for a week. While waiting for the curb to cure, I began work on sloping the shower floor. This portion of the concrete slab had already been processed by the bush hammer and was ready for a bonded mortar bed.

Bonded, Sloped Mortar Bed

To fill the depressions left by the bush hammer and to create a uniformly sloped shower floor, I used a packaged bedding mortar and mixed it with enough water

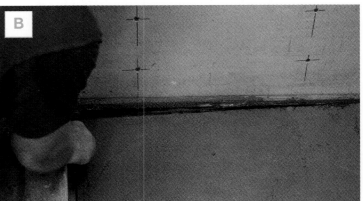

Figure 3-69. To minimize damage to the mortar bed, the author slits the mortar next to the float strips, which can then be easily removed (A) He pries one end of a float strip with a margin trowel and carefully lifts it out of the way (B). After packing additional mortar into the voids left by the float strips, he uses a steel trowel to remove the excess. The slope is evident under the trowel, which he holds level for this task (C).

Figure 3-70. To create a sharp edge where the floor meets the wall, the author uses a margin trowel to remove excess mortar (3V6). He then uses a ¼-inch tuck pointer to detail the narrow circumference of the dish-out (3V6a).

to produce a damp-pack consistency, just wet enough to form a ball when squeezed. To bond the bedding mortar to the slab, I used a thin layer of latex thinset mortar applied to the slab with a ³⁄₁₆-inch V-notch trowel (Figure 3-66). While the latex thinset was still moist and tacky, I covered it with the bedding mortar, which was mixed and ready for immediate use.

The inner screed for the floor was the narrow ring of the original concrete left around the perimeter of the drain. For an outer screed, I used square stock ripped from a 1-by and leveled these float strips with some thinset mortar for support (Figure 3-67). The entire perimeter of the floor must be level, while the remainder of the floor assumes a conical shape as it slopes to the drain. To properly gauge the slope, the ¼-inch-per-foot tolerance should be applied to the point on the floor that is farthest from the center of the drain.

Consistency of the mortar is essential: If too wet, it

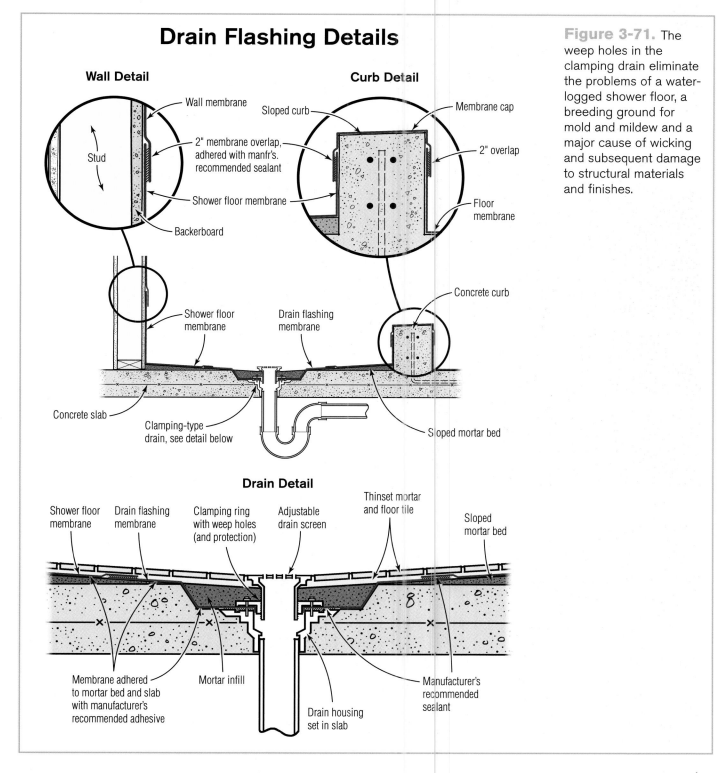

Drain Flashing Details

Wall Detail

Wall membrane
Stud
2" membrane overlap, adhered with manfr's. recommended sealant
Shower floor membrane
Backerboard

Curb Detail

Sloped curb
Membrane cap
2" overlap
Floor membrane
Concrete curb

Shower floor membrane
Drain flashing membrane
Concrete slab
Clamping-type drain, see detail below
Sloped mortar bed

Drain Detail

Shower floor membrane
Drain flashing membrane
Clamping ring with weep holes (and protection)
Adjustable drain screen
Thinset mortar and floor tile
Sloped mortar bed

Membrane adhered to mortar bed and slab with manufacturer's recommended adhesive
Mortar infill
Manufacturer's recommended sealant
Drain housing set in slab

Figure 3-71. The weep holes in the clamping drain eliminate the problems of a water-logged shower floor, a breeding ground for mold and mildew and a major cause of wicking and subsequent damage to structural materials and finishes.

will not pack, if too dry, it will not cure. I prepared the mix using the smallest amount of liquid recommended by the mortar manufacturer and power mixed the wet and dry ingredients in a 5-gallon bucket until the mix clumped when squeezed into a ball. I set all the float strips; distributed the mortar over the floor; and used a flat trowel to pack it into a dense, void-free mass. Then, with a long wood float, I gradually pared away the excess mortar (Figure 3-68), smoothing the perimeter and area around the drain first, then paring down the middle of the bed. I didn't try to remove too much excess all at once, but instead, pared off small amounts taking several passes until the floor had a

smooth, conical shape.

At that point, I slit the mortar around the perimeter float strips, carefully removed them, and backfilled the resulting voids with mortar. I packed the mortar into the void with a margin trowel and used a flat trowel to carve away most of the excess (Figure 3-69). Then I used the wood float (always keeping it pointed toward the drain) to further smooth and finish the slope, a margin trowel to help sharpen and clean up the perimeter of the bed, and a ¼-inch tuck pointer to detail the dish-out around the drain (Figure 3-70). With this done, I let the floor sit for 72 hours to harden, dry, and partially cure.

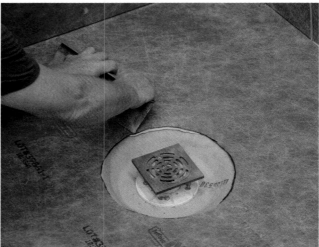

Figure 3-72. A compatible sealant has been applied to the drain flashing, inside corners, and dam corners; and the contact cement on the shower floor is tacky and ready to receive the membrane. The author bundles the membrane section, aligns the edge with the curb, and begins to unfold the material (left). He uses a short straightedge to laminate the membrane to the drain flashing. The squeeze out indicates that the seam is closed (right).

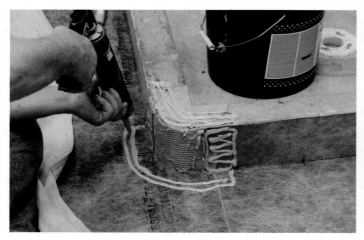
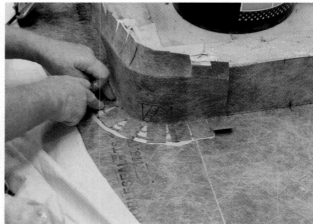

Figure 3-73. Once the contact cement at the corner is tacky, the author quickly applies beads of sealant in a 2-inch-wide path around the adhesive; this assures a watertight seal (left). Next he embeds the corner section of membrane in the contact cement, starting in the center and then pressing the lower tabs into the sealant (right). The tab on the extreme right will get more sealant.

Installing the Membrane

Unlike a traditional shower pan that is located below the tile setting bed, the sheet membrane system used to waterproof this shower was applied to the top of the setting bed, but I followed traditional installation methods by starting at the bottom and working up (Figure 3-71). This allowed upper layers of the sheet membrane to ship-lap over lower sections, but it also meant that the floor membrane had to be protected until covered with tile.

The first step was to dry-fit the drain flashing and all the accessory pieces, outline them with a marker, and cover these areas with the sheet membrane's nonre-emulsifiable contact cement. For this project, I installed the factory-made drain flashing, inside corners, and dam corners, along with the mixing valve and show-erhead opening pieces (that I made using a process described in Chapter 7, page 207). After the accessory pieces were installed, I spread contact cement over the sloped shower floor, 11 inches up the two surrounding walls, and on the two inside curb faces.

It took about 10 minutes or so for the contact cement to become tacky, so I used this time to cut the sheet membrane sections to size and pre-folded the lower section to conform to the upturns at the walls and curb. When the cement was tacky, I quickly shot beads of compatible sealant over the flashing and accessory pieces, bundled the lower portion of the shower's membrane, and pressed it into the contact cement with a short straightedge (Figure 3-72). After the lower section was installed, I covered the bath-room floor with membrane so I could finish the curb before applying the membrane to the rest of the shower area.

Special waterproofing details. For this shower, special detailing was required to waterproof the curb and the coved vertical corner. The curb waterproofing could only be finished after the shower and bathroom floors had been covered with membrane. A square or rectangular curb corner can be finished with lap seams, but an outside curve requires a different approach.

I began by fabricating a section of membrane 4 inches higher than the height of the curb and about 4 to 6 inches wider than the curved section of curb. Next, I covered the affected areas with contact cement and sealant. I applied contact cement on the concrete curb, and when it became tacky, used a compatible sealant where the fabricated section overlapped membrane or accessories. To begin the lamination process, I concentrated on aligning the piece and embedding the central portion of the section in the contact cement (Figure 3-73). Then, working one tab at a time, I gradually flattened all the lower tabs in the sealant, applied additional sealant as needed over the tabs, and used a margin trowel to flatten the sandwich.

While the lower tabs diverge, the upper tabs converge and require different detailing. First, I applied beads of sealant to the contact area on the curb top.

Figure 3-75. The author trowels a uniform layer of sealant on the top and inside faces of the curb (top). For optimal waterproofing of thinbed curbs, the author prefers to bond the sheet membrane to the curb with its compatible sealant, rather than contact cement (bottom).

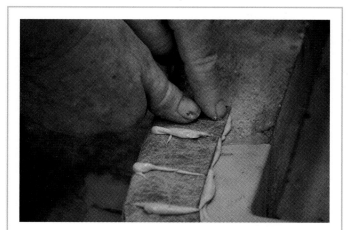

Figure 3-74. Working from one side to the other, the author presses each upper tab against the top of the curb.

Conducting a Water Test, Detecting Leaks, and Weep Holes

The main purpose of a water test is to determine if a shower pan holds water. This also applies to other types of membrane systems designed to protect a structure against moisture intrusion. For example, a water test should be included in the installation spec of an exterior tile deck over an interior living space. The process for testing a shower with curb is relatively simple: Screw in a long nipple or block the drain with a plug made for this task (Figure 3-76) and fill to the point of flooding.

Showers without curbs should also be tested, and for this type of installation, I fabricate sturdy temporary dams from plywood or dimensional lumber that has been carefully wrapped with plastic and sealed with caulk to avoid leaks. Once fitted with temporary dams, exterior decks, curbless shower stalls, and other non-restraining systems can—and should—be tested. The minimum

length of time for a shower pan water test, as specified by the UPC, is 24 hours. My comfort level requires at least 72 hours, and if conditions warrant, I tack on extra hours in varying amounts. For example, I may add 24 hours for a second floor shower test, 48 for the third floor, and up to a week for higher levels.

The first step is to ensure that all construction and materials meet the local code, and that the water level is brought to the appropriate flood point. The test should be conducted for a minimum of 24 hours. During the first 24 hours, as long as there are no visible leaks or a drop in the test water level, the pan can be said to have passed the first part of the test.

Open or easy access to the pan is a plus during the test period in case it leaks. If access is not possible, locating the source of the leak(s) may be more difficult. Regardless of access, I generally rely on the water level and the pan itself to find a leak when there is a loss of test water. If, for example, the overnight loss of all test water is not accompanied by puddles or apparent dampness, the problem usually can be traced to a loose drain plug: Tighten the plug and re-test. If there are puddles or dampness and an overnight drop in the test water level, I can usually find the source of the leak somewhere along the dropped water level. The fix for this is to drain the test water, dry the affected area, apply an appropriate patch, and re-test.

If there are puddles around the shower area and all of

Figure 3-76. To water test the shower, the author first removes the adjustable drain housing and stops the drain with an expandable plug (top). To stop this cast iron, non-adjustable, clamping drain, the author screws a long nipple into the drain's lower half (bottom).

Figure 3-77. The test water should drain quickly until it reaches the level of the drain housing. Then the only exit for the remaining water (and any moisture absorbed by the finished installation) is through the drain housing's weep holes.

the test water within the shower is gone, the first thing I check is the clamping portion of the drain to see if it is seated firmly and squarely on the drain housing and to ensure its bolts are tightened evenly: Loosen all bolts, remove and re-install the clamping ring, making sure it fits snugly. Tighten all bolts gradually and in succession, and re-test.

The second part of the water test begins when the plug or pipe is removed, and again, access to the shower pan and its parts is helpful if there is a leak. This portion of the test focuses on the connections between the drain and the waste line. It determines whether the drain housing is properly connected to the waste water system. Obviously, if there is a problem, the plumber should be consulted, the problem fixed, and the pan re-tested.

The third part of the test begins as soon as the test water level drops below the rim of the drain (Figure 3-77). From this point on, the weep holes cast into the drain housing are the only avenues of escape. The third part of the test determines if the weep holes are working properly; if not, remove obstructions and re-test. Weep holes can easily become clogged or completely blocked by soap, shampoo, and cosmetic and other residues (the stuff we wash off in the shower). In a traditional shower with a thick mortar bed floor, blocked weep holes cause the mortar bed to become saturated with moisture, which allows mold, mildew, and worse to grow and flourish. (Note: Because a bonding flange-type drain lacks weep holes, Step 3 can be skipped.)

The fourth part of the test, checking that all the test water finds its way to the drain, is one of the most important, whether it is performed on a traditional under-the-setting-bed shower pan or a more modern membrane-atop-the-setting bed (Figure 3-78). Does the pan drain completely, or are there birdbaths, flat spots, or worse, a negative slope? All these substrate problems can be repaired, but the pan will have to be cut into or removed to do so; otherwise, after the tiles are installed, residual moisture will collect in low areas and promote growth of mold, mildew, etc.

Figure 3-78. Because the weep holes are located on the underside of this drain, and because the drain itself is located at the bottom of the dish-out, this shower floor shed all of its test water.

Then, working one tab at a time and from one side to the other, I pressed each tab into the sealant and used a margin trowel to flatten the tabs and remove excess sealant (3-74). To complete the top of the curb, I pre-folded and creased membrane sections for the left and right side of the curb and spread contact cement on the outside curb face.

To ensure a higher level of waterproofing, as soon as the contact cement on the outer face was tacky, I used a $\frac{1}{8}$-inch V-notch trowel to spread a uniform layer of sealant on the top and inside faces of the curb (Figure 3-75). After laminating the pre-creased curb top sections, I cleaned up the excess sealant and allowed the curb to sit undisturbed for 48 hours.

After the membrane was extended to all areas in the bathroom receiving tile, after the floor membrane was protected with cardboard and tarps, and after the wall and floor tile locations were laid out, I gave the shower stall a 72-hour water test. After completion of the test, the next step was to trowel on mortar to cove the northeast and southwest corners of the shower walls and the dished-out area surrounding the drain.

Coving Corners With Bonded Mortar

A sloped shower floor is not the only place where an installer can utilize a bonded mortar bed. Practically any structurally sound masonry or concrete surface can be amended with bonded mortar. I am not a big fan of square inside corners in a shower—they get dirty and crack—so I use bedding mortar to cove inside corners. I use the same bedding mortar mix that I used to slope the shower floor, but add slightly more water so the mortar was sticky enough to hang on the wall. Apart from a strong structure, the only other requirement is that the corner to be coved must be plumb on both sides; otherwise, the finished tiles need to be tapered to fit, and this is unacceptable.

On this project, I coved two inside corners (northeast and southwest) following the same basic method: Apply a thin layer of latex thinset mortar for bonding, immediately trowel bedding mortar over the thinset, and remove the excess with a curved screed. I used a ⅛-inch V-notch trowel to apply a thin, 4-inch-wide layer of latex thinset mortar on each side of the corner. While the bonding mortar was still wet and tacky,

I used a hawk and flat trowel to fill in the corner with bedding mortar and gave it 20 to 30 minutes to begin to set up (Figure 3-79). Ideally, there should be slightly more mortar than is required; this allows the mortar to be pared down gradually to its finished shape.

When the mortar had lost most of its plasticity, it was time to screed the cove. To produce coves of dif-

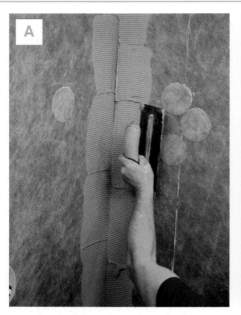
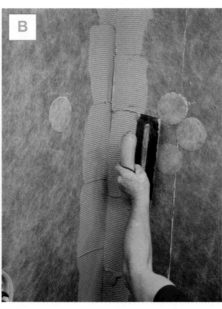
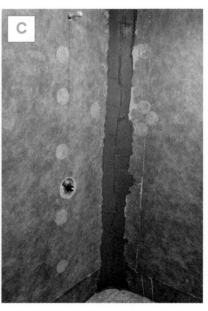

Figure 3-79. For maximum adhesion, the author uses a layer of latex thinset to bond the bedding mortar to the cove area. The mortar must be applied while the thinset is still moist and tacky (A). The author uses a flat trowel and a three-step process to fill in the corner: apply a thin base coat to the entire cove area, a second thin coat to fill in, and a third to top it off (B). The ideal is to float just slightly more mud than is required. A plywood scrap protects the floor membrane (C).

Figure 3-80. The author makes multiple passes with the open end of a coffee can to gradually carve away excess mortar. This must be done firmly, but gently and gradually, to avoid damaging the main body of the cove (top). With the open side tipped slightly away from the corner, he uses the body of the can to compact the mortar on the final pass (bottom).

ferent sizes, I use a variety of tools. I have made several curving trowels for specialty curves, but for this type of coving, my favorite tool is an empty 2-pound coffee can with one end removed. I swept up and down the corner, gradually paring away the excess with the rim of the can until the cove was uniform. To further compact the mortar, I used the body of the can for the final pass (Figure 3-80). After initial screeding, I filled in voids larger then a pea with fresh mortar, re-screeded with the can as needed, and repeated the process for the southwest corner (Figure 3-81). Then I left the mortar to cure for at least 48 hours before covering it with membrane.

Because I wanted maximum protection against absorption and related problems, I covered the shower wall's vertical cove with an additional section of membrane about 48 hours after the mortar was installed. (I decided not to cover the mortar cove on the southwest corner because its potential for absorption is insignificant.) To do this, I laid out an area that extended 4 inches on either side of the cove and filled in most of the area with contact cement. When that became tacky (about 10 minutes at normal room temperature), I laid down two $\frac{1}{8}$-inch beads of NobleSealant 150 on a 2-inch-wide perimeter around the contact cement and laminated the prepared membrane sections over the cove. Where the wall meets the floor, I slit the membrane into 1x2-inch flaps that were closed with sealant (Figure 3-82).

Filling Around the Drain

The dish-out around the drain needed to be filled with mortar, and for maximum performance, some careful detailing was required. To bond the mortar, I applied a thin layer of thinset mortar over the drain flashing and covered that with a skirt designed by the manufacturer (Noble Company) to keep the weep holes open. Next, the drain screen was adjusted to suit the

height of the floor tiles (rocks, in this case), and a damp-pack mortar was compacted into the depression. Then I cut away the excess with a flat trowel, smoothed the mortar with a narrow wood float I use for finishing sloped floors, and thoroughly cleaned the surrounding membrane fabric with a sponge and clean water (Figure 3-83).

Figure 3-82. After covering the cove area with contact cement and the seam area with beads of sealant, the author is ready to install a secondary layer of membrane over the cove. This detail will reduce absorption by the cove mortar and reduce stress on the sliver tiles used in the cove area (top). The lower edge of the membrane piece has been cut into 1x2-inch flaps that the author laminates to the base membrane with sealant (bottom).

Figure 3-81. Coving the southwest corner of the curb is done using the same materials and methods, with the open side of the can pointed down.

Installing the Tiles

When building a shower stall, I prefer to install floor tiles first, then wall tiles. In this case, however, the floor tiles were actually highly irregular rocks, and I wanted a uniform joint between the irregular rocks and the wall tiles, not a wide, grout-filled moat. Creating a smooth transition between the wall and floor tiles required a lot of tedious cutting on the wet saw. To make for an easier install, I set all the wall tiles first (except for the first course), installed the floor second, and installed the first course of wall tiles last, after scribing and cutting each wall tile to fit nicely against the floor rocks.

The wall tiles were made especially for this space, and before firing, their soft porcelain bodies were imprinted with stalks of bamboo. The intention of the artist was to create a wall of bamboo, which meant that all the tiles had to be positioned in the same order as they were imprinted.

To simplify the installation process when setting hand-molded or highly patterned tiles, and to make sure there are no surprises once I put tile to adhesive, I lay out the dimensions of the walls on an open floor as close to the installation site as possible, and dry-fit each of the handcrafted tiles onto the layout (Figure 3-84). When all the tiles are positioned, I use this dry-fit layout to provide dimensions and locations for the

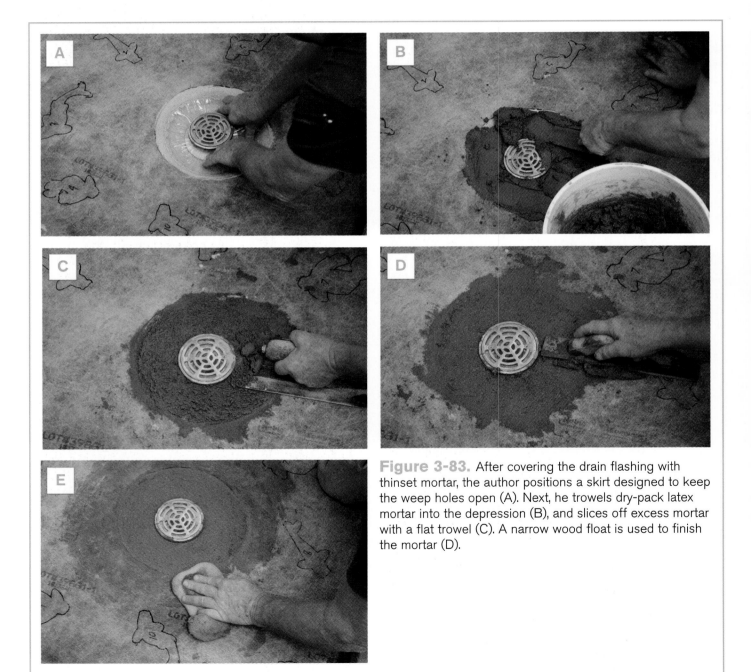

Figure 3-83. After covering the drain flashing with thinset mortar, the author positions a skirt designed to keep the weep holes open (A). Next, he trowels dry-pack latex mortar into the depression (B), and slices off excess mortar with a flat trowel (C). A narrow wood float is used to finish the mortar (D).

real layout lines needed to guide the tiles. The perimeter of this shower floor is about an inch higher than the bathroom floor, so to avoid sliver tiles at the lower edge of the wainscot walls, I began the layout by positioning a wall and floor tile on the bathroom floor and used a laser to mark the elevation (Figure 3-85).

To ensure that the shower wall tiles would be aligned with those installed on the wainscot portion of the wall, I used three straightedges clamped together to simplify the process of creating a temporary ledge for the tiles. The finished setup is typical for all types of wall tile work (Figure 3-86). I use scrap wood blocks, scrap tile, and framing spacers to shim the straightedges level; a couple of scrap tiles to shim each

Figure 3-86. The author uses three straightedges, clamped together, to set up a level ledge for the shower and wainscot tiles (top). The top straightedge will be removed once the lower two are leveled. With the ledges leveled and supported, and tarps and scrap wood protecting the floors, the shower and wainscot walls are ready for tiling (bottom).

Figure 3-84. Whenever installing hand-crafted, highly patterned, or custom mosaic tiles on a wall surface, the author begins by dry-fitting the tiles over a full-sized layout on the floor.

Figure 3-85. The author begins the layout by positioning a wall tile and floor tile. Spacers and a folded cloth under the floor tile simulate grout spaces and the adhesive layer.

Figure 3-87. Tile spacers do not work well with irregularly sized tiles. Here, the author aligns the tiles with the help of small plastic shims, used in various combinations and positions.

straightedge away from the wall; and a couple of piles of tiles to keep the straightedges from falling over while I spread thinset or stack tiles. This is the same basic setup that I use for most shower curb/wainscot work.

When installing handmade tiles, which can change so radically in size, I establish an average size and make sure none of the tiles falls outside the layout grid I plot on the walls. As you might expect, the only way to get irregularly sized tiles into a regular sized layout grid is to be prepared to deal with ever-changing grout joint widths. I never depend on tile spacers when installing handmade tiles, but instead use small tile shims (Figure 3-87), which can accommodate the irregularities between tiles.

After about 90 minutes, most of the tiles on the right wall were set up firm. I began the left wall by positioning a straightedge and installing one row of full tiles and a second row with notches and cuts to accommo-date a corner shelf. To maintain the smoothest transitions between neighboring tiles and adjacent courses, I installed the cove corner segments as each course was completed (Figure 3-88), being careful about spacer and wedge placement. Since the segments are all of equal width, the goal here was to produce grout joints that are as uniform as possible.

Another important detail is to ensure that any shelves in the shower drain properly. To slope this shower's shelves, I used shims to tip the shelf away from the corner (Figure 3-89). After all the tiles were aligned and cleaned, I let them set up while I began working on the floor layout.

Tiling the Floor

This floor was designed to be tiled with rocks inlaid with small porcelain tiles shaped like Japanese koi fish. The rocks came bonded to a mesh backing, and

Figure 3-88. The author installs the corner tile segments course by course to minimize alignment and leveling problems. The segments require a slightly thicker back buttering layer than the whole tiles.

Figure 3-89. The author uses shims to tip the shelf so it will drain without holding water.

Figure 3-90. To help reduce adhesive bleed through and ensure an even layer of thinset mortar, the author flattens the ridges with the notched trowel's smooth edge always pointing towards the drain (top). He carefully positions all four floor sections, embedding them in the thinset (bottom). The plastic mounting film should remain in place until the thinset dries hard.

the manufacturer's instructions extolled its "seamless" installation. After installing several sheets of the product on scrap backerboard as a test, however, I did not like the noticeable gaps between sheets, and I was especially concerned about the mesh backing that significantly reduced adhesive contact. So rather than risk a loss of bond and to avoid the appearance of gaps between sheets, I stripped enough rocks off the backing to cover the shower floor, dry fit them and the porcelain fish on the shower floor, and covered them all with a see-through plastic film made specifically for face-mounting mosaic tiles (available from Mesh-Mount Paper, Fiberglass and Tape, www.meshmount-paper.com). After covering the rocks and tiles, I cut through the film to produce four sections that would be easy to handle and install.

Once the four sections were covered with film, I removed them from the floor and began spreading medium-bed latex thinset with a $\frac{1}{4}x\frac{1}{2}x\frac{1}{4}$-inch U-notch trowel. To reduce bleed through, I flattened the adhesive ridges with the trowel's smooth edge (Figure 3-90). Because the porcelain fish weren't quite as thick as the rocks, I back buttered the fish before setting each section. With only four sections and no cutting, the floor was finished in about half an hour.

Because of their rounded shape, these rocks require a lot of adhesive. The bleed through visible in the lower center of the bottom photo of Figure 3-89 is typical for rocks like these, and because removing the plastic face-mounting film too early would pull rocks and tiles off the setting bed, I had to balance the need to allow the adhesive to cure long enough to hold the rocks firm, but not long enough to make the bleed through thinset mortar super hard and difficult to remove. The thinset mortar I used generally achieved

a sufficient grip after 24 hours to allow the plastic face-mounting film to be removed without loosening the tiles. Typically, the few tiles that came off with the film were easily re-installed (after removing the old thinset) with a bit of fresh thinset mortar.

Sloped Floor Movement Joint

Twenty-four hours later, when I returned to strip off the plastic film and clean up excess thinset mortar bleed through, not one rock was jarred loose. I typically remove soft excess thinset mortar with a $\frac{1}{4}$-inch tuck pointer, but for these thick rocks it was safe enough to use a utility knife for the hardened thinset (Figure 3-91). This work had to be done carefully to avoid accidently cutting the membrane, and since each rock is different, each "joint" had to be detailed individually. I estimated where the grout would finish and tried to keep the top $\frac{1}{4}$ inch of the grout zone free of all thinset mortar residue.

After all the floor rocks were clean, but before I began to install the first course of tiles, the movement joint between the rocks and surround walls and curb had to be filled with a long-life sealant. To ensure compatibility, I used a sealant that is part of the membrane system and designed for submerged applications (Figure 3-92). Once this task was finished, I cut and installed the first course of wall tiles, then tiled the bathroom floor. After a 24-hour wait for the floor tile thinset to setup hard, I tiled the curb. (The bathroom floor installation can be found in Chapter 1.)

Figure 3-91. Careful not to cut the membrane, the author removes excess thinset with a utility knife. Because of their irregular sizes and shapes, these rocks are difficult to bond properly without bleed through.

Figure 3-92. Before installing the first course, the author fills the movement joint between the rocks, the perimeter walls, and the curb with long-life sealant.

Tiling the Curb

Unlike most curbs, this one is covered with two tiling materials. Normally, this is not a big problem when tiling with two flat tiles of dissimilar thicknesses. If that difference is not significant, a smooth finished surface can be achieved by adjusting the amount of thinset mortar. On this curb, though, the difference is more than a difference in thickness. Specifically, the "surface" of the rounded rocks drains differently than the tiles. For this reason, I chose to pitch the top of the curb at a steeper rate than I would for a curb finished with flat tiles only. To help create a smooth transition between the tiles and rocks, the grout line of the rocks should be level with the edges of the tiles.

I began finishing the curb by tiling the entire top right side with 8x8 tiles cut down to fit across the top of the curb. Then, using two straightedges and two large clamps, I set up ledges on the inner and outer faces of the curb to help level and temporarily support

the quarter-round trim pieces (a stationery glass panel will be mounted on this side of the curb). I concentrated on the flat sections of the curb first, and to ensure the trim pieces wouldn't spread, I secured them with painter's tape (Figure 3-93).

The curb's left side is covered with both rocks and tile. I began this side by setting up a level, applying a layer of latex thinset mortar to the face(s) of the curb, and applying back-buttered rocks, one at a time (Figure 3-94). This portion of the curb was tricky, since the surface of the rocks had to be positioned about ¼-inch above the plane of the tiles framing the rock pathway leading from the bathroom to the shower floor. I used the uneven nature of the rocks not just to mask this difference, but also to accentuate the slope of the rock area. I did this by sorting through the stones, installing the thickest at the peak of the curb's slope and using gradually thinner stones as I tiled toward the low end of the curb. The result is a curb top that is more like a swale than a flat incline.

Figure 3-93. The author uses straightedges and clamps to establish a ledge for the quarter-round trim pieces. Here, he uses a sponge to apply thinset mortar to the exposed curb edge (top). The ledges keep the trim pieces level; painter's tape will keep them from spreading (bottom).

Figure 3-94. With a level bridging the rock pathway to help judge the height of the rocks, the author embeds the stones one at a time. The spacers at the base of the curb ensure an open movement joint.

Figure 3-95. Using a few 2x4 blocks and scrap plywood trimmed to fit and stabilized with a couple of tile wedges, the author back butters and fills the quarter-round segments.

Finishing the tiled, curved section required a bit of experimenting with the right cutting angle for the quarter-round segments and another setup to support the tiles while the thinset hardened. I finish curved curb corners in three steps: first, apply tiles to top of curb and allow to harden; second, set quarter-round segments and allow to harden; and third, install the vertical segments.

With the top tiles installed, I began by cutting and setting up a ledge to support the quarter-round segments. I determined the size of the segments by wrapping a flexible ruler around the curve, estimating how many segments would be required, and square-cutting enough to finish the curve. Square-cut segments can be used, but for the best look, I prefer to angle-cut quarter-round segments finishing a curve. To do this for a small number of pieces, I guess at an angle, set up a fence for repeat cuts, and prepare two samples for dry-fitting. It usually takes two or three tries to dial in the correct angle, which changes for the quarter-round segments trimming the interior curve.

With all the segments cut and dried, I set up another ledge made from scrap plywood and 2x4 blocks (Figure 3-95). To stabilize the ledge, I pinned it in place with a couple of tile wedges and used the platform to stage the segments as each was buttered with latex thinset mortar and filled with stiff sanded grout. Working quickly to take advantage of the thinset/grout sandwich's hydraulic nature, I filled all the segments, positioning them slightly away from their ultimate position. When all the segments were installed, I pushed them all into their final position, making sure all wedges were tight, and allowed them to sit undisturbed for a few hours until the spacers and ledge could be removed (Figure 3-96).

After dry-fitting the interior segments, I re-cut them at a different angle, and using methods similar to those used for the outside, I covered the inside curve with quarter-round segments. One of those segments,

visible in Figure 3-98, was cut extra wide so one of its edges could be profile-cut to better fit against the rocks. While the quarter-round segments were hardening off, I cut the tiles needed for the inner and outer faces of the curb, and when it was safe to remove the ledges (about two hours at 90°F.), I installed the last of the segments (Figure 3-97).

Grouting and Finishing

This installation called for different grout colors for the walls and floor. So before packing the wall joints, I used painter's tape and a tarp to mask off the rocks on the shower floor (Figure 3-99). The sanded grout packed and cleaned easily, and the tiles' slightly rounded edges made finishing the grout a relatively simple job.

Cleaning the wall tile indentations made by the bamboo, however, considerably slowed the grouting process. After packing the joints and scraping most of the excess grout off the face of the tiles with the rubber trowel, I had to use my fingers to gouge the excess grout from the indentations (Figure 3-100). Then, after an initial cleaning, I had to use toothpicks to

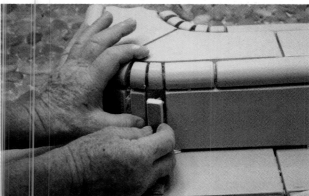

Figure 3-97. To ensure a consistent joint line for the cut tiles needed to cover the face of the curb, the author directly marks tiles positioned over spacers (top). The last tiling step for the curb is to install the outer face segments (bottom).

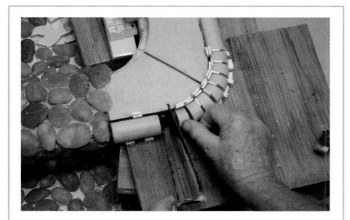

Figure 3-96. After buttering and filling all the segments, the author quickly sets and supports them with tile spacers.

Figure 3-98. The segments for the inside curve include one that has been profile-cut to better fit against the rocks.

remove excess grout trapped in some of the more narrow indentations. I was able to pack and spread one of the shower walls before I had to stop, go back, and clean up. After the second wall was finished, I grouted and cleaned all the wainscot walls. Then I removed tape and tarps and vacuumed the shower and bathroom floors in preparation for the darker grout.

Their rounded surfaces made grouting the sheet-mounted rocks something of a problem: Removing too little excess grout during the cleaning process would assure a smoother surface, but result in a very thin and fragile grout cross-section (Figure 3-101). Removing too much grout makes for a strong joint, but also one that does not drain or clean easily.

As the shape and attitude of each stone, and thus the finished surface of the grout, is constantly changing,

Figure 3-99. Because they are impervious, these porcelain tiles did not require misting or damp sponging prior to grouting. Tape and tarps keep grout off the floor tiles.

Figure 3-100. After scraping the excess grout off the tile surface, the author gouges the excess from the bamboo indentations.

Optimal Grout Depth

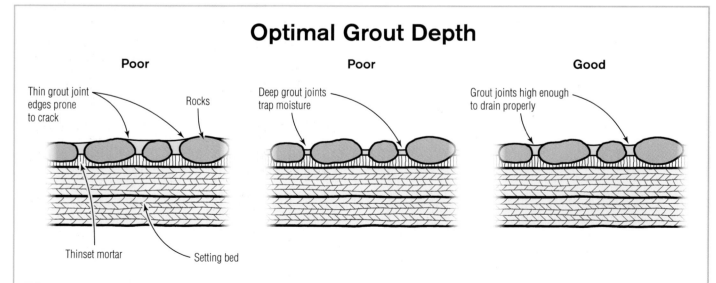

Figure 3-101. The grout on the left is very strong, but the deep joints will tend to trap moisture. The center floor surface is very smooth, but the thin grout joints are prone to cracking. The joints on the right are high enough to drain properly and are relatively robust.

cleaning with the sponge took time and patience. For scraping off excess grout, I found the short edge of the grout trowel far more efficient than the wider edge. The stones are impervious, so I spread and packed the entire floor before stopping to sponge clean. With that done, I used a utility knife to clean out the movement joint between the wall, curb, and floor rocks (Figure 3-102) and let the grout sit for 72 hours to damp cure before filling the joint with sealant.

This shower (and the rest of the bathroom) took far more time to complete than most tiling projects, but its strong construction will ensure that the bathroom will give many years of low maintenance service, and its myriad of details will always make this room a fun place to visit (Figure 3-103).

Installing Ceiling Tiles

On any type of tile ceiling project, the most important part of the installation is support. Will the structure carry the load? Will the tile adhesive retain its grip on the setting bed and the tiles? Normally, tiles installed inside a structure are shielded from extreme temperature swings, but not so in a shower stall—especially if it is a steam shower. The methods I use to produce flat or sloped ceilings acknowledge the energetic expansion/contraction cycles found around shower ceilings.

With the possible exception of industrial-grade tiles made specifically to line the ceilings of tunnels, there are no standards—other than manufacturer's limitations—for tiles that can be applied to ceilings. While some building codes specify that only ceramic or tempered-glass tiles be used in showers or steam showers, nearly any ceramic, stone, or glass tile can be used to tile a shower ceiling as long as certain rules are followed. The key rules cover structural issues, waterproofing, bonding, and movement joints.

Most residential ceiling installations are found in shower stall environments. For information regarding this and other types of tiled ceilings, refer to TCNA C311, C312, and C315. For safety reasons, particular attention needs to be paid to the weight of the installation materials and the limitations of a structure. I prefer 12-inch rafter spacing and cement backerboards for ceiling use, and I locate membranes according to each membrane manufacturer's instructions. Some surface-applied membrane systems may want the membrane installed behind the backerboards rather than on the surface.

Working overhead uses more energy and takes greater patience than wall or floor work, and you have to be extra careful to avoid getting sawdust, backerboard crumbs, mortar, and other construction debris in your eyes. The proper bonding of membrane systems and tile, important on any installation, is especially critical here for safety reasons.

Structural

Although a certain number of minor corrections are inevitable, the desired level of finish needs to be built into the framing, maintained at the adhesive and membrane levels, and carried through to the tiles. For best results, a ⅛-inch-in-10-foot tolerance should be speci-

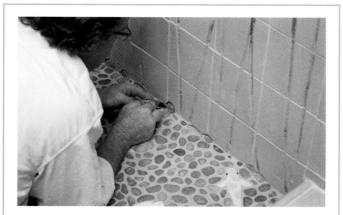

Figure 3-102. As soon as it is practical to get on the floor, the author removes excess grout from the movement joint with a utility knife.

Figure 3-103. Finishing all the details for this installation took time, patience, and persistence, but its beauty, durability, and ease of maintenance make it all worthwhile.

fied for all ceiling rafters and joists, with full-face attachment and edge support for all backerboards (Figure 3-104). Sixteen-inch spacing is the minimum standard for ceiling joist spacing, and 24-inch spacing is allowed under some conditions. However, I recommend 12-inch spacing for ceramic and most natural ³⁄₈-inch-thick (nominal) stone tile, and 12-inch spacing for heavy stone and some fragile glass tiles. Although not necessary for regular showers, canted ceilings sloped a minimum 2 inches per foot are a UPC and UBC code requirement for steam showers (Figure 3-105). The orientation of the slope will determine where the ceiling run off drips.

Backerboard Ceiling Details

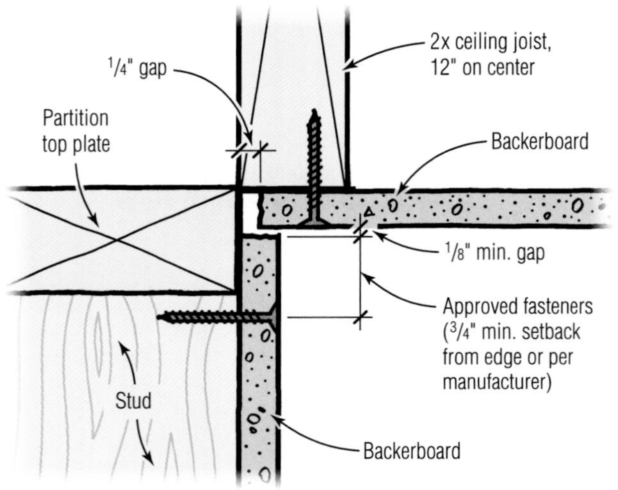

¹⁄₄" gap

Partition top plate

2x ceiling joist, 12" on center

Backerboard

¹⁄₈" min. gap

Approved fasteners (³⁄₄" min. setback from edge or per manufacturer)

Stud

Backerboard

Figure 3-104. For best results, the edges of all backerboards should be attached to the full width (1¹⁄₂ inches) of the framing member.

Waterproofing

Although I generally recommend surface-applied systems, the makers of some brands call for ceiling membranes to be applied to the back side of the backerboard under certain conditions, mostly pertaining to the weight of the tile and its adhesive layer. If there is any doubt about the ability of a particular membrane to safely support ceiling tile, that membrane should be installed behind the backerboard according to the manufacturer's instructions, otherwise another membrane should be selected.

Hot, moist air rises and, confined in an enclosed shower stall, looks for places to escape. For best performance, a shower's light and vent fixtures should be joined to the membrane with sealant. The surrounding ceiling membrane must be joined to the wall waterproofing, but the ceiling tiles must be separated from the wall tiles with a movement joint, and the waterproofing membrane must be built with enough slack in the movement joint areas that normal building movement will not damage the membrane.

Installing Ceiling Tiles

As long as the latex thinset mortar holding the tiles to the ceiling is tacky, there should not be any problem with adhesion, especially if the tiles are back buttered. When properly adhered to a flat ceiling, most tiles should stay put without spacers or wedges until the adhesive hardens. On a sloped ceiling, however, sliding is a problem that can significantly reduce the bond strength and even cause tiles to fall off the ceiling before the adhesive hardens. To prevent this from happening, I begin installing tiles on the low side, use spacers and wedges to stabilize the foundation course, and use additional spacers and wedges to stabilize the remaining tiles until the thinset mortar hardens.

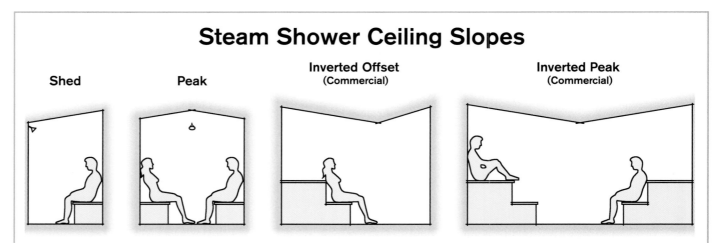

Steam Shower Ceiling Slopes

Shed   **Peak**   **Inverted Offset** (Commercial)   **Inverted Peak** (Commercial)

Figure 3-105. A slope rate of 2 inches per foot is required for ceilings of steam showers. The slope should be built to shed water away from users, as in the four options shown.

NOTES

NOTES

Chapter 4
COUNTERTOPS AND BACKSPLASHES

Tiled countertops are known for their durability and utility in commercial kitchens. They were very popular in homes, as well, until stone slabs, both natural and engineered, became more widely available. Apart from appearance, there are several reasons for the increased popularity of stone slab countertops. Slabs have few joints to collect dirt and stains, provide a smooth working surface, and are easier to clean and maintain than a surface covered with small tiles (Figure 4-1). But slabs are neither universally available nor the only way to produce beautiful countertops that are both highly functional and easily maintained. This chapter will explain some of the details I employ to make a truly functional tile countertop using only thinbed materials and methods.

For most residential and commercial applications, there are three basic types of countertops: dry, bathroom, and kitchen. Essentially, I rely on the same thinbed installation method for all three types; that is, a double-layer plywood base covered with a waterproofing/crack-isolation membrane (Figure 4-2), but I omit some of the finer waterproofing details when building a dry counter. Since countertops have long spans between supports and most backerboards do not offer any structural strength, I rarely specify or use tile backerboards on countertop installations.

Finally, I am not only a tile installer but also a cook who has built and worked in many restaurant kitchens and who likes to cook at home. It is because of my interest in cooking that I stopped building traditional tile counters as I was taught: white-grouted 4¼-, 6-, or 8-inch tiles on the countertop and backsplash. I am fine with tiled backsplashes, even those tiled with uneven, hand-molded tiles. It was the uneven working surface created by all the grout joints that I did not like: tops that were not smooth enough for rolling dough and that made kitchen machines wobble. So I switched to slab tops and tile backs and for about 10 years installed no countertop tiles.

Meanwhile, with improvements in technology, tile manufacturers kept increasing the size of porcelain tiles to the point that (as this book goes to press) 2x3-foot and 3x3-foot porcelain tiles are now readily available. About 10 years ago, it was 2x2-foot porcelain tiles that brought me back to using tile on countertops, because a 2x2-foot tile meant there would be only one grout joint for every two lineal feet of countertop. That's enough space to roll out a pizza and accommodate any kitchen appliance, but with a lot less grout to clean (Figure 4-3).

Figure 4-1. Although more expensive per square foot than many tile installations, this dimensional stone slab provides a smooth, easy-to-clean surface and requires less prep work than tile.

Selecting Tile and Installation Materials

The first step in producing a great tile countertop is to select the right tile. Since they are manufactured primarily for floor use, most large-format porcelain tiles are certainly strong enough to be used on a countertop. However, some may have an abrasive glaze or surface treatment designed to reduce slipping, and this property makes them a poor selection for a countertop. My first choice is unglazed porcelain with an appropriate surface finish for countertop use. Since large format tiles rarely have matching trim, I often pair the large field tiles with complementary trim from another line of tile. With unglazed porcelain, profiling and polishing a bullnose edge is also an option. If possible, I prefer to install only vitreous or impervious trim tiles on high-use, wet-area countertops.

I have a favorite membrane for countertop applications, which I used in Project 1 below, but any surface-applied waterproofing/crack-isolation membrane that is load bearing and rated for ceramic tile floor or wall installations should be okay for countertop use. For maximum grip and performance, I use latex thinset mortar and latex grout. Colored grout? I have no qualms about using colored grout on a dry-area coun-

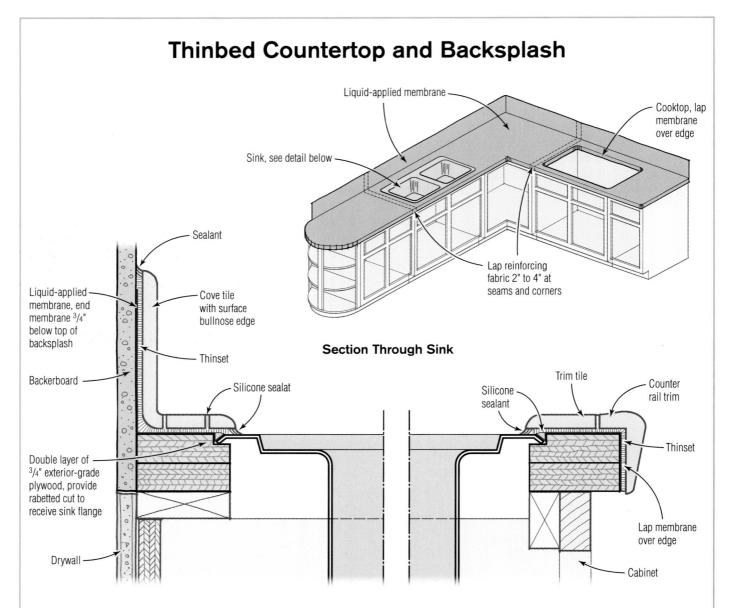

Thinbed Countertop and Backsplash

Liquid-applied membrane

Cooktop, lap membrane over edge

Sink, see detail below

Lap reinforcing fabric 2" to 4" at seams and corners

Sealant

Liquid-applied membrane, end membrane ¾" below top of backsplash

Cove tile with surface bullnose edge

Backerboard

Thinset

Section Through Sink

Silicone sealat

Silicone sealant

Trim tile

Counter rail trim

Thinset

Double layer of ¾" exterior-grade plywood, provide rabbeted cut to receive sink flange

Lap membrane over edge

Drywall

Cabinet

Figure 4-2. The author's preferred tile base for a wet or dry countertop uses two layers of ¾-inch plywood covered by a one-piece membrane. Note that the membrane extends from the lower front edge, across the top of the counter, and up the backsplash. At cooktops, the membrane extends into the cooktop; at a stainless steel sink, the membrane overlaps the sink flange.

tertop, but I prefer to use natural cement-colored grout in wet areas for several reasons:

- People use bleach and harsh cleaners on kitchen and bath countertops, and bleach can lighten or whiten colored grout.

- Food and beverage stains tend to overpower even the most durable sealers and impregnators.

- Natural cement colored grout does not show stains as readily as colored grouts.

Finally, there is a lot of misinformation regarding the use of sealers and impregnators and their ability to "stain-proof" a ceramic or stone tile installation. As we shall see later, these products have their place, but the grout has to be fundamentally sound and specially finished before sealers or impregnators add any real value.

Figure 4-3. With large, heat-resistant tiles and few grout joints, this installation is a practical alternative to a slab countertop.

Project 1:
24x24-Inch Porcelain Tiles Over Membrane

Surface Prep:
Leveling the Cabinets

Aside from waterproofing, a kitchen counter's most important feature is a level surface so cooks do not have to deal with batter leaning out of a cake pan and other such problems. For thinbed countertops, a level tolerance of $\frac{1}{8}$ inch in 10 feet begins with leveling the base cabinets and ensuring that their top edges are all aligned and in plane. I prefer that cabinets be fastened

Materials List: Project 1

Countertop base: Double layer $\frac{3}{4}$-inch Exposure 1 plywood
Laminating glue: Titebond III wood glue (ANSI Type I glue)
Membrane system: ProSpec B-6000, Bonsal American
Tiles: 24x24-inch porcelain tiles, 6x12 cove, counter-rail trim, Stonepeak Ceramics
Thinset mortar: MegaLite, Custom Building Products (CBP)
Grout: Prism, CBP
Sealant: Polyblend, CBP
Sealer: TileLab, penetrating sealer, CBP
Method: A variation of TCNA C512
Performance rating: Heavy

Cabinets Need Full Support

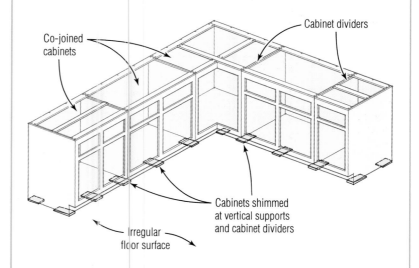

Figure 4-4. When leveling cabinets, give them as much support as possible—not only at the ends of the run. Ensure that all bottom edges are solidly supported with shims or other means.

to each other and to the structure with screws instead of nails. When the cabinets are joined as a group, specify that shims be used in voids beneath all cabinet bottoms and supports, not just at the ends of the cabinet run (Figure 4-4). Inadequate support will cause sagging, door and drawer misalignment, as well as cracked tile.

The cabinets for this project were level and in plane to within $1/32$ inch in 8 feet—perfect for a working wet countertop. I designed this countertop and the supporting custom cabinets to suit the thickness of the cove tile (for the backsplash), the full depth of a 24-inch field tile, the dimension of the V-cap tiles, plus $1/8$-inch grout and movement joints. With stan-

Figure 4-5. The author determines the correct curve for the counter end on a scrap of drywall (left), using a beam compass made from a carpenter's pencil, awl, two clamps, and a wood scrap. After checking the measurements, the curve is precisely duplicated on two sections of plywood and cut with a router bolted to a straightedge (right).

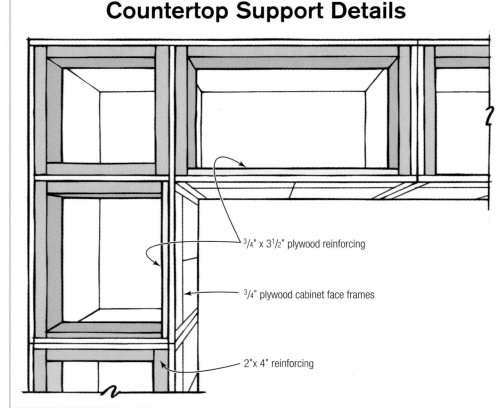

Countertop Support Details

$3/4$" x $3^1/2$" plywood reinforcing

$3/4$" plywood cabinet face frames

2"x 4" reinforcing

Figure 4-6. To provide sturdy attachment for the plywood base, the author reinforces the cabinet walls with 2x4s glued and screwed flush with the top.

dard 24-inch-deep cabinets, that would leave the finished top overhanging the cabinets by about 2 inches. For this project, I needed 4 pieces of ³⁄₄-inch plywood cut to 25⁷⁄₈ inches by 96 inches.

Countertop support is critical because of the long, unsupported spans caused by some cabinets. Standard cabinets are 24 inches deep and range in width from 12 to 48 inches, while the tile industry standard for structural support (based on joist and stud spacing) is 16-inch spacing. To overcome the deflection caused by these extended spans, I fabricated a countertop base made from two layers of ³⁄₄-inch exterior plywood, laminated with an ANSI Type I glue (such as Titebond III), and secured with 1⁵⁄₈-inch backerboard screws (see Figure 4-2, page 106). Because of space limitations, it is usually a good idea to lay out and cut the plywood sheets, including all openings, prior to installing the plywood. However, if there is room to maneuver saws,

I prefer to make sink and cooktop cutouts after the two layers of plywood are laminated.

Trade Tip: After cutouts in the laminated top are prepared, I add supplemental support to narrow sections (in the form of 2x4s, plywood, and in extreme situations where space is limited, angle iron) to reduce deflection.

Plotting the Curved Top

The curve at the left side of the countertop was first determined by laying out the depth of the countertop on a scrap piece of drywall and plotting the curve with a beam compass (Figure 4-5). (This layout also was used later to determine the cutting angle for the V-cap tiles.) After checking the measurements, the curve was

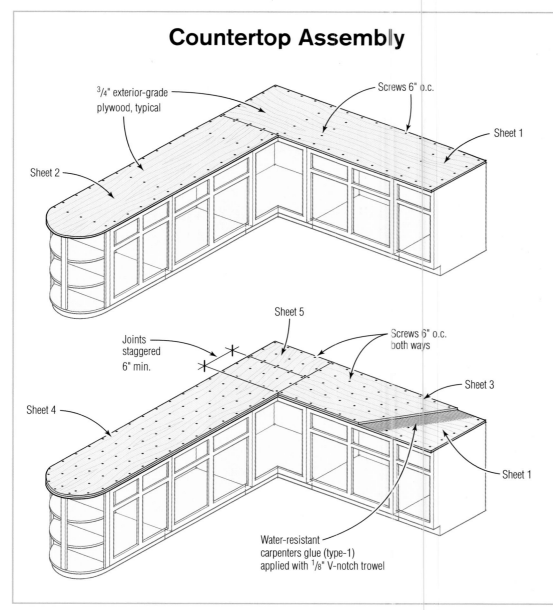

Countertop Assembly

Figure 4-7. The foundation layer of ³⁄₄-inch plywood is attached to the cabinet supports with construction screws, starting with Sheet 1, then 2. Sheet 3 is then glued and screwed in place, followed by 4 and 5 to create the sturdy laminated top.

Figure 4-8. To promote maximum adhesion, the author cleans the first layer of plywood with a damp sponge (A) and spreads waterproof glue over the plywood surface with a notched trowel (B). Next the top layer of plywood is coated with glue and set in place. Clamps secure the leading edge (C) while the author installs screws from front to back, spacing them every 6 inches in both directions.

duplicated on two sections of plywood and then cut with a router.

Installing the Double-Layer Plywood Base

After the curves are cut, the next step is to reinforce the top of the cabinets with 2x4s (Figure 4-6) and install the first layer of plywood over the cabinets with construction screws. Figure 4-7 shows the sequence of

Figure 4-9. A length of 2x4, propped against the ceiling, holds the final section of plywood until it is secured with screws.

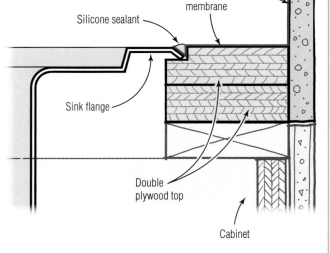

Figure 4-10. The membrane fabric should be trimmed long enough to cover the edge of the rabbet and overlap the sink flange.

installation. It is important to stagger the plywood joints in each layer at least 6 inches to strengthen the top and avoid "creasing," a common problem where joints are aligned in two layers.

After the first plywood layer was installed, I cleaned the top with a damp sponge to remove dust and improve the grip of the glue. Then I spread Type I glue over 100% of the first layer (covering one section at a time) with a ⅛-inch V-notch trowel (Figure 4-8) and sponge cleaned and spread glue on the underside of the top layer.

Next I positioned the top layer over the first layer and temporarily secured it with clamps while I ran screws every 6 inches in both directions, making sure that each screw head was driven just below the surface. Clamps helped to keep the plywood panels flat until they could be secured with screws. In the corner, where clamps don't fit, I used a ceiling prop to secure the small piece of plywood (Figure 4-9) until screws were installed. When all the plywood was laminated, I went over the surface with a block and sandpaper to remove any raised wood fibers.

Cutting the Sink and Stove Openings

Cabinets are built and laid out to accommodate the dimensions of the sink, stove, and other appliances that interrupt the countertop tiles. Like many other countertop installations, the sink and stove on this project are centered above double-door cabinets. Since the cooktop is designed to sit atop the finished tiles, its mounting hole only needed a straight cut and curved corners for the stove base to fit. For this project, I cut the hole large enough for the membrane to lap over the edge of the hole.

Because cleanliness and sanitation are vital issues in the kitchen, I only install sinks below the level of the tile. Self-trimming, top-mounted sinks make even the simplest cleaning chores difficult. Traditionally, quarter-round tile trim was used to cover the edge of the sink. Should the sink need replacement, the quarter rounds can be easily removed without damaging neighboring field tiles, and new quarter rounds can be used to trim the new sink. For this project, I used sur-

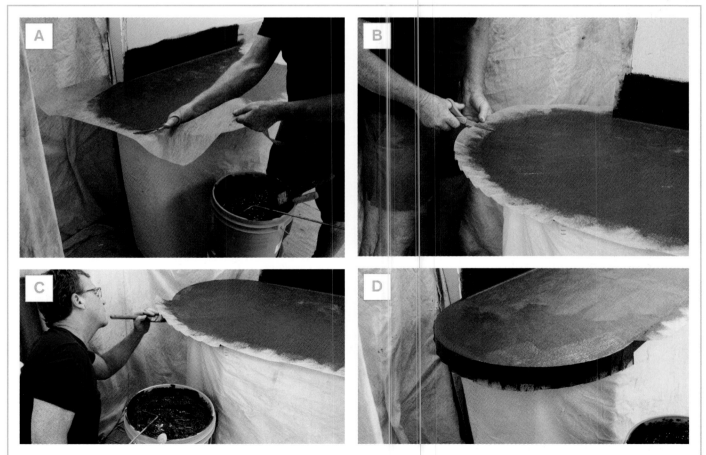

Figure 4-11. The author uses scissors to rough out the curve in the fabric (A). For a smooth fit, he slits the loose edge of the fabric into segments about 2 inches wide (B) and uses a paint brush to fold down and embed the segments in gel (C). Once the all the fabric is embedded in gel, he uses a sharp knife to trim the excess fabric below the countertop edge (D).

Figure 4-12. After embedding the first section of fabric in the gel (A), the author trims around the sink and leaves enough fabric to lap down the edge of the rabbet (B). He then uses a margin trowel to tuck the fabric into the gel-covered rabbet (C).

Figure 4-13. Starting at the backsplash and working out, the author installs the second section of fabric, overlapping the previous section by 2 to 4 inches (A). He then applies a fat coat of gel to the counter's edge to finish embedding the second fabric section (B). The waterproofing should extend around the edge of all openings, with the slit fabric just visible beneath the gel (C).

Figure 4-14. After embedding the reinforcing fabric, the author uses a knife to remove excess fabric (A). A second coat of gel is applied to the countertop and backsplash about two hours after the first has dried (B). To ensure a good seal, the author shoots a bead of silicone in the joint between the membrane and the sink flange (C).

Figure 4-15. To guide the placement of the field, cove, and counter-rail tiles, the author snapped two lines down the length of each leg of the top.

face bullnose trim for the same reason and cut a rabbet around the edge of the sink opening to drop the sink slightly below the surface of the top layer of plywood (see Figure 4-10).

Installing the Membrane

Before installing the membrane, I sponge cleaned the top, dropped the sink into its opening, and cut two lengths of reinforcing fabric—one piece for each leg of the top. I then spread the waterproofing gel with a small diameter paint roller and began embedding the fabric. At the curved end, I trimmed the fabric, slit it into segments, and used a stiff paint brush to embed the segments in the gel (Figure 4-11). After the waterproofing was installed, I went back and trimmed the excess fabric hanging below the bottom of the plywood top.

At the sink, I didn't attempt to trim away excess fabric until this fabric section was embedded in gel. I used scissors to trim the sink fabric, leaving enough to lap down over the edge of the rabbet (Figure 4-12). Using a margin trowel, I tucked the loose fabric into the gel-covered rabbet. When the membrane had cured, I shot a bead of silicone to join the membrane to the sink (Figure 4-14C).

Immediately after installing the first section of fabric, I spread more gel and, working from backsplash out, embedded the second fabric section (Figure 4-13). Each section should overlap the previous one by at least 2 inches; a 4-inch overlap is better. Before trimming the stove opening, I brushed a fat coat of gel on the countertop edge and folded the fabric over. At the stove opening, I trimmed all but 2 inches of fabric, slit it into segments at the rounded corners, and folded fabric into gel. When all the fabric had been embedded in gel, I went back over the entire countertop and cut away excess fabric. Thena I applied another coat of gel to the entire surface of the countertop and backsplash (Figure 4-14) and let the membrane cure overnight. (For commercial kitchens, I apply three coats of gel for extra protection against hard use.) The next day, before installing any tiles, I shot a bead of silicone to join the membrane to the sink flange.

Tile Layout

The layout for this project involved plotting straight lines on the membrane (Figure 4-15), as well as producing a template to radial cut the tile segments used for the counter rail at the curved end of the top (see "Template for Curved Counter Rails," below). I also used the template setup to determine the semi-circular cut on the 24-inch field tile that borders the segment cuts. For the tile layout, I snapped two lines for each leg of the top indicating the joints between the counter rail and field tiles and between the field and cove tiles.

Setting Up the Segment Cuts

To cut accurate angles in counter-rail or V-cap tile trim, I used a cutting jig called the Miter Miser (www.miter-miser.com) to position and support the counter-rail

Figure 4-16. To position the Miser, the author carefully places a straightedge parallel to the saw's fence to make room for the Miser (A, B). Next, he uses the cardboard template (C) to set the Miser at the proper angle against the straightedge. (The narrow kerf on the Miser was made during a previous setup.) The author uses a rock to hold the Miser in place while he positions and tightens the clamps (D). Marking the location of the Miser with a knife makes for a quick setup if more segments are required later (E).

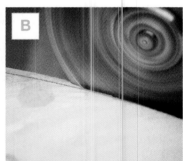

Figure 4-17. The saw is set up to make the left-side cuts on the rail tile segments (A). To make the right-side cuts, the author flips the Miser over, aligns the kerf with the blade, and re-clamps (B). To create a uniform grout joint at the beginning of the curve, the right side of
the first segment along the half-circle must be cut at 90 degrees (C).

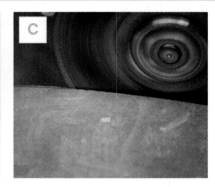

Figure 4-18. The author applies very light pressure with a dry-cutting diamond blade to rough out the curve (A). A few gradual passes bring the blade closer to the line (B). Gradual passes reduce heat that can cause the tile's edge to chip and spall. A final pass brings the blade right to the line (C). To finish the edge, the author uses a tile rubbing stone to smooth the cut and lightly bevel the curved edge (D).

Template for Curved Counter Rails

To make an angled cutting template for the wet saw, I used the scrap section of drywall I used to determine the curved end of the countertop. The first step involved duplicating the dimensions of the plywood top on the drywall (Figure 4-19). The second step required a bit of guessing and a pair of dividers to determine the number of segments needed to cover the half-circle end of the counter. Ideally, I wanted to generate the least amount of waste and get two segments for each counter-rail tile (each factory-made piece measures 5¾ inches). I set the dividers at 2½ inches and stepped off this measurement along the half circle (Figure 4-20), but this measurement did not yield good results, so I spread the dividers to just under 3 inches and re-stepped the half-circle with the dividers. This time, I ended up with full segments with no filler (a partial segment) required to fill in the half circle.

Next, I carefully marked the location of the points indicated by the legs of the dividers. At the apex of the half circle, I laid a tape measure across two of the points and marked the midpoint with a pencil (Figure 4-21). This apex point, plus the point at the center of the circle,

Figure 4-19. The author transfers the dimensions of the curved top to a piece of drywall with a jury-rigged beam compass made from scrap wood, an awl, a pencil, and two C-clamps.

Figure 4-20. The author steps off divisions of the curve with a pair of dividers. This is a trial-and-error process that usually takes several attempts before all divisions are equal.

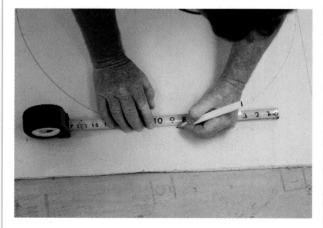

Figure 4-21. The author marks the mid-point of the segment.

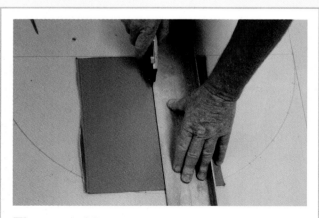

Figure 4-22. To make the first cut, the author aligns a straightedge with the center marks. For easier handling, the author only partially slits through the cardboard.

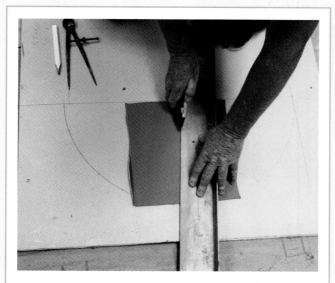

Figure 4-23. The author makes the second cut, again only cutting about two-thirds through the cardboard.

Figure 4-24. For a smoother edge, the author bends the cardboard and slits through from the back side.

helped me cut the first side of the cardboard template I used to setup the wet saw. To do this, I placed a scrap of cereal box cardboard over the drywall, aligned a straightedge with the apex and center-circle marks, and cut through the cardboard with a very sharp blade (Figure 4-22). To finish the template, I repositioned the straightedge, aligning it with the first segment point to one side of the apex mark and the center-circle mark (Figure 4-23), and made the second cut. The finished wedge (Figure 4-24) was all I needed to produce counter-rail segments whose grout joints run parallel, not tapered. Using the dividers to determine full segments— not math—is the method I use to determine segmented cuts for any curved area.

tiles while they were being cut. Ideally, I want to produce all the cut segments before tiling begins, with the least number of setups. To make the first of these two-angled segment cuts, I used the saw's base fence to help align the Miter Miser.

To do this, I used two short straightedges, walking one over the other, to create a new base line for the template parallel to the fence (Figure 4-16). Next, I positioned the Miser gently against the template. To keep the Miser in position while attaching the clamps, I used a rock to hold it in place temporarily (Figure 4-16D) and utilized the saw table's drain holes to secure the clamp bolts. To make the alignment process easier to duplicate should additional segments need to be cut after the first batch was finished, I marked the location of the Miser on the saw's table with a knife (Figure 4-16E).

With the Miser cinched down tight, I could make all the left-side cuts on the tile segments (Figure 4-17). I made two left-side cuts for each full-size counter-rail piece (the second cut was made off a pencil mark made in the middle of each full-size piece). When all the left-side cuts were made, I removed the clamps, flipped the Miser over, aligned the saw blade in the Miser's kerf, reclamped, and made all the right-side cuts. Note: The right side of the first segment needs to be cut at a 90-degree angle so it will transition smoothly with its neighboring full-size trim piece.

Cutting the Half Round

To cut the half-round curve on the 24-inch tile, I re-set the beam compass used to make the template, plotted the half circle, and began the cutting process by roughing the cut with a dry-cutting diamond blade. I made the first cut about ½ inch away from the finished cut line and made several passes—each a bit deeper than the last—until the blade cut all the way through the body of the tile (Figure 4-18). The next cut brought the blade closer to the line, followed by another gentle pass, followed by final passes that took the blade right to the line. Finally, I used a tile rubbing stone to smooth the cut and impart a slight bevel to the curved edge. The only other cuts to be made were around the sink and stove, and these were done as tiling proceeded.

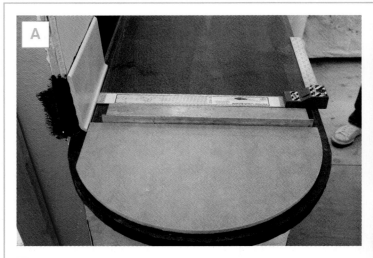

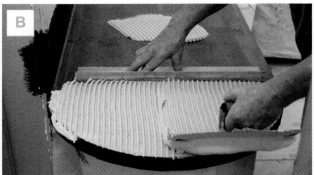

Figure 4-25. To start tiling the counter, the author aligns the half-round tile with a carpenter's square and indicates its position with a short straightedge (A). He spreads only enough mortar to adhere the first tile and uses his right hand to secure the straightedge (B). For convenience, the author back butters the first tile on a nearby work table (C).

Installing the Tiles

I started tiling at the half-round end because it is a focal point of the countertop. Normally, when working with cove tiles, I set the cove tiles first, but because 24-inch tiles require more adhesive than smaller tiles, the 24-inch tiles went in first on this job.

To start the half-round tile on the right path, I positioned it against a short straightedge oriented to the forward layout line and aligned it against the cove tile and the exposed curved edge. I held a straightedge in position while I spread thinset mortar and used it to quickly re-align the first tile (Figure 4-25). Because the laminated plywood top was so flat, I was able to achieve 95% adhesive coverage by spreading medium-bed latex thinset mortar over the membrane with a $\frac{1}{4}$x$\frac{1}{2}$x$\frac{1}{4}$-inch U-notch trowel and back buttering each tile with a $\frac{1}{4}$x$\frac{1}{4}$x$\frac{1}{4}$-inch square-notch trowel. With the first tile properly oriented, I filled in the rest of the top, spreading only enough thinset for one more tile (Figure 4-26) and used a straightedge and level to ensure that all the tiles were aligned in a single, flat plane.

When tiling around the sink, the full or cut tiles on either side should terminate just shy of the sink's rim. I installed the mitered bullnose strips around the sink once all the field, counter-rail, and cove tiles had been installed (Figure 4-27). Around the cooktop opening, two tiles had to be cut carefully to produce the required C-shape at the corners (Figure 4-28). In between the two C-shaped cuts, two slender 24-inch-

Figure 4-26. With tiles this large, the author spreads only enough thinset mortar for a single tile.

long pieces were required at the front and back. A quick check with a straightedge indicated that more thinset mortar was needed beneath the front sliver. I removed the tile, troweled on additional thinset mortar, and re-set the piece. I scraped away excess mortar, cleaned out the movement joint slot at the rear of the countertop, and allowed the tiles to rest overnight.

Sink Trim Detail

Silicone

Liquid-applied membrane

Field tile

Surface bullnose trim tile

Silicone sealant

Silicone

Double plywood top

Thinset

Figure 4-27. To make sink removal easier, only the narrow bullnose strips should cover the sink rim—not the large field tiles (left). The author applies thinset to both the countertop and sink rim to install the bullnose trim (above).

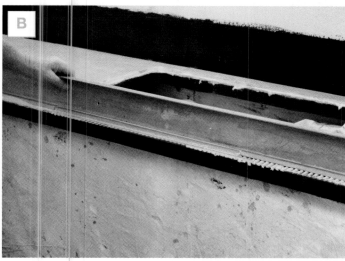

Figure 4-28. After carefully cutting two inside corners on this 24-inch tile, the author back butters the tile and lowers it into position (A). Frequent use of the straightedge ensures a flat surface. Here, the straightedge shows more thinset is needed under the long, narrow tile in front of the sink cutout (B). With the last field tiles installed, the author scrapes off excess mortar and allows the tiles to set up (C).

Installing the Cove Tiles

Allowing the thinset mortar to harden locked the field tiles in place and simplified installing the single-row cove tile backsplash. To make sure the cove tiles on each leg were oriented properly, I used a factory-made inside corner. This created a smooth transition between the two legs and acted as a guide to ensure the faces of the cove tiles were plumb to the countertop (Figure 4-29). To provide an ample cushion for adjustment, I used a ¼x½x¼-inch U-notch trowel to apply mortar to the setting bed and to the backs of each cove tile (Figure 4-30). The mortar is a medium-bed mortar designed for use with heavy stone tiles. Its low-sag formula is ideal for installing these thin porcelain cove tiles, but I still used spacers to help maintain alignment (Figure 4-31).

At the back of the sink, the lower edge of the cove tiles would be exposed until the sink trim was installed. To take advantage of this, I installed wedges to help stabilize the cove tiles and used a straightedge to ensure that all the cove tiles were aligned (Figure 4-32). To trim the right side of the backsplash, I thinned one of the factory out-corners on the wet saw and used spacers and a bit of tape to secure it until its bed of thinset mortar hardened (Figure 4-33). On the left side, I used a full-size factory out-corner, plus another thinned on the wet saw to finish the splash (Figure 4-34). I let the cove tiles rest about 30 minutes

before using a knife and sponge to clean out the grout and movement joints.

Installing the Counter-Rail Tiles

Since the field tiles were sitting rather high, all the counter-rail tiles needed to be shimmed upwards with additional thinset mortar. Also, since these relatively heavy tiles sit on such a small footprint, they needed to be supported from below until the thinset mortar set up hard. I began the counter-rail installation at the top's inside corner and worked outward along the left side (Figure 4-35). I used a straightedge "bridge," assembled with clamps, to support the rail tiles and used shims to fine tune each tile's height. To support

Figure 4-29. This factory-made trim piece makes an attractive corner and serves as a guide for plumbing the faces of the cove on either side of it.

Figure 4-30. The author back butters a cove tile with medium-bed mortar using a $1/4 \times 1/2 \times 1/4$-inch U-notch trowel.

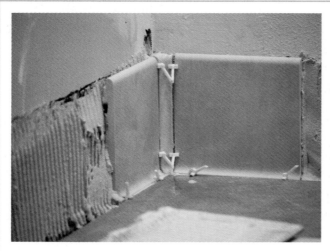

Figure 4-31. Spacers help maintain uniform grout and movement joint widths.

Figure 4-32. The author uses a straightedge to check the alignment of the cove tiles, secured with mortar and adjusted with shims.

the tiles trimming the curve, I made another bridge from scrap drywall and some edges.

The first trim-tile segment installed on the curved section of counter rail had one factory edge so it would meet a full-size trim cleanly. Like the full-size counter-rail tiles, the segment cuts had to be fully supported by adhesive. Squeeze out is messy, but it is also a good indicator that there are no voids behind the tiles (Figure 4-36). The final counter-rail trim required cutting to size, plus notching on the wet saw, to finish the left side of the countertop's edge. With that done, I left the temporary supports in place while I worked on the right side of the top. Compared with the left side, the right side of the countertop's edge installed quickly. I used another factory-made trim to finish off this side's square corner.

Figure 4-33. A factory-made outside corner, thinned by $1/2$ inch on the wet saw and held in place with spacers and tape, is used to finish the right side of the splash.

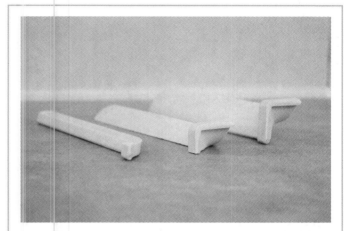

Figure 4-34. On the right is a full-size trim, in the middle is the thinned trim piece, and on the left is the off-cut.

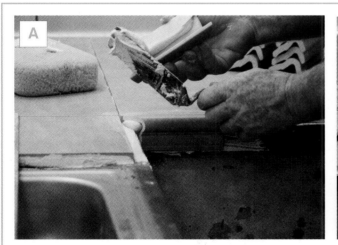

A

B

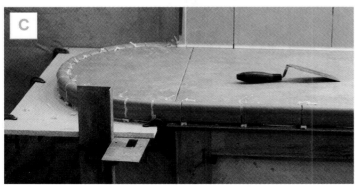

C

Figure 4-35. To keep the counter rail tiles correctly aligned, the author starts with a pair of miter-cut trims at the inside corner (A). The sponge in the background is used to spread thinset mortar on the face of the counter's edge. This straightedge bridge, assembled quickly with clamps, ensures that the counter rail trim tiles won't sag out of alignment (B). Shims are used to fine-tune the height of each tile (C).

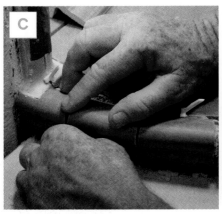

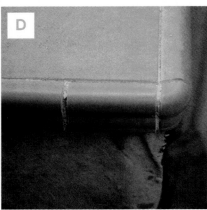

Figure 4-36. To make the smoothest transition between full-size trim tiles and the segment cuts, this trim retains one of its original 90-degree ends (A). Although messy, adhesive squeeze-out indicates there are no voids behind the tiles (B). With a bit of trimming and notching on the wet saw, this tile finished the left side counter edge (C). This factory-made outside corner helps speed the work of finishing the countertop's right side (D).

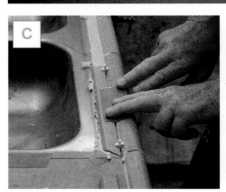

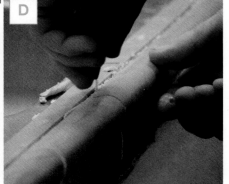

Figure 4-37. The author prepares to install the surface bullnose trim by spreading thinset mortar on the setting bed around the sink's perimeter (A). Spacers and tape are used to secure the trim tiles (B). Full adhesive support is critical at this thin leading edge of the countertop (C). After allowing the trims to set for about 30 minutes, the author uses a knife to clean out excess thinset and a sponge to clean the tiles (D).

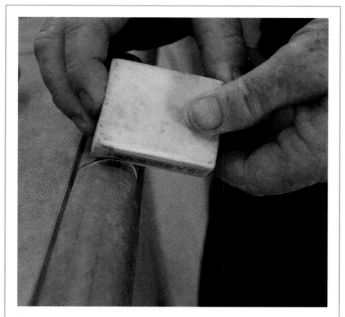

Figure 4-38. The author uses a small tile rubbing stone to smooth the edges between the segment cuts.

Counter-Edge Tile Detail

Counter rail trim

Cold-applied asphalt gum

24" field tile

Extra-thick layer of thinset mortar causes lower edge of top to become visible

Use sander to remove exposed edge

Figure 4-39. Thick layers of medium-bed thinset may lift V-cap tile and trim high enough to expose the lower edge of a double-plywood top. The author recommends sanding off the exposed wood edge for a finished appearance.

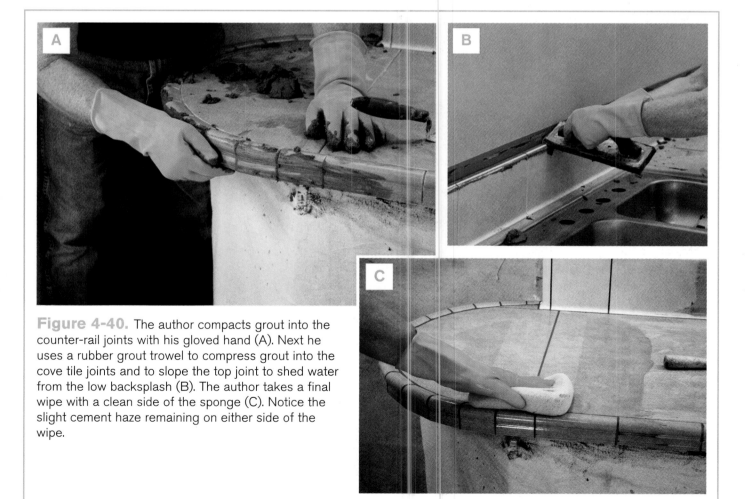

Figure 4-40. The author compacts grout into the counter-rail joints with his gloved hand (A). Next he uses a rubber grout trowel to compress grout into the cove tile joints and to slope the top joint to shed water from the low backsplash (B). The author takes a final wipe with a clean side of the sponge (C). Notice the slight cement haze remaining on either side of the wipe.

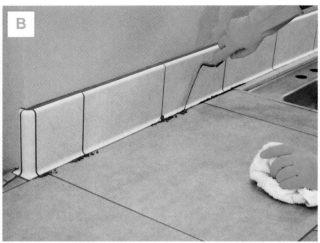

Figure 4-41. The author buffs the tiles with a clean, soft cloth to remove the last traces of cement haze (A). He cleans out all movement joints by slitting through any remaining grout with a ¼-inch wide margin trowel (B). To ensure easy maintenance and cleaning of the finished grout joints, the author uses a length of brass tubing to strike all joints (C).

Finishing the Sink

The first step in trimming the sink was to pre-cut, miter, and dry fit all the surface bullnose pieces required to trim around the sink's perimeter. Next, I spread a layer of thinset around the sink's left side, back buttered, and began installing the tiles (Figure 4-37). Alignment was critical with these trims because they will be right under the gaze of whoever is using the sink. When the first side was finished, I secured the tiles with spacers and tape. Because the front and rear edges are so narrow, the trim tiles installed here had to have 100% adhesive support (Figure 4-37C). After all the trim tiles were set, I let the thinset mortar harden for about 30 minutes before cleaning the excess with a knife and sponge.

Grouting the Top

Prior to grouting the top, I smoothed the transitions between the counter-rail tiles with a small tile rubbing stone (Figure 4-38). Next, I ensured that all movement joints were clean, and the top two thirds of each grout joint was free of all adhesive residue. I also made sure that the underside of the overhanging edge of the countertop was smooth. Normally, V-cap type trim tiles conceal the edge of a 1½-inch-thick setting bed. When a thick layer of medium-bed thinset mortar raises countertop tiles and trim, however, the lower edge of the

Figure 4-42. To cut notches for the cooktop, the author aligns the chisel for another light hammer blow. Notice the other relief cuts made with the chisel.

plywood top may be exposed. In that case, a little sanding will keep the plywood from sight and keep counter edge smooth to the touch (Figure 4-39).

Using my hands to compress the grout, I began filling the counter-rail tile joints at the curved end of the top and worked my way along the edge to the right side of the top. There, I used a rubber grout trowel to compress the grout into the cove tile joints and used

Figure 4-43. The author fills the movement joint between the field and cove tiles with color-matched caulk (left). The joint between the tiles and sink flange also must be filled with caulk to stop leaks and prevent the appearance of cracks (right).

Surface Bullnose Sink Trim

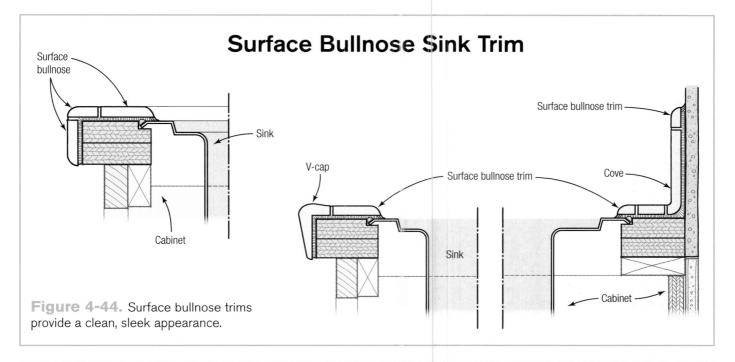

Surface bullnose

Sink

Cabinet

Surface bullnose trim

V-cap

Surface bullnose trim

Cove

Sink

Cabinet

Figure 4-44. Surface bullnose trims provide a clean, sleek appearance.

Traditional Sink Trim Details

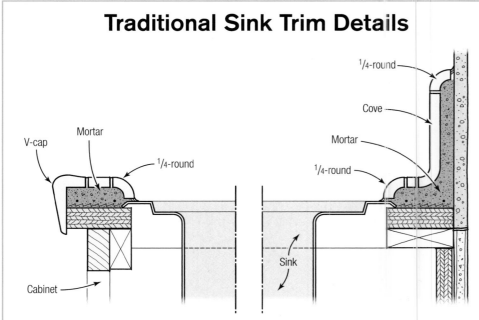

¹/₄-round

Cove

Mortar

¹/₄-round

V-cap

Mortar

¹/₄-round

Cabinet

Sink

Figure 4-45. V-cap tiles on the counter's edge, quarter rounds lining the sink, and cove tiles are traditional trim shapes used to finish a countertop.

the trowel to produce a sloping edge to the top joint (Figure 4-40). Because of the small size of the top and backsplash, and because there were so few grout joints to fill, I packed grout over the entire top before stopping to sponge clean. With crisp, narrow joints, this top was easy to fill and clean. As soon as the grout had set up (15 minutes after cleaning), I removed the masking tape, gave the top a final rubdown with a clean cloth, cut through any grout remaining in the movement joints (Figure 4-41), and ran a striking tool over all the joints on the counter's field tiles and counter-rail tiles.

Finishing the Top

After the top had rested for 72 hours, the movement joint was ready to be filled, but one other task had to be finished first: fine-tuning the countertop range opening. I used a narrow cold chisel and light hammer blows to cut notches in the opening to accommodate the installation clips (Figure 4-42). This method is quicker for me than marking and cutting with a wet saw before installing. The next step was to carefully install a color-matched caulk in the movement joint between the field and cove tiles and in the joint around the perimeter of the sink (Figure 4-43). As

soon as the caulk had cured (24 hours for most brands of latex or siliconized latex), the tiles and grout joints were ready to be treated with a quality sealer or impregnator.

Trim Options

There are numerous ways to trim a countertop edge with tile and other materials. Some are primarily functional, some beautify the edge, and some achieve both. Below are sample details for trimming countertop edges and openings. The countertop edge in the first example (Figure 4-44) uses only surface bullnose tile for a clean, sleek appearance. The second example (Figure 4-45) is traditional and covered with V-cap tile, while the sink is trimmed with quarter rounds. Another approach that I use with stone tile is to use a narrow, fabricated stone slab to trim the vertical face of the edge. To finish the top, I profile and polish trim pieces and install them like surface bullnose (Figure 4-46). In all these examples, notice the extra layers of plywood used to reinforce the edges of openings. In examples where traditional mud-cap trim is used to trim sink (or other fixture) edges, the plywood setting bed will need to be rabbeted prior to installing the membrane and tile.

Fabricating Stone Trim

| #1 Whole tile | #2 Stripped | #3 Profiled | #4 Honed | #5 Polished |

Figure 4-46. To make trim pieces finish around the sink, stone or color-through porcelain tile can be cut into strips and profiled, then honed and polished with a wet grinder (left).

Project 2:
Self-Leveling Countertop Underlayment

Another way to build a setting bed for countertop tiles is to use self-leveling underlayment (SLU) poured over a ¾-inch exterior plywood base. Wet-area SLU countertops should be covered with a waterproof membrane system before tiling. The SLU countertop method can be used for below-mount sinks trimmed in either surface or radius bullnose, as well as for surface-mounted sinks and appliances. The only difference is that, with below mounts, the SLU forms need to set up to create recessed lips for the sink flange (Figure 4-47).

Figure 4-48 shows a countertop prepared for an SLU pour with a foam strip at the back to create a movement joint, front and side dams to contain the SLU, and a tar paper dam around the perimeter of the sink. Expanded metal mesh and 9-gauge galvanized wire are in place to reinforce the top. Four layers of tar paper

Materials List: Project 2

Base for countertop: ¾-inch Exposure 1 plywood
SLU: Custom MegaLite plus primer, Custom Building Products
Reinforcing: 2.5-pound (minimum) galvanized expanded metal mesh, 9-gauge galvanized wire
Spacer for movement joint slot: ¼ x 1¼-inch, self-adhering camper-shell mounting tape, available from ACE Hardware
Dam construction: Scrap tar paper (folded into 4 plies), drywall, and lumber, plus staples or screws

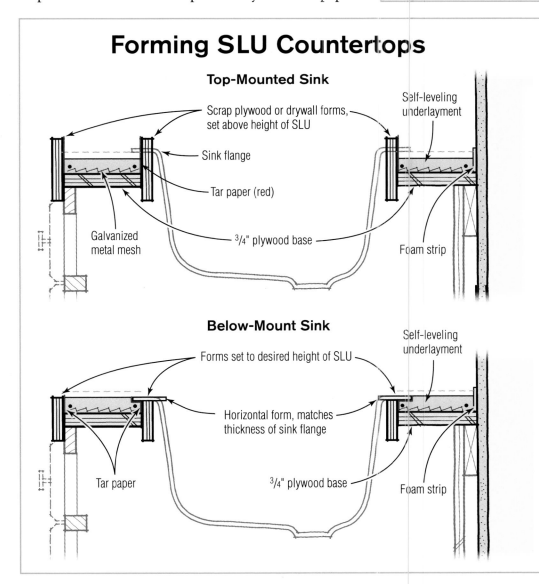

Forming SLU Countertops

Top-Mounted Sink

Scrap plywood or drywall forms, set above height of SLU

Self-leveling underlayment

Sink flange

Tar paper (red)

Galvanized metal mesh

¾" plywood base

Foam strip

Below-Mount Sink

Forms set to desired height of SLU

Self-leveling underlayment

Horizontal form, matches thickness of sink flange

Tar paper

¾" plywood base

Foam strip

Figure 4-47. For self-trimming, top-mounted sinks (top), set the forms above the finished height of the self-leveling underlayment. Forms for undermount sinks (bottom) must create a lip for the sink flange.

Figure 4-48. The ¼-inch thick foam strip at the back of the countertop is camper-shell mounting tape. Galvanized mesh and wire reinforce the SLU. The dams are made from scrap tar paper and drywall.

Figure 4-49. To dam this area, the author stapled four layers of 15-pound tar paper around the curve and sealed the top/dam joint with leftover caulk.

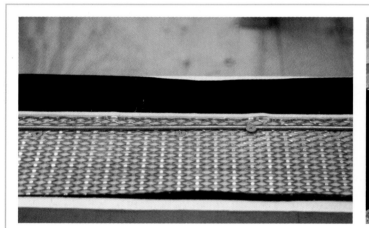

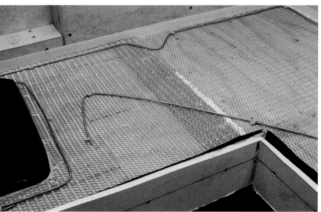

Figure 4-50. The edges of the SLU top are reinforced with 9-gauge galvanized wire held in place by backerboard screws, which also secure the galvanized mesh (left). The author positions 9-gauge wire at inside corners to prevent cracking (right). A bend at each end of the wire helps to anchor the reinforcing.

were also used to dam the curved end of the countertop. Figure 4-49 shows the curved dam stapled temporarily in place. Notice the bead of caulk used to seal the joint where the dam attaches to the plywood top. The beauty of working with SLUs is that none of the dams need to be level—just secure enough to hold back the wet mix and contain it until the SLU hardens. The SLU's plywood base does not even have to be level (results will be better if it is!), but the plywood base must be securely fastened to stable cabinets.

After the dams were temporarily affixed to the plywood and all holes and seams filled to prevent drainage of the SLU, a primer was applied to the plywood substrate, and a layer of galvanized expanded metal mesh was stapled over that. I used 9-gauge galvanized wire to reinforce the countertop's front and back edges, inside corners, and openings. I used backerboard screws to hold the mesh, and tucked the 9-gauge wire under screw heads to keep it positioned until the SLU hardened (Figure 4-50). To increase the tensile strength of the SLU, I laid 9-gauge wire across inside corners, bent the wire ends for greater hold, and staked it in place with backerboard screws. As a final step, I examined the top for any cracks or holes the SLU could seep through and made certain that nothing remained to be done other than mix, pour, and distribute the SLU.

Pouring the SLU

Using simple math to determine the volume of the

Figure 4-51. To save time and steps, the author mixes the SLU right where he needs it (above). An extra pair of hands is required to lift the mixing bucket for pouring. Narrow sections in the front and back of sink or stove openings restrict the flow of most SLU mixes. After pouring, the author will use a trowel to help the mix along and ensure it is evenly distributed (right).

Figure 4-52. The hardened raised edge, common with most SLU brands, is easily removed with a few strokes of a masonry rubbing stone or with a sanding block, as the author is doing here.

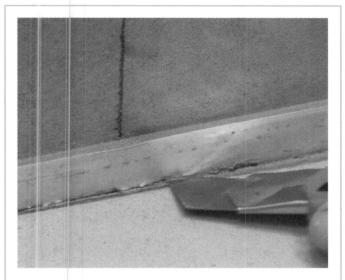

Figure 4-53. After the foam strip used to fill the movement joint is trimmed flush, the top is ready for membrane or tile.

anticipated pour, I estimated that three sacks would be more than enough. Because I generally don't save partial sacks of SLU (unless they will be used within a week or two during dry weather), I mixed full-sack amounts so that extra material would be available if needed. The critical part of this pour was to achieve the required thickness (5/8 to 3/4 inch thick) and ensure the mix was flat. Producing the top was simply a matter of pouring the SLU into the form, quickly distributing the material (Figure 4-51), helping the poured material to flatten where needed, and allowing the mix to harden and cure. This particular mix hardens in about an hour, but I let it set up overnight to lose excess moisture and build strength. Once the level was on mark, I poured the remaining SLU into empty

boxes for disposal after hardening.

With the materials used in the project, the forms were ready to be stripped within 4 hours. To allow the SLU to cure more fully, however, I waited overnight before stripping the forms and plugs, and another 24 hours for the material to fully evaporate and dry at normal room temperatures, with no air conditioning or de-humidifying that could draw moisture out of the SLU and negatively affect the cure. As soon as the forms were removed, I used a masonry rubbing stone to make any minor corrections to the casting and to remove the raised edge caused by capillary action (Figure 4-52). After slitting the foam strip flush and vacuuming the surface, I could begin installing a membrane system or tiles (Figure 4-53).

Project 3:
Building a Cement Backerboard Countertop

In general, I do not recommend cement backerboard (CBU) as a setting bed for ceramic or stone tiles on a countertop. That said, I have worked on many projects where CBUs were specified. Not only are cement boards not structural, they also do not stop water or moisture from entering the structure. Although cement backerboards may be unaffected by water, they require a membrane in wet areas to prevent the board from absorbing water and to protect the underlying materials, as well as materials stored in the cabinets. In cases where CBUs are specified on counters, they should be limited to light-duty residential applications.

When used for countertops, most CBU manufacturers require a layer of 15-pound asphalt felt (tar paper) between the board and the plywood substrate. The board may be fastened with approved screws or hot-dipped galvanized roofing nails. I am uneasy pounding nails through tough backerboard into a flexible substrate, so I recommend backerboard screws. I am even uneasier with dry-installing a sheet of asphalt felt because once the backerboard is installed, air spaces above and below the paper create capillary-action zones that can wick moisture onto the plywood, cabinets, and the wall and floor cavities. To guard against this, before installing the asphalt felt, I make sure the plywood base is level and secure, and then spread a layer of cold-applied asphalt to the plywood base with a $1/8$-inch V-notch trowel (Figure 4-54).

Next, the top is covered with a sheet of 15-pound asphalt felt, sized to lap up the backsplash wall $1\frac{1}{2}$ inches. The felt paper does not require any fasteners, but it is important to smooth out all the air beneath the paper while laminating it to the asphalt-covered plywood. The upturn also should be laminated and stapled to the drywall (or backerboard) splash (and, in turn, covered with one or more rows of tiles). With the tar paper installed, a layer of thinset mortar is spread with a $1/4$x$1/4$x$1/4$-inch square-notch trowel, and the pre-cut and dry-fitted boards positioned and secured with screw fasteners. (To prevent damage, nails should not be used for tile work on cabinet structures.) A movement joint space of at least $1/4$ inch must be maintained between the board and backsplash wall.

Note that if the above construction is used for a wet-area installation, the surface of the backerboards should be covered first with a waterproofing membrane system that must also extend to just below the field of tiles planned for the backsplash.

Finally, to provide a solid base for trim tiles along the front edge of the countertop, I attach a narrow strip of backerboard, cut with a diamond saw and pre-drilled and countersunk to prevent damaging the fragile piece. I attach the strip of board to the front edge of the counter with screws and thinset mortar and cover the joint between the edge and top backerboards with alkali-resistant mesh tape.

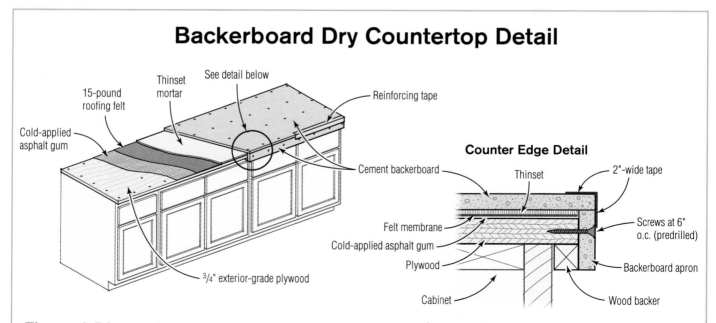

Backerboard Dry Countertop Detail

See detail below
Thinset mortar
15-pound roofing felt
Reinforcing tape
Cold-applied asphalt gum
Cement backerboard
3/4" exterior-grade plywood

Counter Edge Detail

Thinset
2"-wide tape
Felt membrane
Cold-applied asphalt gum
Plywood
Cabinet
Screws at 6" o.c. (predrilled)
Backerboard apron
Wood backer

Figure 4-54. A uniform layer of cold-applied asphalt, spread with a $1/8$-inch V-notch trowel, helps eliminate air below the cement backerboard. A $1/8$-inch layer of thinset mortar provides a support plane for the backerboard. The author pre-drills and countersinks thin strips of cement board (detail) to cover the apron edge.

NOTES

NOTES

Chapter 5
SELECTING TILE AND INSTALLATION MATERIALS

Technology and consumer demand have resulted in an almost endless array of tiles and tiling materials, each with very specific properties to match specific applications. In particular, floors, countertops, ceilings, baseboards, pools, fountains, and exteriors have rigorous demands that require a precise combination of materials. This applies to ceramic, stone, glass, agglomerated, resinous, cast concrete, and metal tiles, as well as to installation materials, including backerboards and their fasteners, membrane systems, adhesives, grouts, caulks and sealants, and impregnators and sealers. There is no one set of materials that would be suitable for every job. Tiles and installation materials need to be carefully selected for each application.

For me, the selection process begins with a tile or a design idea chosen by, or for, the customer. My first task is to ensure that the tile is suitable for the application and, once that is established, to keep the customer steered in the right direction with the help of a designer or showroom. With so many tiles and installation materials available, selecting the right combination may seem daunting, but the initial process I use is simple and nontechnical. It begins with the answers to a few questions:

- where is the installation located (interior, exterior)

- what type is the installation (wet area or dry, functional or artistic)

- how much use will the installation receive

These questions tell me a lot about the physical properties of the tiles and materials that are needed for the installation and allow me (and the client) to narrow the selection process to only those tiles and materials that will work.

Tile selection is usually best done with the help of a sales associate at a local tile showroom. The selection of installation materials depends on the demands of the installation, job budget, and availability. I recommend, to the greatest extent possible, that all installa-

tion materials for a project be single sourced from one manufacturer. Additives, thinset mortars, and grout powders of different brands can often be used together with no compatibility issues. However, to ensure good performance and avoid warranty problems, I always recommend single sourcing the grout, adhesive, and if possible, the underlayment and membrane from a single manufacturer and through a single, local source. This produces the best results at a reasonable cost.

Ceramic Tile

While the variety of ceramic tiles today is vast, at one time there were only two major types of tile: glazed and unglazed. Glazed tiles were generally used on walls, and unglazed tiles were used on floors (and countertops). Traditionally, unglazed tiles—whose surface color extends throughout the entire body of the tile—were made with clay bodies that were high fired. Glazed tiles used for decorative purposes were usually low fired. Tiles that are low fired cost less to produce and have a corresponding loss of wear resistance, while high-fired tiles generally cost more but have

Figure 5-1. Trim tile comes in a variety of shapes, but availability sometimes can be a problem because many trim items are not stocked with field tiles. If trim will be needed for an installation, make sure you can get it before settling on a tile selection.

hard, long-wearing surfaces. The advantage of either type of through-color bodies is that even after being worn down by heavy use, these tiles still retain their original color.

One example of unglazed tile is quarry tile, whose red clay body has been used in factories, stores, restaurant kitchens and food service areas, as well on residential floors. This tile is very robust, but because footprints show and linger, quarry tile, in my opinion, is better suited for commercial applications such food preparation areas. Another example, one that has been used in residential bathroom and shower floors in particular, is unglazed porcelain mosaic tile (Figure 5-2A). Until recently, porcelain mosaics only were available in 1-, 2-, and 3-inch squares or rectangles, but today much larger porcelain tiles are available from numerous manufacturers in sizes ranging from 8 inches up to 36 inches (Figure 5-2B). Also currently being produced are sheets of porcelain measuring 1 x 3 meters (about 39 x 118 inches) and less than ⅛ inch thick.

In the past, making tiles involved a lot of experimentation, guesswork, a local source of clay, plenty of firewood, and a lot of trial and error. The resulting tiles exhibited a wide range of properties because of impurities in the clay, temperature variations within the kiln, and a lack of precise timing as the tile bodies (and glaze) heated up and cooled down. Today, however, tile manufacturing is an international business using highly refined clays, advanced glazes, sophisticated machinery, precise timing, and energy efficiency to produce tiles with highly consistent properties.

Applying a glaze to a tile allowed for unlimited design, but the soft glazes available at the beginning of tile's history were suitable only for use on interior walls (special floor designs were usually produced with stone mosaic techniques instead of glazed tiles). Then and now, glazes can be applied to an unfired or fired clay body and nowadays, because of advances in glaze technology, are used on both wall and floor tiles—depending on the materials used, the kiln temperature, firing time, and other factors. As a general rule, glazes applied over soft, low-fired tile bodies are designed for wall applications, while glazes applied to dense, high-fired bodies are formulated for use on high-traffic floor applications. With ceramic tile, though, there are plenty of exceptions, making tile selection today a bit more challenging.

Because so many tile installations are exposed to water and because porous materials can absorb moisture and harbor unwanted organisms, absorption is one of the most important properties of tile, whether it is ceramic or made of stone, cast cement, or other hard materials. In wet-area applications, absorption can affect health and safety due to the growth of mold, bacteria, and other microorganisms. On exterior applications, absorption can also cause significant freeze/thaw damage. This is why water absorption is No.1 on the list of properties in the "Properties of Ceramic Tile" (pages 293).

The water absorption characteristics are classified from impervious (least absorbent) to non-vitreous (most absorbent) (Figure 5-3). I select impervious tiles whenever possible because, within certain limits, porcelain tiles, or stone and other tiles with impervious properties, can be used for most floor, wall, or countertop applications and are the easiest to maintain. In the real world, however, other types of tile are often desired, and the installer must balance a tile's rate of absorption with how much use and water exposure an installation will receive. For example, while I would not specify a non-vitreous or semi-vitreous ceramic tile for shower walls or bathroom floors that receive

Figure 5-2. Unglazed porcelain mosaic tile is commonly used for residential bathroom applications [A]. Once available only in small squares and rectangles, unglazed porcelain nowadays comes in a wide variety of sizes and shapes [B].

heavy daily use, I might consider installing the same tile in an infrequently used guest bathroom. In wet or exterior areas, I don't specify any tiles in the non-vitreous or semi-vitreous range because the only way to limit their absorption is through regular scheduled application of a topical sealer—not a practical solution. Since most of my work is focused on high performance wet-area installations, I rarely use non-vitreous tiles. When I do, they are used only for dry-area interior wall installations that are decorative rather than functional.

Porcelain Tiles

All porcelain tiles are ceramic, but not all ceramic tiles are porcelain. Porcelain tiles are distinguished by the composition of the tile body (the type and purity of the clay), the temperature within the kiln, and how long the clay is fired. Porcelain tiles are made from clays so resistant to heat that they vitrify only at very high temperatures. Since porcelain clays are so pure, the fired tile body has impervious properties well suited for wet areas.

From a sanitary perspective, only impervious tiles should be used in residential, commercial, or institutional food service areas, since these tiles absorb minimal moisture that can support the growth of harmful organisms. Impervious porcelain tiles are also recommended for high-performance residential and commercial wet areas—kitchen and bath countertops, stall showers, master and family bath floors, and entry hall and mudroom floors in freezing climates.

For commercial surfaces exposed to foot and wheeled-cart traffic, impervious tiles designed for that purpose are recommended. Such tiles can withstand the daily onslaught of traffic as well as the usual daily cleaning and maintenance such floors receive.

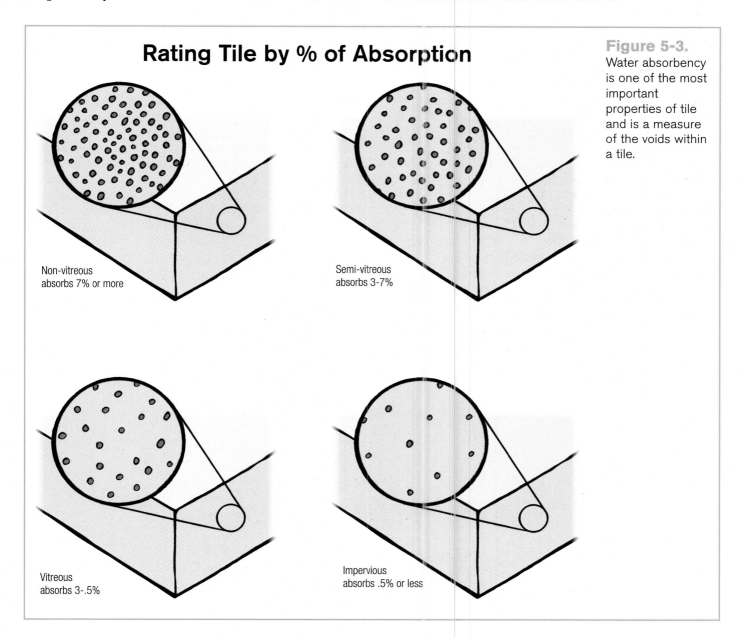

Rating Tile by % of Absorption

Non-vitreous
absorbs 7% or more

Semi-vitreous
absorbs 3-7%

Vitreous
absorbs 3-.5%

Impervious
absorbs .5% or less

Figure 5-3.
Water absorbency is one of the most important properties of tile and is a measure of the voids within a tile.

Since some porcelain tiles are quite delicate and only suited for decorative purposes, I use the terms porcelain, porcelain tiles, impervious, and impervious tiles in this book to refer to tiles made for practical, functional use in a home or business. Depending on the manufacturer and type, porcelain tiles may be either glazed or unglazed. Homogenous, color-through, unglazed tiles are available in varying sizes ranging from less than an inch to 3 feet square. Highly colorful glazed porcelain tiles are also available, but their intense colors only extend to the thickness of the glaze covering their otherwise dull white bodies. Still other through-color porcelain tile bodies are made with a clear glaze to sharpen and brighten the color of the body and give the tiles a smooth glass-like surface.

One precaution concerns a special type of porcelain floor tile made with a textured finish molded into the tile body to provide additional traction. These are most often specified for commercial and industrial floor areas where the most aggressive cleaning methods (steam or high-pressure wash) will be used daily, a floor in a food preparation area, for example. The same surface irregularities that give these tiles their extra traction also prevent dirt and grime from being thoroughly removed by household cleaning methods and materials. These tiles belong in commercial and industrial settings only—not in a home or business where floor drains would not normally be installed.

The fact that porcelain tiles absorb minimal amounts of moisture makes them somewhat difficult to bond. While a number of thinset mortars are specifically formulated for use with porcelain tiles, these are not always readily available. If a specially formulated thinset is not available, I use a premium-grade latex or polymer thinset mortar for bonding and a latex or polymer grout to fill the joints.

Porcelain tiles have a reputation for being difficult to cut, but they can be trimmed to size quickly and easily using a snap cutter and a small amount of light oil (SAE 10 or lighter) or kerosene. I set the snap cutter's fence for repeat cuts, and before scoring a tile, I paint a stripe of light oil in the area of the desired cut (Figure 5-4) and then run the scoring wheel though the path of oil. After snapping the tile apart, I wipe off the oil with a clean rag. With porcelain, I prefer to use the snap cutter for all cuts except Ls, which are best

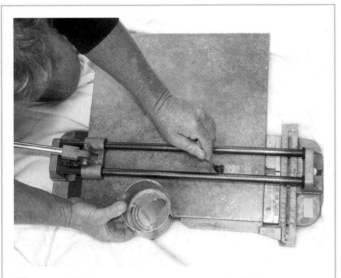

Figure 5-4. Painting the score path of this porcelain tile with light oil results in more consistent snap cutting with less erratic breakage.

Figure 5-5. The author uses a diamond core bit, a plywood guide, and the water bath of a wet saw to drill through a hard porcelain tile.

done on a wet saw. For wet-saw cutting, I use a blade designed for cutting porcelain tiles and keep the cooling water as clean as possible. After cutting, each tile should be rinsed in clean water and dried completely before bedding in thinset mortar. Both dirty coolant water and clean rinse water are bond-breaking materials that should be removed for greatest adhesion. The body of an unglazed, color-through porcelain tile can be ground, profiled, polished, and fabricated with the same tools and abrasives used to work stone tiles. It is possible to drill through porcelain tiles with some high-performance carbide bits if you work slowly and clamp the tile to the cushioned base of a drill press, but if you want to be practical, use diamond drills and core bits for this type of work. Unless I am using dry-cutting core bits, I always use a water bath to extend the life of the cutting tools (Figure 5-5).

Vitreous Tiles

The clays used in vitreous tiles are not as heat resistant or as pure as those used to produce impervious tiles. As a result, vitreous tiles absorb more moisture, are less stable in freeze/thaw conditions, and are less stain-resistant than impervious tiles. Generally, vitreous tiles also have less compressive strength, require lower kiln temperatures and shorter firing cycles, and consequently are less expensive than impervious porcelain tiles. Vitreous ceramic tiles can be used wherever maximum resistance to moisture absorption is not required. Some vitreous tiles also may be used in exteriors not subject to hard freezing, and most are suitable for wet use in interior applications, such as shower floors. Vitreous ceramic tiles and stone tiles with vitreous properties can be cut with wet or dry diamond blades and drilled with carbide or diamond bits. Vitreous ceramic tiles can be cut with a standard snap cutter. Vitreous tiles may be used in all residential interior wet areas and in most residential and commercial exterior areas that are not subject to freeze/thaw conditions.

Semi- and non-vitreous tiles. Although some artistic versions are available at a considerable cost, most semi- and non-vitreous tiles are low-performance commodity tiles more suited for dry walls than in wet areas or on floors. Non-vitreous tiles were used extensively in bathrooms in the past, but with the increased water usage in today's homes and the increasing incidence of mold and mildew, it is wise to stay away from tiles that can absorb moisture. This caution applies to stone, cast-cement, resinous, and ceramic tiles. If your dealer cannot provide porosity information for any tiles you want to install in wet areas, it is better to assume the tiles in question fall into the semi- or non-vitreous range than to assume they have vitreous or impervious properties.

Non-vitreous ceramic tiles, also referred to as glazed wall tiles, at least have a covering of vitrified glaze that will prevent moisture from penetrating through the face of the tile. However, with semi- and non-vitreous stone tiles, the porous nature means there will be plenty of absorption through the face of the tile, as well as through its edges and back. At a time when some marble is being sold as granite—and vice versa—it is difficult to generalize, but marble, limestone, sandstone (in order of increasing absorption) can be considered semi- or non-vitreous, while granite, quartz, quartzite, and some slates can be put into the vitreous, impervious range. Yes, it is possible to apply a water-resistant top coating to porous stone tiles, but waterproofing absorbent stone tiles in wet areas requires absolute vigilance on the part of the user, plus extensive cleaning and lengthy drying for every re-application, which may be required every 4 to 12 months—a routine no user would ever tolerate. For this reason, I recommend semi- or non-vitreous ceramic tiles only for dry areas. Stone or other tiles having the absorption properties of a non-vitreous ceramic tile should be used in dry, interior applications only. The best way to determine a stone tile's suitability is to request from the stone-tile dealer (such as a tile store) the location of a similar installation, in a similar climate and exposure that you can examine. If a similar example is not available for inspection, choose another stone tile.

Selecting Ceramic Tile

Ceramic tiles produced today possess a wide range of properties, making certain tiles better suited to some applications than others. Few tiles can satisfy the needs of every application, so knowledge of the properties is important to achieve the desired performance.

The "Properties of Ceramic Tile" (page 293) provides a complete list of properties for ceramic tile. The first seven properties have useful ANSI reference tables (found in the ANSI A137.1 booklet) that are relatively easy to access and understand. The entire list contains the key properties of most interest to consumers and end users: Does the tile absorb moisture? Will the installation show wear? Can the tile be stained? Damaged by frost or freezing conditions? Hurt by cleaning chemicals? Are the tiles slippery? Slippery when wet? Are all the tiles the same size? Will the installation be difficult to maintain? Will it be beautiful? Altogether, there are 21 properties for which ASTM tests or ANSI test methods exist.

With so many other properties to evaluate, how can you determine what tile is right for a given application? The best way is to communicate the needs of the installation to your supplier or showroom dealer and then develop a list of tiles and materials that make sense for that project. For my own installations, I sometimes have to work with unfamiliar tile and materials from an unknown supplier. Since most of my work involves low-maintenance, wet-area installations, I typically use vitreous or impervious ceramic or stone tiles with vitreous or impervious levels of moisture absorption.

The following properties are what I look for in an ideal tile for a wet or exterior area receiving heavy, continuous use:

Property	Value
Aesthetic Class	V0 to V4
Water absorption	P-, E-, O-1 or P-, E-, O-2
Visual abrasion resistance	Class II, III, IV, or V
Chemical resistance	Class A or B
Freeze/thaw resistance	15 cycles with zero defects
Coefficient of friction	No less than .5 wet, .6 is better
Stain resistance	Class A is preferred
Deep abrasion resistance	P-, E-, O-1 or P-, E-, O-2, only
Crazing resistance	Passes
Thermal shock resistance	Passes
Facial dimensions	Passes*
Warpage	Passes*
Wedging	Passes*
Thickness	Passes*

It is assumed by consumers, designers, and installers that tiles for a specific installation will share certain physical qualities, for example, a common thickness, uniform linear dimensions, and a certain degree of flatness. All tiles, however, are usually shipped with somewhat erratic dimensions that require a careful installation. The size of a particular tile can only be determined with the tile in hand, and even then, variations in dimensions should be expected. For example, manufacturing tolerances for 12-inch-square tiles allow over $^1/_8$-inch difference in length and width; this is in addition to an allowable tolerance of $^1/_8$ inch for warpage. Values for smaller or larger tiles are proportional to 12-inch tiles.

In addition, I look for the following physical properties for all types of tile:

Bond strength	≥50 psi
Breaking strength, glazed wall tiles	≥90 pounds
Breaking strength, floor tiles	≥250 pounds
Facial and structural defects	Passes
Evaluation of shade value	V1 to V4
Thermal expansion	Passes
Moisture expansion	Conforms
Mounting	Conforms*

Mounting pertains to a set of testing methods for mosaic tiles that are sheet mounted. Passing this test indicates that the grout joints are uniform.

When selecting tiles and installation materials for a specific project, I begin with the above lists, which represent an ideal with compromises made for a combination of appearance and performance.

But here's a trick to further simplify the task: By simply selecting tiles from the P-, E-, or O-1 water absorption group, practically all other desirable properties (except coefficient of friction) for wet or exterior applications are attained. The physical strength values represent minimum strengths that are often exceeded by tiles in this group.

Stone Tiles

One hundred years ago, most available stone tiles had been on the market for hundreds or thousands of years. In the early 1900s, there were few standards for determining the properties of stone tiles. In the past, most stones were taken from known quarries, and in place of standards, a stone tile producer would use a book of installations to show suggested uses for a particular stone. The process of natural selection rooted out stone materials that failed in construction.

Today, most stone tiles have been in use for less than a hundred years—many less than 20 years. The source quarry of many stone tiles may be impossible to identify or locate, and samples that are submitted for the most demanding suite of tile industry testing may not necessarily represent the properties of the lot from which they are taken. The properties of stone tiles not only change from lot to lot and from tile to tile, but the properties of a particular stone tile may change within the same tile. Testing may not always reveal the entire story of a stone tile or its suitability for an installation.

The list of properties above relates to ceramic tile only. The Marble Institute of America (MIA), the leading association of the stone industry, references the ANSI A108 standards for the installation of stone tiles, but the tests MIA uses to determine the various properties of stone are based on dimensional stone, which has a far greater cross section than stone tiles. (The term dimensional stone has a strict interpretation that applies to very thick—6 to 36 inches—stone building blocks and to some stone slabs used for exterior cladding, interior countertops, sills, thresholds, and sculpted baseboards.)

In my opinion, thin stone tiles should be evaluated using the same ASTM tests as ceramic tiles—not those used for stone building blocks. When I am evaluating a stone tile for critical installations—such as exterior cladding, exterior or interior floors, or wet-area showers and baths—and ASTM ceramic tile test results are not available, I rely on a much simpler form of test: I ask the stone tile dealer to direct me to a similar installation that is subject to the same environmental conditions as the installation I am considering. If no examples are available to prove that a particular stone tile is durable, easy to maintain, does not discolor and absorb moisture, and does not deteriorate when exposed to moisture, I counsel the designer or building owner to make another selection. I use the same thinking when evaluating glass, metal, resin, concrete, and other types of hard tile.

For noncritical installations such as dry-area countertops and walls less than 8 feet high, I don't think the qualifications have to be so stringent as long as the installation is functional. Many granite, some marble, and a few limestone tiles have the same relative properties as impervious or vitreous ceramic tiles, and they can be used for most interior and exterior applications. The others, because of high absorption rates, low abrasion resistance, and other problems, are not suitable for exterior walls and floors, interior floors, and wet-area interiors.

Some designers, sellers, installers, and consumers of stone tiles think that the application of a "sealer" will render an absorbent tile fit for use in an exterior or an interior wet area. While there are some top coatings that, when properly reinforced, can produce an impervious surface (at the expense of the appearance of the stone), there are no penetrating sealers or impregnators that can impart vitreous or impervious properties to any stone. Impregnators are designed to prevent stains or make a treated surface easier to clean and maintain; they were designed as a shield against graffiti.

Trim Tile

The type of trim chosen for a job depends on several factors, not the least of which is whether the manufacturer makes trim to match the field tile. Availability of trim tile can often be a problem since many trim items are not stocked by local showrooms or distributors. Trim tiles require special handling during manufacture, have special needs within the kiln environment, and are usually made apart from the field tiles. Trim tiles are often slightly smaller or larger than their field tile counterparts, and there is often a slight shade variation between trim tiles and their companion field tiles, since kiln conditions are difficult to reproduce. With enough planning and lead time, however, finding appropriate trim is possible, even if it requires some ingenuity.

For this book, I break trim into two distinct classes: surface and radius, with surface trim having a flat surface with one or more curved edges (Figure 5-6A) and radius trim having one or more extended curved edges (Figure 5-6B). Radius trim is shaped to conceal the traditional mortar bed on which it usually sits, although the same effect can be achieved on walls with a double layer of ½-inch backerboard.

On floors, I don't use any trim tile (with the exception of cove tiles) except at the edge of a stair tread. When floor tiles abut another finished surface, the tiles should be flush (Figure 5-7). On walls, although I sometimes need the crisp edge that surface bullnose provides, I prefer the traditional look of radius trim and find its curve both elegant and sensuous. In spite of the extra work involved with their installation

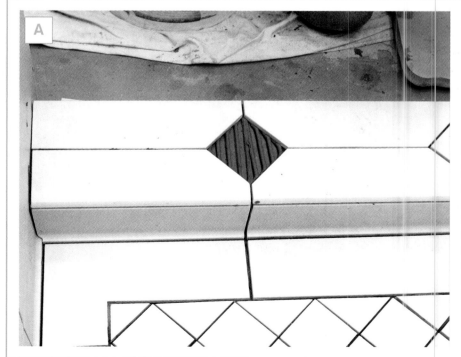

Figure 5-6. Trim tiles come in two styles: Surface bullnose [A], like those shown along the top of this shower curb, are flat tiles with the surface rounded over on one side to create a finished edge. Radius bullnose tiles [B] have a curved edge that provides dimensionality to the tile and is useful for covering over the setting bed.

(Figure 5-8), cove tiles are one of my favorite trim pieces because of the clean way they finish a floor's perimeter and the way they simplify regular maintenance. One of my least favorite "trim" tiles is the glazed edge tile. This is a square-shouldered field tile with one edge covered in glaze that is used as a substitute for surface bullnose.

Not all ceramic or stone field tiles have companion trim, yet most installations need some trim tiles. When a full line of trim pieces is not available, I use local sources and a variety of manufacturers to help select alternate trim tiles whose properties most closely match the original. Bullnose trim can also be fabricated from through-color porcelain or stone tile stock. For short-run production of through-color porcelain or stone tiles into bullnose, I profile tile stock on a wet saw and polish them with standard diamond

Figure 5-7. Inlayed into a wood strip floor, these art and decorative tiles have been installed flush with the floor and require no trim.

polishing pads (see Figure 4-46, page 126). For large production runs, I'll contract with a fabrication shop to do this work and deliver it to the installation site.

Installing Trim Tiles

In spite of slight variations in size or color, trim tiles are useful and essential for many tile installations, and when given careful installation, they provide a beautiful finish unmatched by any other material. Above all, trim tiles require patience and skill to install.

Most surface bullnose tiles can be installed along with the field tiles with no changes to the adhesive layer. But radius bullnose trim and hollow trim shapes need additional support beneath their curved edges. To accomplish this, the hollow areas must be filled with a bonded mortar. For most installations, I use thinset mortar as the bond coat (Figure 5-9A) and sanded grout for the filler mortar (Figure 5-9B).

This technique works fine for most wall work. On floors, I use a setting-bed mortar instead of sanded grout for greater compressive strength. The main part of the technique is the application of a thin bond coat of thinset mortar whose ideal thickness is $3/32$ inch, not to exceed $1/8$ inch. This bond coat, while still fresh and wet, will bond the filler mortar to the tile, and when installed, the combination provides support for the curved edge (Figure 5-9C). To prevent cracking, it is important to extend the setting bed as close to the trim tile's curved edge as possible. The technique of using sanded grout or light mortar as a filler should apply only to the curved portion of the trim tile.

For hollow tile (Figure 5-10A), I use a damp sponge to apply a layer of latex thinset to the irregularly shaped back (Figure 5-10B), fill the cavity with sanded grout (Figure 5-10C), and cut away the excess (Figure 5-10D) before installing in fresh thinset (Figure 5-10E). The curved portion of a piece of cove tile is vulnerable

Figure 5-8. Cove tiles offer a smooth transition between tiled floor and wall planes. Corners can be joined by a simple cope joint, as show here.

if installed unsupported.

Cove tile can be handled in similar fashion for better performance and durability. Prior to installation, butter the back curved edge with thinset mortar, add a layer of grout, then install the cove piece. Filling trim pieces and hollow tiles eliminates air spaces behind the tiles and allows them to withstand greater loads and impact without damage. Hollows should also be avoided in wet areas where they may help develop and harbor mold growth. Grout used for such filling should be mixed to a stiff—but plastic—consistency.

One further note about trim tile is that it is important to accommodate variations between trim and field pieces: If you are using spacers to space the field tiles, make certain you know the average trim size. Trim larger or smaller than the field tiles will require alternate means of spacing to compensate and align with field tiles.

Alternate Field and Trim Tile

Over the years, I have used a very wide variety of materials as substitutes for ceramic tile, including shells, beach glass, marbles, mirrors, barrel bungs, metal castings, river rocks, petrified wood, lava bits, and other materials. I fully recommend the use of found and natural materials as tile substitutes provided the material you want to use meets some of the criteria we would apply to a ceramic tile: Is it absorbent? Is it hard or soft? Will it support foot traffic? Does it discolor easily? These are some of the practical questions you need to ask before lugging rocks up a cliff or out of a ravine. Test your samples with simple absorption and scratch tests, and try bonding your target material with latex thinset to test for adhesion. Keep in mind that some metal tiles and metal tile substitutes may cause grout-staining oxidation if used in a wet-area application. Use your imagination, but use common sense, as well!

Small-diameter, red-clay sewer pipe and glass bottles can be cut, lengthwise, in quarters to substitute for cove tiles or large quarter-rounds. In addition to sewer pipe and bottles, I have used stainless steel, copper, and brass pipe, slit lengthwise into quarter or half sections, as trim for ceramic and stone tiles. In the early and mid-1980s, I used beach glass extensively as both field and trim tile.

The beach where I collected glass and ceramic bits was located north of a California coastal industrial town that happened to make porcelain toilets, sinks, and electrical insulators. For over 50 years, garbage and waste from the ceramics plant and from all the town's other businesses and residences was dumped off a cliff overlooking the Pacific Ocean. Over time, the dump became a 300-foot peninsula composed of

Figure 5-9. The author applies a thin layer of thinset mortar to the back of the curved section of this piece of 4¼-inch radius bullnose (A). While the layer of thinset mortar is still wet, the author applies a thick layer of sanded grout over it (B). The thinset/grout combination helps provide support for the curved edge (C).

glass, ceramics, stainless steel, nickel, Monel (a nickel alloy) and other metals. Another favorite alternative tile of mine is mother-of-pearl lined shells.

Installation Materials

Thin-bed installation materials need to be applied in tight, neat layers with a minimum of lumps that will mar a smooth tiling surface.

When dealing with a subsurface floor or wall that is just outside the desired tolerance, I can usually make minor corrections by using a small, extra amount of thinset mortar to raise the tiles over the imperfection. However, regular thinset mortar should not be used in layers thicker than ⅜ inch, or as indicated by a spe-cific manufacturer, to make corrections to a floor. That can only be done with a self-leveling or featheredge underlayment.

Concrete Slabs

Because slab-on-grade concrete can be so stable, it is one of the best setting beds for tiling. Unfortunately, a lot of slabs in the U.S. are not fit for tile because their surfaces are too slick or covered with curing com-pound or other bond-breaking materials. They also may be inadequately prepared, placed, or reinforced for tile, or their surface may be too rough or out of level. When properly specified, though, a clean, cured concrete slab-on-grade with a steel-troweled, fine-broom finish has greater strength, durability, and

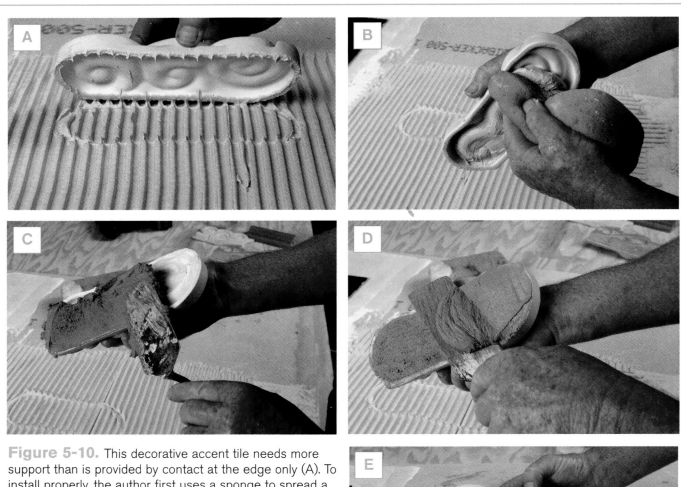

Figure 5-10. This decorative accent tile needs more support than is provided by contact at the edge only (A). To install properly, the author first uses a sponge to spread a thin layer of thinset on the back of the tile (B). The entire back of the tile should be filled with sanded grout or mortar (C). Before setting it in place, all excess sanded grout should be sliced off the back of the tile with a trowel (D). Once it is filled with the thinset/grout combination, this piece will be fully supported, with no voids that could harbor moisture and mold (E).

other advantages over alternative types of construction. Concrete is not harmed by moisture, and its expansion/contraction cycles are more in line with ceramic tile than is wood construction.

Post-tensioned, suspended, and cracked concrete slabs-on-grade are all capable of supporting heavy loads. However, none are stable and all require an isolation membrane before tiles are installed to prevent cracks and movement from damaging tiles or the entire installation. When working as designed, the surface of post-tensioned concrete floors is in almost constant motion. This alone is enough to cause plenty of damage to any material applied directly to the concrete surface. But post-tensioned plank systems are also capable of telegraphing cracks generated at plank-to-plank junctions upward through the leveling coat or topping and into the tiles. Suspended concrete slab floors—like suspended wood floor systems—are designed to bend and flex within certain limits. If those limits exceed the L/360 requirement for ceramic tile or the L/720 (or higher) requirement for stone tiles, an isolation membrane will be needed to protect the tiles. All post-tensioned floors need to be smoothed with a mortar, self-leveling underlayment, or other acceptable patching material before any membrane or tiles can be installed.

Some cracked concrete slabs can be tiled successfully while others cannot. A few small shrinkage cracks in a new concrete slab may not seem to be much of a problem, but the cracks indicate a deficiency in the way the concrete was batched, reinforced, placed, or cured. Also, cracks in a new floor indicate that additional cracks may appear over time. For this reason, I do not recommend the band-aid approach to crack isolation —that is, placing a strip of membrane just over the cracked area. Instead, if there is a problem with cracks, I specify a full-coverage system for those floors that can be rehabbed with a membrane.

However, some concrete slabs cannot or should not be tiled. Conditions unsuitable for ceramic tile installation include:

- where the surfaces of the concrete on either side of the crack are not level—this indicates a structural problem with the slab that cannot be solved by a membrane system

- where cracks are too wide—generally, cracks wider than ⅛ inch are considered too wide to renovate successfully, although there are exceptions depending on the brand of membrane

- where there are too many cracks—when examining a floor before tiling or submitting a bid, I assign 1 square foot for every lineal foot of cracked slab and only consider tiling those floors with no more than a 15% cracked surface

Ideally, concrete should be cured a minimum of 28 days before covering with tile or a membrane and before rehabbing with self-leveling compound or other surface prep materials. A fine-broom finish promotes the best adhesion; without it, mechanical methods such as bush hammering or shotblasting should be employed to eliminate slick surfaces. A latex or polymer-modified thinset mortar is recommended for installing tiles on slabs, a latex or polymer-modified grout is recommended for filling the grout joints, and movement joints must be a part of every concrete slab installation—on grade, suspended, or cracked. Detailed information on preparing slabs for tile is found in Chapter 6; information on creating movement joints for tile is provided in Chapter 8.

Plywood Subflooring and Underlayments

There are several reasons for using double-layer plywood as a base for ceramic tile. The first is strength. When properly installed, certain grades and sizes of plywood are structural. When two layers of plywood are laminated, they produce superior strength and ample support for tiles. The only drawbacks to a double-layer plywood base are:

1. The flatness and level of the floor depend on the straightness of the joists (both at the time of installation and years down the road, after the wood has reached equilibrium).

2. Plywood expands and contracts more than tile, which over time can undermine the bond between the two and shorten the life of the installation. To counter that problem, I always apply a waterproofing/crack isolation membrane to the surface of the plywood underlayment prior to tiling, and I'm scrupulous about maintaining a network of movement joints to further protect the tiles.

Best practices for installing plywood subflooring are provided in Chapter 6.

Backerboard Underlayments Over Wood Subfloors

Backerboards were developed for wet-area tile setting as an alternative to using mortar beds or drywall as the setting bed. The skilled labor needed to produce traditional mortar beds has grown increasingly scarce, and regular and treated drywall has proved to be unsuitable for most wet-area tiling. Due to their popularity, numerous brands of tile backerboards are now available throughout the U.S. Backerboards are being made in four basics types (see "Types of Backerboards" page 144). They also are sometimes made from a wide range of ingredients, including processed newsprint, chopped or shredded foam, resilient resins, sand/foam/cement combinations, ground glass, microspheres, fly ash, clinker, and other materials, some of which are already being used for brand-name boards. Over the past 30 years, numerous boards have come and gone, and no doubt the next 30 years will bring numerous other boards to the market.

Backerboard and membranes. In the past, the makers of most tile backerboards have promoted inexpensive and low-performance waterproofing materials and methods, such as a layer of 15-pound roofing felt or 4-mil plastic sheet between the boards and studs. But most manufacturers now accept the use of surface-applied membranes and approve their use in warranties.

To reduce the risk of mold, waterproofing membrane systems should be an integral part of every wet-area backerboard installation. Regardless of whether the installation is mortar bed, plywood, or cement backerboard, I specify and use surface-applied membranes. Yes, mortar beds and cement backerboards are unaffected by exposure or saturation, but both are also porous and can hold a surprising amount of water—horizontally and vertically—that can harbor permanent, thriving colonies of mold and mildew.

To me, it makes absolutely no sense at all to attempt installing a waterproofing membrane behind a setting bed. The nails or staples used to attach reinforcing wire for a mortar bed and the nails or screws used to attach backerboards and plywood all puncture this type of membrane, plus the entire setting bed (mortar bed, backerboard, or plywood) can absorb a lot of water—8 pounds or more for every 15 square feet of $\frac{1}{2}$-inch-thick cement backerboards, up to 12 pounds or more for every 15 square feet of $\frac{3}{4}$-inch-thick mortar bed, and up to 27 pounds or more for 15 square feet of a typical $1\frac{3}{4}$-inch-thick floor mortar bed. These conservative figures add up to about 30 pounds of water or more absorbed by a typical cement backerboard tub/shower surround; up to 44 pounds or more for a $\frac{3}{4}$-inch-thick mortar bed shower; up to 144 pounds of water or more for a 100-square-foot, $1\frac{3}{4}$-inch-thick mortar bed floor.

Of course, the addition of high-solids latex to the mortar setting bed would reduce absorption to around 5%, but rather than think that latex will cure all waterproofing problems, it is better to think of latex as a strength-building component instead and apply a membrane for waterproofing protection.

Nonstructural attachment planes. With few exceptions, most current backerboards are nonstructural attachment planes that are unaffected by exposure to moisture or water. An attachment plane is nothing more than a surface that can easily be installed over a suitable subflooring and to which tiles or a membrane system can easily be installed. It is not a structural member, but rather is a structural load. Most tile backerboards are available in nominal $\frac{1}{4}$- and $\frac{1}{2}$-inch thicknesses, with panel sizes ranging from 3x5 feet to 4x8 feet. Depending on the brand, they are designed to meet minimum performance standards when installed over single-layer plywood or OSB subfloors. Minimum performance means just that. Consequently, I tend not to recommend most tile backerboards for floor installations (unless installed—in dry areas only—over a double-layer plywood floor) and prefer the double-layer plywood/membrane method described above. When using backerboard on floor installations, keep in mind that most $\frac{1}{2}$-inch-thick backerboards offer no more strength than $\frac{1}{4}$-inch-thick boards. In fact, $\frac{1}{4}$-inch boards should provide better performance on floors because they add only half as much weight to the structural floor load as do $\frac{1}{2}$-inch boards.

Wet-area wall installations. For thinbed wall installations, cement backerboards are unaffected by exposure to moisture and are considerably stronger than regular gypsum walls. These two properties alone make them well suited as bases for tiles installed in wet areas, such as showers and tub surrounds, whose setting bed walls will be protected by surface-applied membrane systems (Figure 5-13). I do not recommend $\frac{1}{4}$-inch boards for wall or ceiling applications because they are too flexible and are not recommended for these applications by the manufacturers. On floors and counter-

Types of Backerboards

Cementitious backer units (CBU) are the first generation of sand and cement backerboards and are generally recognized by a gray color and a partially visible skin of woven fiberglass mesh (Figure 5-11). Some of these boards are shipped with visible cracks, and unless handled like sheet glass, this type of board will continue to crack during handling and installation. The more cracks, the weaker the board. Fasteners cannot be positioned close to the edge or cracking will occur. Nail and screw fasteners are known to cause "blowouts" that eject

material from the backs of the boards. Although encapsulated by thinset mortar when applied to a floor or countertop, these blown-out crumbs can be a problem on vertical installations. To prevent hard crumbs from interfering with stud contact, fastening should proceed from top to bottom, with boards pulled out slightly from the plane of the wall so the crumbs have an escape route.

CBUs are completely unaffected by exposure to water or moisture, but since they will absorb and wick moisture, a membrane is required for wet areas. This board can be

Cement Backerboards

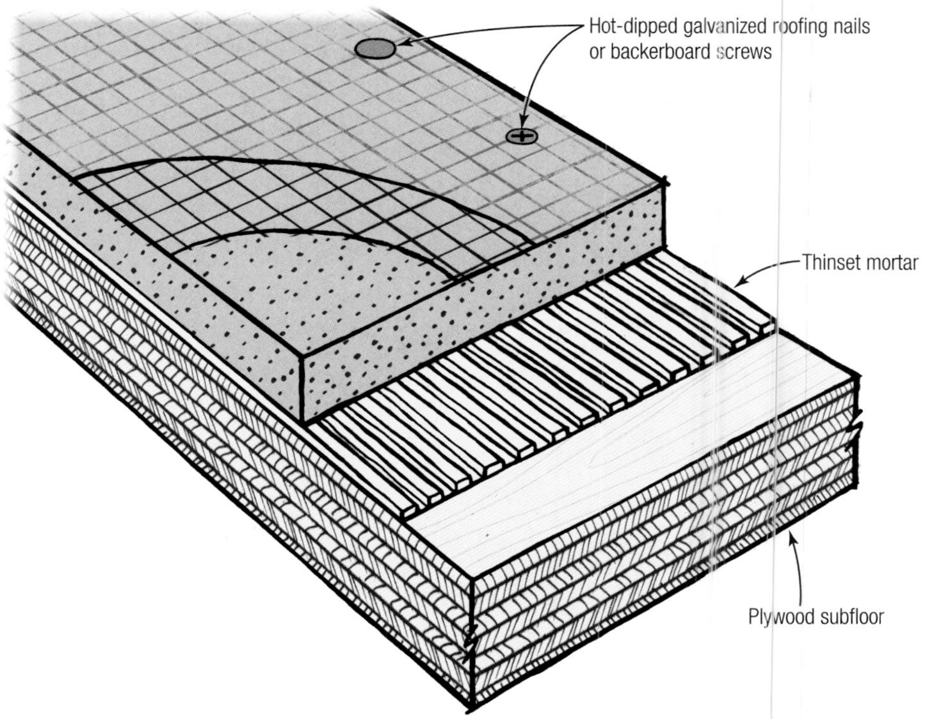

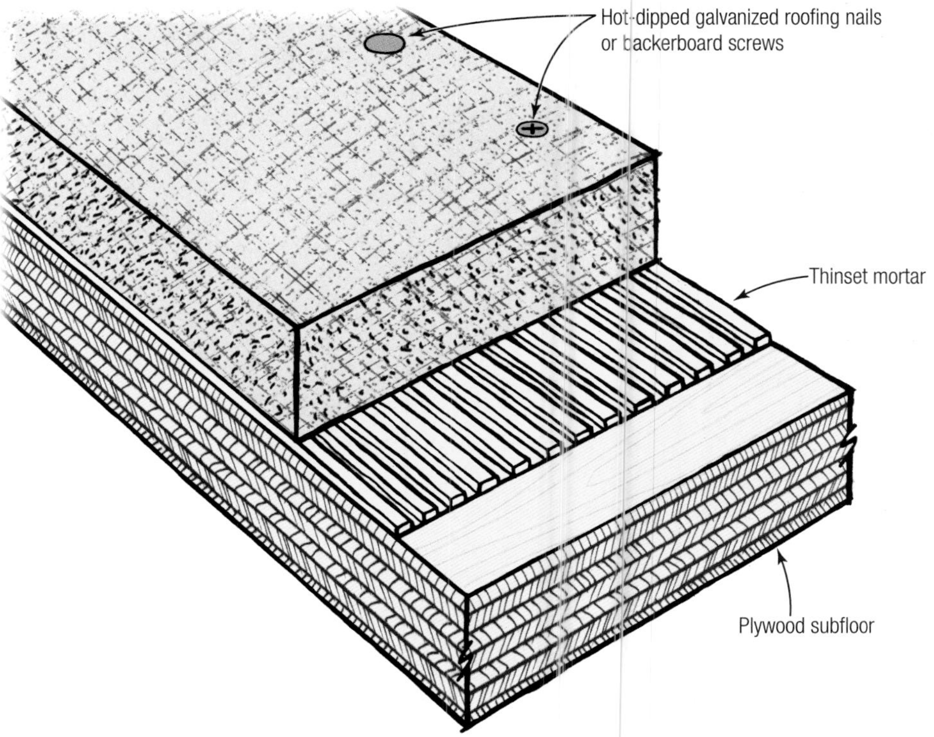

Hot-dipped galvanized roofing nails or backerboard screws

Thinset mortar

Plywood subfloor

Figure 5-11. The CBU at the left, identified by an external skin of fiberglass or other reinforcing mesh, is made with portland cement, gritty sand particles, and an exterior reinforcing mesh. The fiber cement board below is made from portland cement, fine grades of sand, with chopped mineral fibers added as reinforcing.

Hot-dipped galvanized roofing nails or backerboard screws

Thinset mortar

Plywood subfloor

Other Types of Tile Backerboards

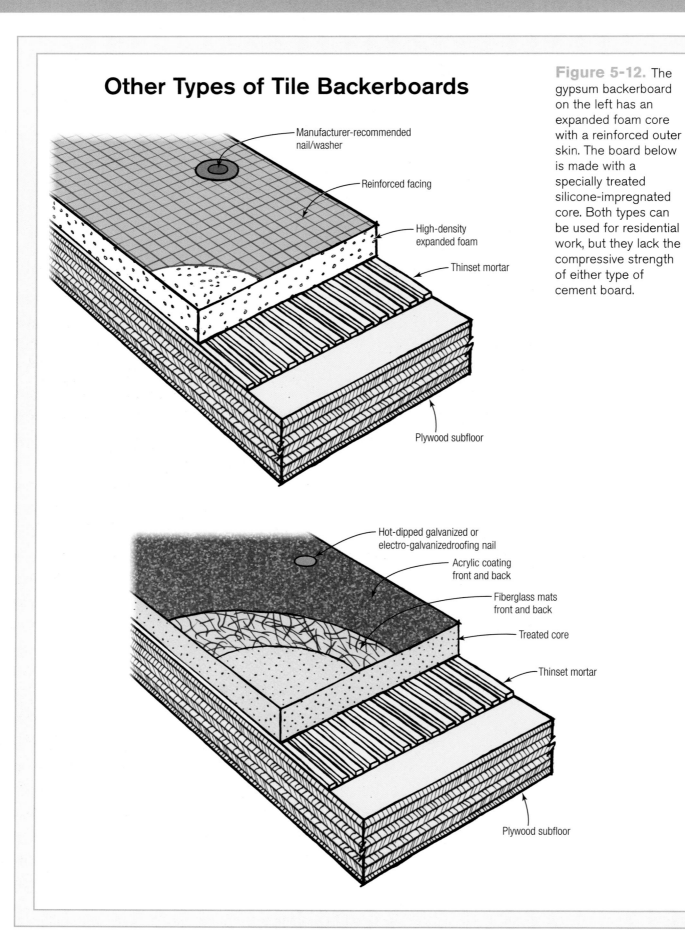

Manufacturer-recommended nail/washer

Reinforced facing

High-density expanded foam

Thinset mortar

Plywood subfloor

Hot-dipped galvanized or electro-galvanizedroofing nail

Acrylic coating front and back

Fiberglass mats front and back

Treated core

Thinset mortar

Plywood subfloor

Figure 5-12. The gypsum backerboard on the left has an expanded foam core with a reinforced outer skin. The board below is made with a specially treated silicone-impregnated core. Both types can be used for residential work, but they lack the compressive strength of either type of cement board.

used for both residential and light-commercial applications. It can be cut with score-and-snap methods, but the cut edge is ragged and may require smoothing with a stone or grinder. Cutting with a dry-cutting diamond blade creates clouds of dust. Although a hammer can be used to punch holes through a CBU, this practice usually causes more cracks to appear. Holes should be drilled through using a carbide or diamond core bit.

Fiber-cement boards (FCB), made of sand, cement, and chopped mineral fibers, are the second generation of tile backerboard—designed to overcome cracking problems encountered in the first (Figure 5-11). The technology to make panels using reinforcing fibers is relatively old, and this type of board goes a long way toward eliminating cracking, splitting, and damage caused by fasteners. In spite of its impressive strength, however, this type of board will still absorb and wick moisture and, thus, requires a membrane for wet-area installations. This board can be used for both residential and light-commercial applications. It can be cut using score-and-snap methods that produce a much smoother cut edge than can be achieved with a CBU cut the same way. This board can also be cut with power shears made for the purpose. Holes should be drilled using a carbide or diamond core bit.

Coated gypsum-core backerboards (CGB), with spun, nonwoven fiberglass mesh reinforcing, are part of the third generation of backerboards designed for easier installation and waterproofing (Figure 5-12). The boards have a water resistant core and a waterproof covering on the front face of the board. Sold under the brand name DensShield (www.gp.com), it carries a good warranty, but the waterproof skin can be damaged during installation, requiring application of a surface-applied membrane to the damaged area (a surface-applied membrane is also required by the manufacturer when the board is used for steam applications). Gypsum-core backerboards do not have the compressive strength of cement backerboards, and tiles installed over gypsum-core board must be 2x2 inch or larger. This board is useful on light and regular-duty residential installations, but should not be used on passive solar or radiant heating installations. Cutting is accomplished with a utility knife using score-and-snap methods. Holes can be made with wood core bits, and either backerboard screws or galvanized roofing nails can be used to install the boards.

Cement-coated, extruded-polystyrene foam backerboards, reinforced with woven fiberglass mesh, are another version of the third generation of tile backerboards (Figure 5-12). Foam boards are extremely lightweight, very easy to work, and easy to install with nails or screws and special large-diameter washers. Foam backerboards have a waterproof core and will absorb virtually no moisture, but moisture can travel through fastener holes. It is recommended that these holes be filled with a surface-applied membrane. There are minimum tile-size restrictions for foam boards, and some foam backerboards claim noise-reduction properties. While foam backerboards may be fine for wall installations, I do not recommend them for use on floors, since they do not have high compressive strength. Even if the installation method results in a floor that is solid, I do not like the hollow sound that is made when one walks over a foam-board floor. This board is easily cut with a utility knife; holes can be drilled with a wood core bit.

tops, though, they provide good performance (general installation instructions are slightly different for these three locations). Half-inch boards can be used on floor, wall, ceiling, and countertop applications. When two floors covered with tiles of different thickness meet, the use of 1/4-inch boards under the thicker tile and 1/2-inch boards under the thinner tiles can help minimize the height difference.

Floor installations. All tile backerboards used for floors need to be installed over a support bed of thinset mortar. The purpose of the thinset is not to fasten the board but to provide a support plane for the board and any tiles installed over it. An air pocket beneath either a backerboard or a tile will cause tiles to crack, come loose, or both. Some installers use panel adhesive instead of thinset mortar, but this actually reduces support because the ribbons of adhesive lift the board off the subfloor and create air pockets that reduce the floor's compressive strength. Some installers claim that residential installations do not require the support bed of thinset, but all board manufacturers require it. If installed over single-layer plywood or OSB subflooring without thinset support, backerboard systems are bound to fail and are not protected by the manufacturer's warranty. Details for installing backerboards for floor installations are provided in Chapter 1.

Currently, cement backerboard manufacturers okay the use of 15-pound roofing felt or 4-mil plastic behind wall and ceiling installations, but there are no instructions for these two materials when cement backerboards are installed on floors or countertops. As a result, when protection against moisture is desired, a surface-applied system must be used, as described in detail in Chapter 7.

Wall and ceiling installations. On steel-framed walls and ceilings, cement backerboards can be installed with approved screw fasteners, spaced at 12- or 16-inch centers (I do not use or recommend nails for wall or ceiling work). Over wood studs and ceiling joists, backerboard screws can be used alone, but panel adhesive is recommended, especially on ceiling applications. All board ends should be supported by framing. Inside corners—especially at the wall/ceiling juncture—require the right detailing so that all boards are properly supported by full-face contact with studs. I recommend that waterproofing be applied to the surface after all boards are installed. This gives the greatest level of protection against moisture, but since some membrane systems call for their membrane to be installed behind the backerboard, check the manufacturer's instructions before you proceed.

Although cement backerboards were designed as a durable setting bed for tile, they make excellent drywall in wet or high-humidity applications. When I am designing or building a bathroom from scratch, for example, I frequently spec cement backerboards in place of gypsum drywall on the walls, and I always spec cement backerboards for the ceiling—whether or not these surfaces will be tiled. Half-inch-thick cement boards can be painted and finished with the same materials (only alkali-resistant joint tape should be used, though) and techniques that are used for gypsum drywall, and no need for the extra blocking that CBU-to-gypsum-board joints require.

Countertop installations. On countertops, there are several ways to install backerboards depending on the brand, with some manufacturers calling for a support bed of thinset while others do not. For better support, I prefer to use thinset mortar and fasteners, and as with floor installations, I prefer to install backerboards over a double-layer plywood base for extra strength. This is important since most of the structural support comes from cabinet uprights that are often spaced at 24- or 36-inch centers. On dry-use counters, I comb roofing asphalt over the plywood base with a $\frac{1}{8}$-inch V-notch trowel to laminate 15-pound roofing felt to the surface of the plywood and cover this surface with a thinset mortar support bed and CBU. For the best protection in wet areas, a surface-applied membrane should cover the countertop from the front to the back and extend upwards to protect the backsplash areas. Details for tiling countertops are provided in Chapter 4, with additional information about surface-applied membranes for wet-area counters provided in Chapter 7.

Sealers and Impregnators

The market is filled with all kinds of sealers for tile. Some are effective, others are not. It is important to put the issue of sealing tile and grout in the proper context. First, for wet-area installations, I don't recommend using any tiles that require the application of a sealer to achieve vitreous or impervious properties. Over time, sealers tend to be forgotten, tiles absorb moisture, and problems can begin. So sealing porous tiles to be used in a wet-area installation is not recommended. Instead, it's important to select the right tile for the job!

Most sealers and impregnators are not designed as waterproofing materials. Rather, they are designed to reduce staining from food, spills, and other household materials. Staining can affect ceramic tiles, stone tiles, and grout, regardless of porosity, but the incidence of staining can be reduced or eliminated through the careful use of sealers or impregnators. Another factor affecting whether tile or grout will stain is the quickness of response to a spill. Where cleanup is prompt, staining is less of an issue, whether or not the tile or grout has been sealed.

Impregnators are considered a step up from ordinary silicone sealers and were developed primarily to simplify maintenance and repairs on stone that has been

Figure 5-13. Cement backerboards are unaffected by exposure to moisture and are considerably stronger than regular gypsum walls, making them a good choice for shower and tub surrounds, provided they will be protected a by surface-applied membrane.

marred by graffiti. Impregnators are usually more expensive than sealers and are applied by brush, roller, clean and lint-free rag, and sometimes, airless sprayers. After application, they are allowed to penetrate for a short period of time (usually less than 20 minutes), after which the excess is removed and the surface of the tiles is buffed with a clean, dry cloth. Impregnator absorbed by the tiles and grout needs to cure for 24 to 72 hours (depending on brand) before the installation is put into use. Impregnators, like sealers, should never be applied to a dirty or stained surface. Make certain the surface you want to protect is clean and dry and that the grout has fully cured before application. Impregnators and sealers can be used on both tile and grout. I have seen installers go to great pains to spread sealer or impregnator on grout joints only in the belief that the tiles will absorb buckets of sealer. Stone and ceramic tiles, depending on their porosity, will absorb some material, but hardly enough to justify the economy of protecting the grout only. If a tile is porous, it needs protection, too.

Grout issues. Grout is considered by some to be a weak link in many tile installations, and because a lot of grout is improperly mixed, installed, cleaned, or cured, to a large extent, it is. But when installed carefully, grout can help keep stains and moisture penetration to a minimum and contribute to an installation's long life. Unfortunately, people spend a lot of money on sealers to treat grout whose surface is rough, porous, and not worth the effort and expense to seal. When struck smooth, though—especially in food service areas—sanded grout and a high-quality sealer or impregnator make perfect sense. However, not even the highest quality impregnator can improve a gritty, dirt-grabbing surface. So if you are aware that an area will be sealed, ensure that the grout is smoothed with a striking tool so that the sand grains are forced flush and the surface does not feel like sandpaper.

Another issue, especially around food service areas, is grout color. When tiling a kitchen, I try to determine how much activity will take place on the floor or countertop. In very active kitchens, I avoid boutique colors and, instead, specify natural cement-colored grout. This neutral color does an excellent job of masking the appearance of food stains, unlike white, pastel, or light-colored grouts. The advice to use natural cement-gray grout applies, as well, to kitchen floors, where light colored grout near work areas is often stained or discolored from constant countertop spills.

Selecting a practical color and smoothing the surface texture will help reduce future maintenance, but unless the grout is proportioned, mixed, slaked, re-mixed, packed into the joints, cleaned, and cured properly, it will lack the density to resist moisture and staining. In this case, even with a superior sealing product, the stain- and water-resisting properties of the grout will be marginal. Grout that is installed, finished, and cured properly, though, already has excel-lent stain- and water-resisting properties that can only be enhanced by a good sealer or impregnator. Consult Chapter 6 to learn more about grout and the process of grouting.

The impregnator I prefer (511 Porous Plus by Miracle Sealants Company, www.miraclesealants.com) imparts no sheen or luster and appears to have no effect on the color or light-reflecting qualities of any material to which it is applied. It was designed primarily to reduce maintenance on porous materials, but even marginally absorbent materials like porcelain tiles can benefit from its protection. For this reason, I never use an impregnator or sealer only on the grout or only on the tile, but always on both surfaces and usually with a minimum of two applications. Multiple applications are required because, especially with stone tiles, there are usually differences in porosity between the tiles and the grout. On very porous tiles, I also use this material as a grout release.

Tile Cleaners

The best approach to keeping tile and grout clean is to promptly clean up spills or dirt, use neutral soaps and cleaners, avoid abrasive cleaners, and only use acids designed for cleaning tile as a last resort. If there is adequate ventilation around wet-area installations, no special cleaners should be required. Showers built with sloped subfloors beneath their shower pans and open weep holes rarely present any cleaning or maintenance problems. Showers built on flat shower pans, though, absorb and retain moisture, and provide all the essentials for mold and mildew to flourish in spite of their owners' best efforts to keep them as clean as possible.

Assuming that the cleaning we are discussing here is related to ordinary dirt and grime on well-built installations in good condition, then we are talking about cleaning what gets tracked into our buildings on our shoes; what we spill and slop in our kitchens; and whatever ends up on our bathroom walls, floors, and countertops. Most fresh spills are food or cosmetic related and can easily be cleaned with a damp sponge or mop or eliminated with a rag and some nail polish remover. For dried-on dirt, food residues, and stains where grease or oil may be present, all cleaning water should be augmented with a neutral soap or detergent powerful enough to emulsify the oil and rinse without leaving a film or residue.

For heavier stains, scrubbing, soaking, or a poultice may be required. Cleaners containing bleach should not be used, except in limited amounts on white grout. In restoring the grout on an old floor, wall, or countertop, some initial scrubbing with detergent and a stiff-bristle brush are usually required to effectively clean the surface of the grout. If the condition of the floor requires heavy-duty cleaners or even acids, I try to identify the manufacturer of the grout and use a companion product for cleaning. If that is not possible

Applying Impregnators and Sealers

The first step when applying a sealer or impregnator to new tilework is to ensure that all tile installation materials are dry. For most portland cement products, this takes approximately 72 hours, unless otherwise indicated by the sealer or impregnator manufacturer (a minimum moisture content also may be required). If a tile installation is put into service before sealing, it is imperative that you protect the installation and ensure that the tiles and grout are clean and bone dry prior to sealing. When sealing existing wet-area installations, the biggest problem is drying the tiles and setting bed enough so that resident moisture does not discolor, cloud, or weaken the sealer or impregnator.

To apply the impregnator, I use either a wide brush or a paint roller and spread a liberal amount over the surface. On vertical applications, I spread just enough to avoid runoff and excessive dripping. I prefer to do this work with a helper, who can begin wiping off the excess about 5 or 10 minutes (or as specified in the manufacturer's instructions) after I begin. That way the operation is continuous, with no obvious start/stop lines showing. Also, I prefer to apply sealers and impregnators at lower room temperatures—around 65°F —because evaporation is slower than at higher temperatures. That provides additional time for the impregnator to soak into the tiles and grout and more time for buffing off the excess. During the soaking period, it is important to keep a watchful eye on where the material is being absorbed and where it is not; areas that absorb quickly may require a second or even third application.

When removing the excess, I use lint-free cotton towels or rags and remove in two stages: swab up the bulk of the excess with the first pass and follow that immediately with a second wiping using fresh rags or towels. On the first pass, I try to blot out large areas, but on the second pass, I work the towel vigorously to buff individual tiles and joints; it is essential that all traces of impregnator be removed, without leaving any visible film on the surface. Impregnator residues are sticky, never dry tack-free, and are difficult to remove. In fact, the removal process usually requires re-application of the impregnator in the affected area. After a minimum 24-hour wait, the installation can then be opened to traffic. For exposure to water or moisture, I prefer to wait an additional 24 hours.

Re-applying a sealer or impregnator. Most tile sealers or impregnators do not need the same kind of stripping that a top-coating material like varnish requires. However, at a minimum, they do require a very careful cleaning and thorough drying before fresh sealer can be applied. Otherwise, the new application will encapsulate whatever is deposited on, or has stained, the surface. Also soap film, oil, grease, dirt, and grime all act to repel the application of the sealer or impregnator. Freshly cleaned surfaces should be allowed to dry overnight in heated, well-ventilated conditions. Some surfaces, particularly those in very wet areas, such as a shower stall, may require more time for drying. Some brands of sealer or impregnator claim to vent moisture vapor. Consult the manufacturer's requirements for moisture content in the surface being protected.

or practical, though, I turn to my local tile supplier because most grout and mortar manufacturers offer a line of cleaning and maintenance products suitable for use with most brands of grout.

Muriatic acid has been used to clean tile and grout in the past, but it is such a potentially harmful material, even in dilute amounts, and it requires such extensive surface preparations, that I do not recommend its use for ceramic or stone tile installations. The only acids I will recommend come from the grout and mortar manufacturers. These cleaners have generally been tested for compatibility with stone and tile materials and are relatively safe to use in the concentrations available to contractors and the public without elaborate protection or the need for deep rinsing.

To reiterate: The best way to keep a tile installation clean is with regular light cleaning and prompt cleanup when there is a spill.

Floor Treatments for Slip Resistance

There are numerous products on the market that claim to increase the slip resistance of ceramic and stone tiles. As with other materials, some are more effective than others. Most are etches that are applied to the tiles, given time to etch into the glaze, and then rinsed off the surface. The resulting gains in slip resistance are made at the expense of the glaze or surface of the tile, which, although not always, gets dulled in the process. When contemplating such action, it's best to work directly with the manufacturer to ensure expected results.

It is hard to imagine a single material that can be applied to countless ceramic and stone surfaces to reduce slipping. If possible, get a performance warranty in writing and always test this type of material on a spare tile or in an out-of-sight location, so you can assess the treatment.

NOTES

NOTES

Chapter 6
SURFACE PREPARATION

Whether I'm starting with a sketch on a napkin, full-blown blueprints, or the installation site itself, I take a methodical approach to every installation. I always start with an examination of the underlying structure to see if it is strong and stiff enough to support tile. Once the soundness of the structure is established or corrected if found inadequate, I take the following steps:

- determine the most effective method of installation

- develop a complete materials list

- plot layouts for the placement of backerboard or other panels, membrane systems, and tiles

- install and finish the tiles

For this book, surface preparation refers to any work that is required before a membrane system or tile can be added to a structure. By structure, I mean any area to receive tiles, such as a concrete slab or the subfloor on wood-frame construction, a masonry or stud wall, a ceiling, or countertops.

Surface preparation always includes examining a structure to ensure that its parts (joists, subflooring, and/or studs) are fit for tiling. During the installation phase, it also includes maintaining a clean installation site. On some installations, surface preparation tasks may be done by other trades, but the responsibility for checking surfaces to make sure they are tile-ready or membrane-ready falls to the installer (ANSI A108.02.4.1).

Structural Support
Tile is a durable cladding—not a structural material. Tile installations depend on a sturdy and stable base for their longevity. Even the best materials and methods cannot overcome an inadequate structure.

Although concrete and masonry structures, in general, provide a strong and stable base for tile installations, concrete itself is not a perfect setting bed for tile. On the plus side, tiles installed directly to concrete slabs-on-grade typically have the highest compressive strength—and load-carrying capacity—of all floor tile installations. Yet on-grade and suspended concrete slabs present three major hurdles for the tile installer: cracks, surface impermeability, and flatness. Many cracks can be rehabilitated with the addition of a surface-applied membrane. Impermeability, caused by coating compounds and other coatings on the concrete surface, can interfere with the bond but can be overcome with abrading, blasting, and leveling compounds.

Wood structures, unlike concrete and masonry buildings, are not ideal for tile because flexing and deflection of the structure can cause tiles to crack or shear off the setting bed (problems also found on some suspended concrete floors). Not only are concrete and masonry structures usually more stable than wood-frame buildings, but directly bonding tiles to concrete and masonry is much simpler than bonding tiles to a wood surface. For these reasons (along with a shrinking pool of skilled mortar-bed workers), cement backerboards were developed and marketed as a replacement for labor-intensive traditional mortar beds.

Today, the market is filled with many types of tile backerboards. No matter which you choose to work with, however, all tile backerboards are nonstructural attachment planes. This means that most backerboards do not increase the strength of the structure and, due to the added dead load, may actually weaken it. Also, most backerboards require the addition of a membrane in wet areas. The proper selection and installation of tile backing is critical to the overall performance of the tile work.

Deflection
Deflection is not an issue with most concrete slabs-on-grade, but suspended concrete (and wood) floors can be very problematic for ceramic and stone tile if the deflection of the floor structure exceeds the standard ceramic tile deflection limit of L/360. The deflection limit may vary with the type of tile. When in doubt, always consult the manufacturer or supplier.

Because stone tiles do not have uniform properties from tile to tile, and because some are not as strong as ceramic tiles, many stone tiles require deflection ratings of L/480, L/720, and even L/1080 for very fragile stones.

Uniform Versus Concentrated Deflection

Deflection for ceramic-tile and stone-tile installations must be measured in two ways: uniform and concentrated. Uniform deflection is the movement of the subflooring or setting bed measured across the entire floor span with a load spread over the floor. Concentrated deflection in a framed floor (or wall) system is the movement of the subflooring or the setting bed between two joists subjected to a concentrated or "point" load. Knowledge of both is essential to the success of any floor tile installation.

Deflection occurs in both wood and concrete floors. In simple terms, deflection is the amount of sag or bounce that results from loading a particular floor with home furnishings, office equipment, people, and whatever else usually occupies the space. In the industry, it is defined for ceramic and some stone tiles by the following equation: allowable deflection = L/360; that is, the maximum allowable deflection cannot exceed 1/360th of the length (L) of the span.

To measure uniform deflection, span is the overall length of the floor from one support to the other. For measuring concentrated deflection in a wood floor, span is the distance between two joists. For example, to determine the allowable deflection for a 30-foot (360-inch) span, the equation for L/360 is: 360 inch ÷ 360, or 1 inch. Allowable L/360 deflection between joists for 16-inch joist spacing would be 14.5 inch ÷ 360 or .040 inch, just under 3/64 inch (14.5 inches is based on 16 inches minus the 1 1/2-inch thickness of a typical joist).

To test deflection, I typically measure an unloaded and loaded section of floor using tile, sacks of mortar, or water containers to load a 4-square-foot area with at least 300 pounds and measure the movement with a dial indicator or laser (Figure 6-1). A laser is helpful, but it lacks the precise accuracy of the indicator I use, which has a .001-inch readout from .000 to 1.000 inch.

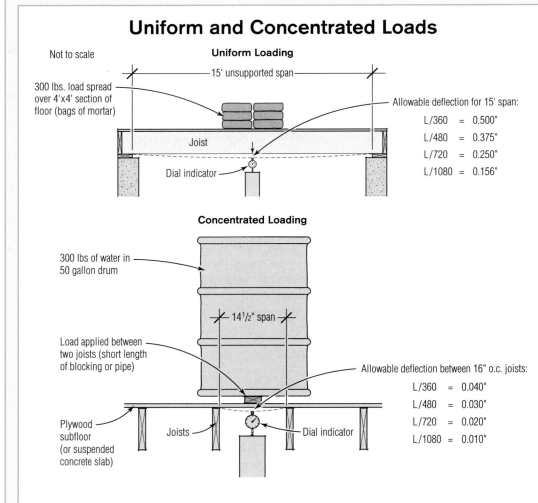

Uniform and Concentrated Loads

Not to scale

Uniform Loading

15' unsupported span

300 lbs. load spread over 4'x4' section of floor (bags of mortar)

Joist

Dial indicator

Allowable deflection for 15' span:

L/360 = 0.500"
L/480 = 0.375"
L/720 = 0.250"
L/1080 = 0.156"

Concentrated Loading

300 lbs of water in 50 gallon drum

14 1/2" span

Load applied between two joists (short length of blocking or pipe)

Plywood subfloor (or suspended concrete slab)

Joists

Dial indicator

Allowable deflection between 16" o.c. joists:

L/360 = 0.040"
L/480 = 0.030"
L/720 = 0.020"
L/1080 = 0.010"

Figure 6-1. For ceramic and stone tile, deflection must be measured both across unsupported spans (uniform loads) and between joists (concentrated loads). Floor systems that meet ceramic tile's L/360 requirement for uniform loading may fail the concentrated loading test. Stone tiles may require L/480 to L/1080, depending on stone type and thickness. To test for uniform loading, place a 300 lb. weight (e.g., sacks of mortar or stacks of tile) in a 4-sq.-ft. area at the center of the span and directly over two joists (top), then measure the deflection at the center of the span. To determine concentrated deflection, the load should be midway between joists (bottom).

Before beginning any stone tile installation, check with the supplier for a deflection spec in writing.

Scheduling, Cleanliness, and Contracts

Scheduling is important because thinbed materials need to cure properly, and for maximum adhesion, they need to retain their virgin surfaces and avoid contamination. A single contractor/installer is likely to continue the proper work flow and respect each layer of an installation. However, with multiple contractors each handling a specific layer (one installing self-leveling underlayment, another a waterproofing membrane, and a third tiles, for example), the installation is often left exposed between stages to traffic, dust, paint overspray, and other bond-breaking materials. Solving these problems often requires additional work and puts the project behind schedule.

It is a good idea to hold off installing setting bed materials until just before they are needed to avoid contamination and additional cleaning steps. To further protect the installation, I write contracts that allow back charging the general contractor or owner for time spent scraping drywall compound, removing paint overspray, or picking up trash left behind by the GC or other subcontractors. By contract agreement, the only surface prep required upon my arrival at the jobsite should be some light vacuuming or damp mopping of setting-bed surfaces like backerboards, membrane systems, and self-leveling underlayments.

In addition to a provision for cleanup, there also should be contract language giving the tile installation contractor authority over (and access to) the space to be tiled. Such authority allows a contractor or installer to effectively restrict traffic or use of the space until the materials in all layers have properly cured. This eliminates any surprise cleanup chores and ensures the best possible performance from all materials, including patching mortars and other surface-prep materials; the adhesives holding down the membrane systems and tiles; and the grouts, sealants, and sealers.

Single-source responsibility. While some installers would rather just set tile on an installation, I prefer to handle all tile-related work—everything except building or installing the concrete slabs, subfloors, stud walls, and cabinets that will hold the tile. With this approach, I can ensure the desired results for all the layers and materials required for the installation, create single-source responsibility and authority over the space being tiled, reduce scheduling problems, and improve efficiency and productivity.

Equally important is the issue of securing enough hours of labor to make a contracting business pay: By installing all the materials, including surface prep and membrane systems, a contractor can increase billable hours or per-square-foot charges by two, three, or as much as four times that which the same contractor might earn for installing tiles only. Single sourcing the labor also helps eliminate the idle or down time that is a part of every tile installation. With so many different tasks to complete, there is usually always something to do to fill in the waiting periods, rather than continually changing and re-arranging a completion schedule.

Surface Preparation Guidelines

In addition to any specific requirements for the materials to be used in a tile installation, the following general requirements should always be followed. These will help assure the best possible performance from the materials individually and from the installation as a whole:

1. maintain optimal temperatures from staging to the end of curing

2. provide adequate housekeeping and ventilation

3. restrict access to the tile area

4. provide a safe workspace with GFCI power for wet saw and other tools

5. maintain clean, flat, and smooth conditions that meet industry minimums for tiles and membrane systems

6. maintain virgin bonding surfaces wherever possible

Flatness. Since small tiles more easily conform to irregular surfaces, tiles less than 10 inches on any edge need subsurfaces that are flat, plumb, or level to within 1/4 inch in 10 feet (the industry minimum standard), with no abrupt irregularities greater than 1/32 inch in 12 inches. Larger tiles, however, require a stricter standard, depending on the size of the tile. Table 6-1 below shows the tolerance range I use for tiles less than 10 inches (on edge) to tiles measuring more than 24 inches.

Very flat, 1/2-inch-thick (nominal) porcelain tiles are now available in 2x3-foot, 3x3-foot, and larger sizes. And a new generation of very thin porcelain tiles now can be made as large as 1x3 meters. In the future, the ultimate size of dust-pressed porcelain tile may only be limited by the capacity of the kiln in which it is fired. It is essential for designers, architects, builders, installers, inspectors, and building owners to understand the need for increased flatness as the size of tiles

Table 6-1 Recommended Setting Bed Flatness	
Tile Size	**Surface Tolerance (longest dimension)**
Up to 10 inches	1/4 inch in 10 feet
10 to 16 inches	1/8 inch in 10 feet
16 to 24 inches	1/16 inch in 10 feet
Over 24 inches	1/32 inch in 10 feet

passes 8 or 10 inches.

To reduce lippage to acceptable levels, the laws of geometry demand that setting bed accuracy increase proportionally as tile sizes increase. For quality-finish thinbed surfaces receiving tiles over 12 inches, $\frac{1}{8}$-inch-in-10-foot surfaces would be the minimum; tiles over 16 inches require a setting bed surface accurate to within $\frac{1}{16}$ inch; and tiles 24 inches or larger need a surface tolerance of $\frac{1}{32}$ inch in 10 feet. To simplify your large-format tile installation, ensure that desirable tolerances are maintained in the floor, wall, ceiling, and countertop surfaces receiving tile.

A smooth finish is determined by the flatness of a setting bed, the flatness of the tiles covering it, and the adhesive layer in between.

Renovation Issues

When working with new materials, it is not too difficult to maintain clean conditions. With remodeling or renovation work, surfaces are sometimes covered with sheet goods, coatings, paint, paint overspray, waxes, grease or oil, dirt, curing compounds (also a potential problem with new concrete slabs), and other materials that reduce the bond strength of adhesives used for installing tiles or tile membranes. These often have to be removed or covered. Certain thinset mortars can be used over some coatings and adhesive residues, but the adhesive bond between the tile and substrate is never any greater than the lesser bond of all the coatings.

Tiling over an existing setting bed. I'm frequently asked whether tiles can be installed over an existing setting bed whose tiles have been removed. With a concrete slab, the answer is almost always yes, unless there is something structurally wrong with the slab. In this case, chippers, chisels, or other tools are used to strip off the tiles and clean adhesive residues off the surface of the slab. To remove tiles, I use a pneumatic chipping gun and chisel for the fastest removal. If the resulting exposed surface is smooth enough, tiles can be installed as usual.

Setting bed removal. If tiles are removed from mortar beds, plywood underlayment, or backerboards, damage to these materials during tile removal is usually great enough that these setting bed surfaces cannot be reused. Consequently, when ripping out tile installed over these surfaces, instead of chipping off the old tiles first and then removing the setting bed, I remove both at once. First, I cut through the grout joints every 2 feet or so in both directions with a dry-cutting diamond blade set to the bottom of the mortar bed or backerboard setting bed. Then I use pry bars to lever out 2-foot squares of the tile/setting bed sandwich. When ripping out tile over plywood underlayment, I set the dry-cutting blade to the bottom of the tiles, cut along straight lines only, leave a kerf at least $\frac{1}{4}$-inch wide, then cut the underlayment with a wood blade set so the blade does not make contact with the subflooring.

Concrete slab surface problems. When removing tiles from a concrete setting bed, ideally adhesive residues should be found on both the back of the tiles and the surface of the slab (an indication of a good bond). Sometimes when a tile is removed, the adhesive bond is so great that the tile, the adhesive layer, and a por-

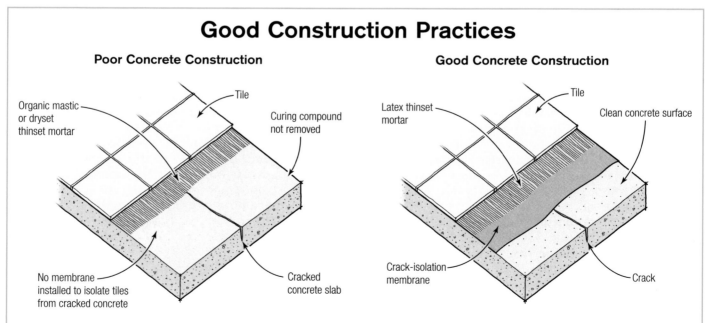

Good Construction Practices

Poor Concrete Construction

Organic mastic or dryset thinset mortar

Tile

Curing compound not removed

No membrane installed to isolate tiles from cracked concrete

Cracked concrete slab

Good Concrete Construction

Latex thinset mortar

Tile

Clean concrete surface

Crack-isolation membrane

Crack

Figure 6-2. Poor concrete construction details include installing tiles over uncured, coated, sealed, artificially cured, or cracked concrete. Good concrete practices include installing tiles or crack-isolation systems over properly cured, finished, and untreated concrete.

tion of the setting bed comes off in a single chunk. On the other hand, if the tiles separate cleanly from the concrete slab, taking all the adhesive with them and leaving none behind on the slab, this is an indication of a poor bond. While the slab can be re-used, it must first be renovated to remove the layer of curing compound, sealer, or contaminant that is preventing a good adhesive bond.

Concrete Slabs

Although concrete can provide a strong and stable base for tile installations, the concrete slab must be constructed properly to limit cracking. For thinset applications, a crack-isolation membrane is recommended, and the slab should be flat, level, and have a fine-broom finish for bonding to thinset (Figure 6-2).

Concrete needs the proper mixture of portland cement, aggregate, and water and must be cured under carefully controlled conditions to reach its maximum strength. Also, concrete requires steel reinforcing and must be placed on carefully prepared forms, footings, and compacted sub-soils to perform properly. When there is enough time, an adequate budget, and skilled applicators, concrete work of great precision can be produced. Examples of crack-free, super-flat concrete slabs specifically produced for tile installations are found throughout Central and South America. These feature incredibly flat, yet coarsely textured, surfaces offering maximum adhesive potential.

Unfortunately, though, most concrete surfaces found in the U.S. are not flat enough for tile, and most are covered with bond-breaking curing compounds that must be removed before tiles can be installed. Damp curing results in near perfect conditions for tiling, as long as the slab's surface has a steel-trowelled, fine-broom finish, but at 70°F, damp-cured concrete will be fragile for a week and won't be completely ready for tiling until 28 days (the time needed for a concrete slab to cure) have passed.

On the other hand, applying certain curing compounds to the surface of fresh concrete can bring normal 28-day strength in as little as three or four days. Unfortunately, the same curing compounds that hold moisture inside the slab to promote curing also prevent adhesives from bonding to the surface of the slab. Because curing with compound is less expensive than traditional damp-curing, and because most other construction materials (wood or masonry components) do not require the concrete to have adhesive bite, most concrete today uses compound for curing. Knowing whether or not a slab has been compound-cured is essential to the performance of membrane systems and tile for the simple reason that even the best tile adhesives will not stick to concrete treated with curing compound.

Shrinkage and cracking are also critical issues with concrete setting beds. All concrete is known to shrink, and most concrete is expected to crack—two problems for tiling regardless of a slab's construction or orientation. Shrinking concrete can dislodge tiles from the setting-bed surface, and cracks within a concrete slab can telegraph through and damage the overlying tile. With minor cracking, it is possible to protect the tiles by using a crack-isolation membrane system. But when concrete has excessive movement or cracks, protective membrane systems made for normal building movement cannot protect the tile, and another finish material should be used instead.

Inspecting a Slab

The first step is to visually inspect any concrete slab you want to tile, checking for flatness, level, surface hardness, surface texture, movement joints, and penetrations. It's important to check the surface for curing compounds, paint and other coatings, and absorbed oil or grease, any of which will interfere with the adhesive bond. The surface of the slab should be clean and uncoated and have a flat, coarse finish. Coarse, flat, and absorbent are the ideal conditions, but unless the concrete slab in the tile area has been specified and installed to industry standards with a fine-broom finish, its surface may not be flat, level, or toothy enough for tiles.

Testing for curing compounds. Curing compounds will interfere with the adhesive bond of the tile or membrane. The first way to determine this is to ask the general contractor or the concrete finishing subcontractor. A low-tech method of testing requires about 15 minutes and a dozen or so drops of water spread over the surface of the slab. The air above the slab should be around 70°F and still, with no drafts or breezes that could affect the outcome of the test:

1. First, sprinkle drops of clean water over the surface of the concrete.

2. After 10 minutes, observe whether the drops have been absorbed.

3. If the drops have not yet been absorbed, there is a high probability that a curing compound was used.

If the slab is sealed with a coating or curing compound, it can only be eliminated by removing some of the concrete. For most coatings or curing compounds, removing about ½ to ¾ inch from the surface of the slab and restoring the surface with a self-leveling underlayment will cure the problem.

Documenting cracks. Concrete also needs to be inspected for cracks that might impair the performance of tile. Because of tight schedules, poor workmanship, and the job-site abuse of slabs before they can properly cure, cracks are an almost inevitable sight on residential and light-commercial concrete slabs.

During my inspection, I use an indelible marker and write directly on a slab to indicate start and stop points for cracks (see Figure 7-7, page 195). I write the date and initial each marking, then transfer the general location of all cracks directly to whatever blueprint or sketch I am using to work up the bid (a photograph of the marks is an excellent way to document the cracks). Marking the location of cracks is a highly effective way to demonstrate to a general contractor or building owner that a crack is actually moving. If it is not possible to personally inspect a slab, it is a good idea to treat it as if it were cracked and submit bids and proposals accordingly.

When inspecting a slab, in addition to observing the condition of cracks, it is important to note the number of cracks. There are no fixed rules, but counting one square foot of floor space for every running foot of crack, I tend to be uncomfortable bidding on floors whose cracks equal more than 10% of the total area of the floor. When inspecting a floor located in an existing house or building, I keep a sharp eye out for cracks in walls and ceilings that might point to a structural problem that could impact the floor.

Why is it so important to note cracks in proposals and bids? In my opinion, a crack-isolation membrane is a requirement for all tiles installed over on-grade or suspended slabs, and all proposals and bids should include references to cracks and methods of rehabbing with a suitable membrane system. As an installer, it is easier for me to sell the tile installation first and list the cost of installing a membrane "should cracks prove to be dynamic" as a separate item to be automatically approved if conditions warrant it. Whenever enough time has elapsed between my inspection and the beginning of the tile installation (about 30 days or more), my experience over a variety of conditions, climates, and building methods has been to find cracks advanced past their original marks by the time I show up to tile. I am then able to install the needed membrane under the terms of the contract.

Cracks in Concrete

Not all cracks are equal, and there are general limitations for all crack-isolation membrane systems and specific limitations for each membrane product. For example, the only cracks that can be rehabbed for tiling are small shrinkage cracks no wider than 1/8 inch, or as indicated by the individual manufacturer. Shrinkage cracks are the result of a problem with the moisture content of the concrete when it was poured or while it was curing and are not necessarily an indication of a structural problem.

Structural cracks, however, cannot be tiled over using any known system without damage occurring to the tiles. Structural cracks are caused by a weakness or failure of the structure and can be identified by uneven surfaces on either side of the crack (Figure 6-3). To determine if a crack is structural or shrinkage, I lay a straightedge perpendicular to the general direction of the crack and check to see if both sides of the floor are in plane. If in plane, the crack is most likely from shrinkage of the concrete, and tiles should not be installed without a crack-isolation membrane. If the two sides of the crack are out of plane, neither tile nor membrane should be installed until the structure is repaired or renovated.

It should be noted that crack-isolation systems do not provide absolute protection against the future appearance of cracks in the finished tile installation, nor do they substitute for a structurally sound setting bed. The installation of a crack-isolation membrane, instead, is a way to reduce the number and severity of cracks—not eliminate them. With this in mind, the appearance of a particular type or brand of membrane in this book does not indicate that it will solve all cracking, waterproofing, or sound reduction functions. Instead, each tile installation must be evaluated on its own merits before any membrane system is applied. It is critical with membrane systems that you read and follow individual brand instructions, especially those regarding movement joints.

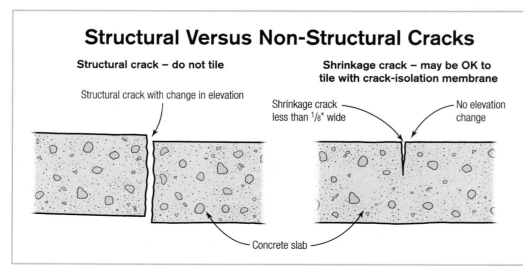

Structural Versus Non-Structural Cracks

Structural crack – do not tile

Structural crack with change in elevation

Shrinkage crack – may be OK to tile with crack-isolation membrane

Shrinkage crack less than 1/8" wide

No elevation change

Concrete slab

Figure 6-3. Uneven surfaces on either side of a crack (left) indicate a structural crack that should not be tiled over. Crack-isolation membranes should only be used to tile over nonstructural shrinkage cracks no wider than 1/8 inch (right).

Industrial or institutional concrete requires thicker cross sections, precise reinforcing, and controlled placing and curing conditions. Independent on-site inspection of the work in progress is usually mandated, and the finished product tends to be as you might expect, remarkably free of cracks. Still, I treat all concrete slabs—new or old—as susceptible to cracks even if none are present. I assume that any crack that is present will continue to advance its way into and across the slab. I also do not rule out the likely possibility that new cracks will appear down the road.

Bond-Breaking Coatings and Curing Materials

Concrete surfaces that are treated with curing compounds or covered with paint or coatings are a problem for tile and any other finishing material requiring a solid adhesive bond. On slabs not produced with curing compounds, nonpenetrating paints can sometimes be removed by scraping, and the exposed concrete surface can then be etched with a mild acid. This process requires extensive clean-water rinsing to produce the kind of smooth but coarsely textured surface that is ideal for bonding agents, leveling compounds, and thinset mortars. Yes, it is possible to renovate a slab this way, but the health and safety risks of using strong acids, the extensive precautions that must be taken with surrounding finishes, the multiple clean-water rinses that are required, plus the possibility that some contaminants will remain on the surface and reduce the adhesive bond make this method somewhat impractical and expensive.

Penetrating sealers, paints, epoxies, and other such coatings or applications cannot be scraped off at the surface, nor can their bond-breaking qualities be scraped away. Such surfaces can only be rehabbed by removing portions of the slab itself, at least to the penetrating depth of the contaminating material. To be certain, for most coatings and curing compounds, a nominal half inch of concrete should be removed to expose a 100% uncontaminated concrete surface.

If the surface you are tiling is large enough, or if you frequently work over concrete, you may want to consider renting or purchasing a shot-blasting unit made for renovating concrete, either a walk-behind model or a larger, self-contained drive-around unit. For smaller installations, though, the most effective concrete removal tool is the bush hammer, a tool available in an escalating range of sizes and capacities, each requiring more and more physical strength to operate. The unit I use falls somewhere in the middle of the performance range and can be handled by one reasonably strong person (see "Using a Bush Hammer," below).

Smooth Concrete

A concrete slab that is otherwise perfect, but produced with a slick, steel-troweled finish, is not an appropriate base for the direct application of either tile or membrane systems. The smooth surface of the concrete acts more like a concrete form than an attachment base, and adhesives don't want to stick to it. With a smooth surface, tiles can become unbonded when there is normal movement within the slab. Such concrete is great as a base for a nonbonded mortar bed installed over a concrete slab (TCNA F-111), but not for thinset installations. For thinset installation, the industry standard requires a steel-troweled slab to be finished with a fine-bristle broom made specifically for imparting a coarse, toothy texture to flattened, fresh concrete.

For the best bonding, slick concrete should be prepared for tiling. It is possible to do this with a bush hammer, but this tool may remove so much material that the surface will need to be repaired with featheredge or self-leveling compounds. On floors less than 2,000 square feet, a better approach is to use an angle grinder with a diamond cup wheel or other suitable abrasive wheel that will not burnish the concrete. Use the wheel to roughen 95% of the surface while digging into only the top $1/64$ inch of the slab. After vacuuming away the dust, the treated slab immediately can be covered with a membrane system or finished with tile.

Etching Concrete with Acid

An alternate method is to use muriatic acid to etch the concrete. This is done with a diluted solution of acid and requires extensive precautions before application. (Never use undiluted acid to etch concrete!) Acid is highly corrosive and can damage other building finishes—especially metals (and your body)—and the fumes are very hazardous. Acid-resistant gloves and high-topped boots, an acid fume filter mask, a full-face shield, and ventilating fans are necessary to provide relative safety when working with dilute acids.

Acids—even when diluted—are difficult to work with, require substantial prep work to avoid damaging the concrete and other surfaces, and are a nuisance to dispose. In addition, it is difficult to remove all traces of acid from the concrete after treatment. Because acid etching is so problematic and requires such extensive precautions for the workers and surrounding materials, I do not recommend this approach, and use mechanical surface treatments instead.

Grinding and Abrading Tools

Dry-cutting carbide and diamond blades mounted in small angle grinders are a part of most tile installer's tool kits. They can be an effective way to cut tile or perform a variety of grinding chores. Dry-cutting carbide and diamond discs are not only capable of removing practically anything hardened on a concrete or masonry surface, they also can remove portions of the surface of the concrete or masonry.

Unfortunately, there are two problems with whirling discs: They generate heat, which can drive some coatings or penetrants deeper into the concrete, requiring more concrete removal. And while they may be efficient at cutting through some hard materials, they are far less efficient at removing concrete—a necessity on many tile-over-concrete installations. Even worse, heating and burnishing a surface with a clogged disc can actually close the open pores in concrete and masonry, rendering the surface impervious and making good bonding difficult or impossible. High-speed rotating discs also are ineffective at removing asphalt floor covering adhesive residues.

The most efficient uses of such abrasive discs are

- removing the steel-troweled sheen from otherwise acceptable concrete finishes

- removing thinset residues (unmodified only)

- scarifying the glaze on existing tiles for tile-over-tile installations

For all other concrete or masonry surface prep chores—dealing with curing compounds and removing coatings, penetrants, or contaminants such as motor and cooking oils—I prefer to use a much quicker demolition process, such as bush hammering or shotblasting. After removing the material, I rehab the resulting rough surface with self-leveling underlayment.

Using a Bush Hammer

Maximum bonding is essential to the durability and performance of any installation. With curing compounds and other suspect concrete or masonry surfaces, I prefer to use a bush hammer over less aggressive surface prep machines because it quickly removes enough depth of concrete to eliminate most problem

areas, and it produces a very rough surface that is ideal for finishing with a self-leveling compound. This provides a renewed surface rather than one that has only been roughened. The bush hammer is my preferred approach on most residential or light-commercial jobs of up to about 500 square feet.

The bush hammer is a powerful, aggressive machine, so before any demolition can begin, careful preparations must be made to avoid personal injury or damage to the surrounding surfaces. To protect myself, I begin with a double pair of work pants and at least three shirts (the thicker the better) and add a dust mask, ear protection, a full-face shield, and heavy gloves. To retard dust, I dampen the surface with water and keep a vacuum hose close by to clean the slab from time to time while bush hammering.

Prior to bush hammering, turn off all water supply lines located in the work area. Next, remove anything bolted to the floor (for example, toilet, bidet, and pedestal sink), and protect all protruding or neighboring supply lines or drain pipes with a wrapping of packing foam and tape. All waste lines should be plugged or stuffed with wads of paper or plastic to keep out debris that could clog those pipes. Windows and any mirrors that are permanently mounted, obviously, will require padding and protection. To protect wall surfaces, I use multiple layers of tarps or packing quilts (Figure 6-4). The work shown in Figures 6-4, 6-5, and 6-6 was part of the surface prep required for Floor Project 1 (page 4) and demonstrates how to use a bush hammer on a typical installation.

Also, turn off appropriate circuit breakers to interrupt current to any power lines running through conduit that may be embedded in the slab. When working around embedded, pressurized water lines, I prefer to

Figure 6-4. The author makes three passes with the bush hammer to achieve a uniform depth. Notice the tarps protecting the walls.

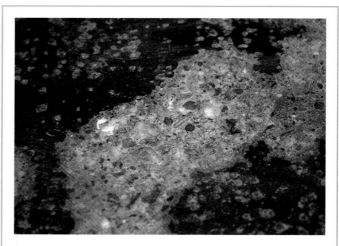

Figure 6-5. A coat of spray paint helps the author gauge how much material has been removed. It can also help him preserve some of the slab, like the edge of the circular depression cast for the shower drain.

keep the pressure on while bush hammering for instant leak detection should there be an accident.

To help control the amount of concrete removed on large commercial floors, a horizontal laser beam can be used with a target stick to check slab height. On small floors, though, I sometimes give a slab a light coat of high-color-contrast paint so I can tell at a glance whether any part of the floor has not been hammered (Figure 6-5).

Working a bush hammer requires a fair amount of strength, but an operator also has to be surprisingly light-handed when using the tool without trying to wrestle it. I stop occasionally to clear away the concrete chips and am careful that I don't bore too deeply into the slab. It helps to work the entire floor rather than concentrate on a single section; that way, some of the original floor surface is always visible and acts as a reference for how much has to be removed. It is important to understand that the bush hammer is not a finishing tool. Stay an inch or two away from plastic, copper, or cast iron plumbing or conduit to prevent damaging those surfaces. A hammer and chisel is used to work around sensitive areas and complete the demolition (Figure 6-6).

After the last pass, the final step is to give the floor a thorough vacuuming so chips and dust are not ground into the open pores of the exposed concrete. The cleaner the surface, the stronger the bond will be between a slab and its topping of self-leveling underlayment.

Shotblasting Machines

Another concrete prep option is to blast the surface with metal or ceramic shot beads to remove the top surface of concrete. The best shotblasting machines automatically recycle the shot, and use it again in a continuous cycle to impact and dislodge undesirable concrete material while the debris is vacuumed from the surface into temporary storage for later disposal.

The machines use a variety of proprietary technologies and range in size from push models about the size of a lawn mower to self-contained riding units suitable for the largest projects. Each brand of shotblaster is different, and not all brands recycle their shot or have integral vacuum systems.

Compared with bush hammering (operating a jackhammer), shotblasting machines are relatively easy to use and operate, and they are capable of removing fairly uniform amounts of waste material. Once properly adjusted to suit a particular slab, most shotblasters can remove ¼ to ¾ inch of the surface in a single pass. Shotblasters typically employ a shrouded impact zone whose space is also used as a removal and separation conduit for the shot, dust, and concrete chips. Push units (imagine pushing a lawn mower) are the entry level, but tether-guided, self-propelled, and even riding units are currently available for ever larger projects.

In spite of its current sophistication, shotblasting results in a surface that is not tile ready. For job sites where the units are maneuverable, it is often the most consistent method for concrete surface removal and the easiest in terms of human labor required per square foot of floor. Shotblasting is almost always paired with self-leveling underlayment as the standard fix for renovating the surface of curing-compound-covered concrete that is to be tiled.

Shotblasting is ideal for large floor areas, but the smaller-size units suitable for residential jobs are difficult to rent, and all units require some specialized training for the operator.

Scarifiers and Scabblers

Scarifiers and scabblers are often used to roughen the slick, steel-troweled surface of concrete slabs that are otherwise sound enough for tiling. The machines, which look vaguely like lawn mowers, have different

Figure 6-6. While the bush hammer cab removes large amounts of unwanted concrete quickly, a hammer and chisel are safer to use around sensitive areas, like this plastic drain pipe.

Caution: Bush Hammer Safety

Because the bush hammer is an aggressive power tool that makes quick work of this small bathroom floor, steel-toe shoes are an appropriate addition to the safety equipment. Dust generated by concrete demolition is difficult to avoid and can have long-term effects on your respiratory system. Because tile renovation projects may generate toxic substances, a NIOSH-approved respirator should be used for all demolition work.

features and operating capacities, but most can be adjusted to produce the desired rough surface required by membrane or tile. Some are self-propelled for a more uniform surface texture, and some have built-in vacuum systems. But whether or not the unit is equipped with an integral vac, every attempt should be made to prevent trampling dust and debris back onto the treated surface.

A job-rated vacuum is the only effective way to deal with the dust and grit generated by scarifiers and scabblers. A broom does not remove surface dust, so using only a broom ensures that proper bonding to the treated surface will be impossible. For best results when preparing slick, steel-troweled concrete with a scarifier or scabbler, hold off using these tools until just before you are ready to tile to avoid having the open pores of the treated concrete contaminated by other construction work.

Some scarifiers and scabblers are able to remove significant amounts of concrete and may be used to remove concrete treated with curing compounds. Such projects should include patching or self-leveling compounds to bring the surface smoothness up to an appropriate level for the tiles you need to install. Generally, larger tiles require a flatter surface. Flat and smooth to within $\frac{1}{4}$ inch in 10 feet is the industry minimum, but $\frac{1}{8}$ inch in 10 feet (or smoother) is better for 10-inch and larger tiles (see "Surface Tolerances for Tiles and Membrane Systems," below).

Tiling Over Existing Mortar Beds

Existing mortar beds may be bonded to a concrete slab or separated from the slab by a membrane or slip sheet. In some cases bonded mortar beds can be stripped of tile and retiled. With unbonded mortar beds, it is relatively easy to remove the mortar bed and

---

Surface Tolerances for Tiles and Membrane Systems

Tiles are flat and require a flat substrate to, well, sit flat. Flat can be a subjective term, but with tile, flat applies to
- the structure supporting the tile setting bed
- the setting bed
- the tiles
- the finished installation

All four "flats" must be considered from two perspectives: technical and aesthetic. For typical residential and light commercial tile work, the industry standard for flat, level, or plumb varies depending on the application (floors, ceilings, walls), the setting bed, and the tile adhesive. There are slight differences, but if you average out the applications and adhesives, the industry minimum standard for a substructure (wood subfloor, concrete slab, masonry or stud wall), a surface-applied membrane system, or a finished tile installation is:
- $\frac{1}{4}$ inch in 10 feet
- no abrupt irregularities greater than $\frac{1}{32}$ inch in 12 inches

The standard I use has a sliding scale that is determined by the flatness of the substructure and the flatness of the tiles. It is based on the fact that small imperfections in a setting bed become greatly exaggerated as tile size increases. For example, if a setting bed rolls, undulates, and grossly exceeds the minimum standards, it might still be possible to produce a beautiful tile installation—if the surface was relatively smooth with no abrupt "steps" and if the tiles were relatively small. But if 10-inch or larger tiles were bonded to such a surface, the installation would be both a

technical and an aesthetic disaster.

A case in point is the installer faced with a sagging but otherwise sturdy, nonspringy wood floor that is often found in structures built 50 or more years ago. Fifty years ago, floor tiles were typically 1, 2, or 3-inch porcelain; tiles more than 8 inches long or square were rare. If such a floor is otherwise strong and meets industry deflection limits (L/360), it will look fine when tiled over as long as the sag is not extreme and as long as period tiles smaller than 8 inches are used. I have seen some tile remodeling projects that looked out of place because their perfectly flat floor did not match all the other floors that had sagged over the years.

As tiles get larger, they need a correspondingly flatter setting bed for the surface of the finished installation to look smooth. Here is the smooth, flat, level, or plumb guideline I use for floors, walls, countertops, and dry-area ceilings:

Tile size	Setting bed tolerance
1 to 6 inches	$\frac{1}{4}$ inch in 10 feet
6 to 12 inches	$\frac{1}{8}$ inch in 10 feet
12 to 18 inches	$\frac{1}{16}$ inch in 10 feet
18 inches or greater	$\frac{1}{32}$ inch in 10 feet

For floors that slope to one side (an outdoor tiled walkway or porch, for example), I keep the same tolerances listed above with the addition of the slope tolerance of $\frac{1}{4}$ inch per foot. A slope tolerance of $\frac{1}{4}$ inch per foot should also be added to any wet-area ceiling and 2 inches per foot for steam room ceilings.

replace it. Both types of mortar beds require an experienced tile setter skilled in mortar-bed work.

Bonded mortar beds are mortar beds that have been laminated to the concrete slab with an adhesive or a primer (Figure 6-7). These typically range from ½ to 2 inches thick and are commonly used for leveling concrete slabs. If a project calls for the tiles installed over such a setting bed to be replaced, it may be possible to remove the old tiles without causing too much damage to the mortar bed. Damaged mortar can usually be repaired with a patching material made for tile, or if height is not a problem, a self-leveling compound can be used over the old mortar and adhesive residues—as long as they are completely bonded to the concrete.

On the other hand, if the process of tile removal damages up to 20% of the old bonded mortar, I prefer not to rehab the old bed, but instead remove it completely and replace with new mortar. I am not always comfortable working over another person's mortar-bed work and am careful to inspect the old bed for sand pockets, soft spots made of poorly compacted mortar, excessive cracking, poor bed-to-slab bonding, and any other negative condition that could damage the new tiles.

If the bonded mortar survives the tile removal process with its surface more or less intact, but a crack has telegraphed from the slab to the bonded mortar bed, it may be possible, depending on the size (width and length), number, and condition of the cracks, to renovate the bonded bed with a crack-isolation system. It is important to note that not all crack-isolation systems made for tile meet the same performance levels.

Unbonded mortar beds that are separated from the concrete slab with a cleavage or separating membrane are a greater problem to prepare for re-tiling (Figure 6-8). Such unbonded beds use a membrane or "slip sheet" to prevent bending stresses or cracks in the slab from telegraphing through to the tiles. For that reason, unbonded mortar beds are commonly used for suspended (above-grade) concrete floors. They typically range from 1½ to 2 inches thick and are tricky to install. It is challenging to place the reinforcing correctly and eliminate all voids under the cleavage membrane.

Usually, when removing tiles from unbonded mortar beds, the mortar bed may be too damaged to be repaired or renovated, and for this reason, I normally do not make any attempt to save unbonded mortar beds. This type of installation can usually be pried off the concrete surface easily, leaving behind only a damaged slip sheet, which should be discarded.

It should also be noted that unbonded mortar beds should be produced over rather slick concrete. A smooth, steel-trowel finish is normally specified for this type of installation. The slick concrete finish allows the mortar bed to move unimpeded over the concrete. Depending on the project, another unbonded mortar bed can be floated over a new cleavage membrane, or the surface of the slab can be prepared for a bonded mortar bed or self-leveling underlayment.

Removing Tile and Mortar Installed Over Concrete

Tiles are sometimes installed directly over concrete without a membrane system. During renovation proj-

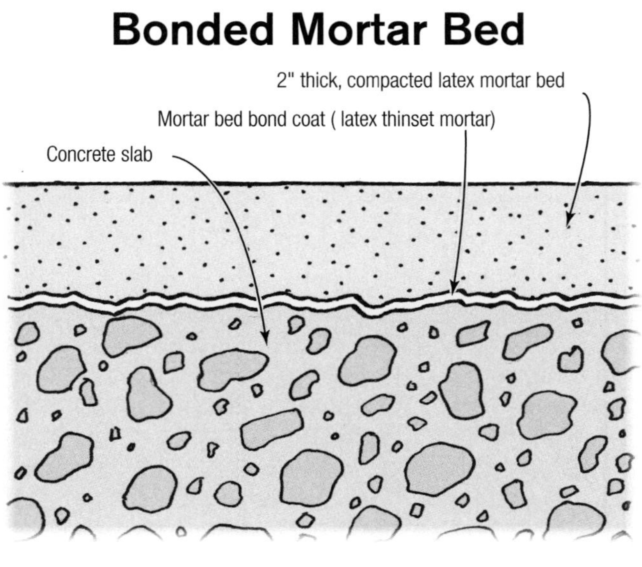

Bonded Mortar Bed

2" thick, compacted latex mortar bed

Mortar bed bond coat (latex thinset mortar)

Concrete slab

Figure 6-7. A bonded mortar bed is often specified to level a rough-finished concrete slab. This type of mortar bed application can produce a very strong setting bed for tile.

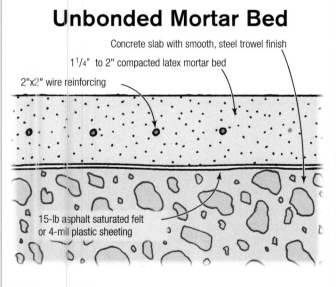

Unbonded Mortar Bed

Concrete slab with smooth, steel trowel finish

1¼" to 2" compacted latex mortar bed

2"x2" wire reinforcing

15-lb asphalt saturated felt or 4-mil plastic sheeting

Figure 6-8. Unbonded mortar beds, which are isolated from the slab floor with a cleavage membrane, are often specified where deflection and structural movement are a concern.

ects, it has to be decided whether to install new tiles over old or to remove the old installation and install new tiles over a freshly prepared, uncracked setting bed. If cracks are present, if the area to be tiled is a wet area, or if sound reduction is desired, a protective membrane system will need to be installed prior to tiling.

Removing tiles directly installed to a slab is fairly straightforward work: Expose the edge of one or more tiles, hold a 1- or 2-inch chisel at a low angle to the surface (and between the tile and the slab) and pound away with a suitable hammer or maul. I use a 3-pound maul paired with a 1- or 2-inch chisel for close-in work and a 3- or 4-inch chisel with a 5-pound maul for open sections of flooring. A maul and chisel are the most basic removal tools. Whenever possible, however, I use a pneumatic chipper to make the task less arduous.

Before beginning the demolition work, though, surrounding surfaces need to be protected. If a network of soft movement joints exists around each field of tile to be removed, I can begin removing tiles immediately. If there are no movement joints, however, I use a close-cutting blade to slit through the grout joints and mortar or underlayment at regular 3- to 5-foot intervals to minimize stress to surrounding surfaces (Figure 6-9).

Once the demolition area has been masked off from the rest of the structure and all finished surfaces protected, I begin by removing two perpendicular rows of tiles that run through the center of the field of tiles (Figure 6-10). This cross pattern creates a massive "movement joint" that allows the surface to relax and give up its tiles with less effort. These first demolition rows will be the toughest to remove, but removal of the remaining tiles should go much easier.

Hand-removal methods are OK for most residential-size projects, but most installers who regularly renovate or repair tile work use power tools to remove tile and adhesive residues. When properly installed with thinset mortar, tiles are usually very difficult to remove. Many concrete slabs are sturdy enough for tile removal and repair, but most wall, countertop, and ceiling setting beds are destroyed during the act of tile removal and cannot be repaired or reused.

Ideally, when removing tiles directly installed over concrete or masonry, half the adhesive should remain on the back of the tile, with half still stuck to the concrete. This indicates a good bond. In practice, with thinset mortar, most tiles get destroyed, and most non-concrete setting beds get damaged. For this reason, when I cut through the grout joints, I set the blade deep enough to cut through the setting bed, too. Often, when the tiles to be removed are installed over concrete, the biggest task is removal of the hard (or soft) adhesive residue. Tiles that part with no residue or with all of the adhesive indicate a poor installation.

Because there are so many different tile/adhesive combinations, I sometimes have to use one set of tools to remove the tiles and another to remove the adhesive residue. I rely on hand, small power, and pneumatic

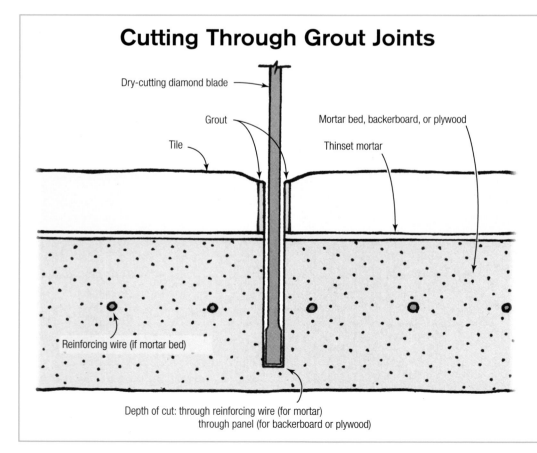

Cutting Through Grout Joints

Dry-cutting diamond blade

Grout

Tile

Mortar bed, backerboard, or plywood

Thinset mortar

Reinforcing wire (if mortar bed)

Depth of cut: through reinforcing wire (for mortar) through panel (for backerboard or plywood)

Figure 6-9. Cutting through grout joints and underlayment with a dry-cutting diamond blade relieves pressure and allows tiles, or groups of tiles, to be more easily removed.

tools for demolition projects less than 200 square feet or so. Stand-up, hand-held, air-powered scalers, with chisel bits made specifically for removing ceramic tile and ceramic tile adhesive residues, are the next step above hand chisels and hammers. However, these tools still require considerable down-force on the part of the scaler operator to remove all thinset mortar residues, and they require a high-volume compressor.

For large floors, even large residential concrete slabs, the easiest way to remove tiles and thinset mortar residues is with the latest generation of shotblasting machines. These machines are narrow enough to pass through most doorways. They are expensive to purchase ($10,000 to $20,000) but may be available at larger tool rental agencies. Often, a single, large-floor demolition project can pay for one of these units.

Mortar beds over wood construction. When working with mortar beds over wood construction, I prefer to use cutting and prying tools to do the work. I start by making cuts every 3 to 5 feet with a portable worm-drive saw fitted with a dry-cutting blade set to the depth of the mortar bed (or backerboard). Next, using thin pry bars pounded into the resulting kerf, I pry sections of the tile/mortar-bed sandwich off the substructure. You may have to snip through any reinforcing wire or mesh that does not break when prying apart the tile installation.

Dealing with cut-back adhesive residues. So-called cut-back asphalt adhesive residues are left behind after carpet or sheet goods have been removed. This type of adhesive is very difficult to remove completely. The bulk of the residue can be sliced off with a wide-blade pneumatic scaler, but even if all the residue is removed from the surface, cut-back adhesive penetrates concrete. It generally leaves a bond-breaking residue that penetrates the setting bed surface a quarter inch or more. Scraping the surface only is inadequate preparation for membrane or tiling; removal of a portion of the surface of the slab is required. It is possible to tile over these residues with special asphalt-compatible thinset mortars, but the bond strength and stability of the tiles will never exceed that of the asphalt, which is generally much lower than a tile-to-slab bond with thinset mortar.

Caution: Adhesive Removal

Never use abraders or shotblasters unless all excess asphalt or other gummy types of adhesive have been scraped off the surface; otherwise, the abrading wheel or shot will heat the coating and carry the unwanted adhesive deeper into the slab, making the situation worse.

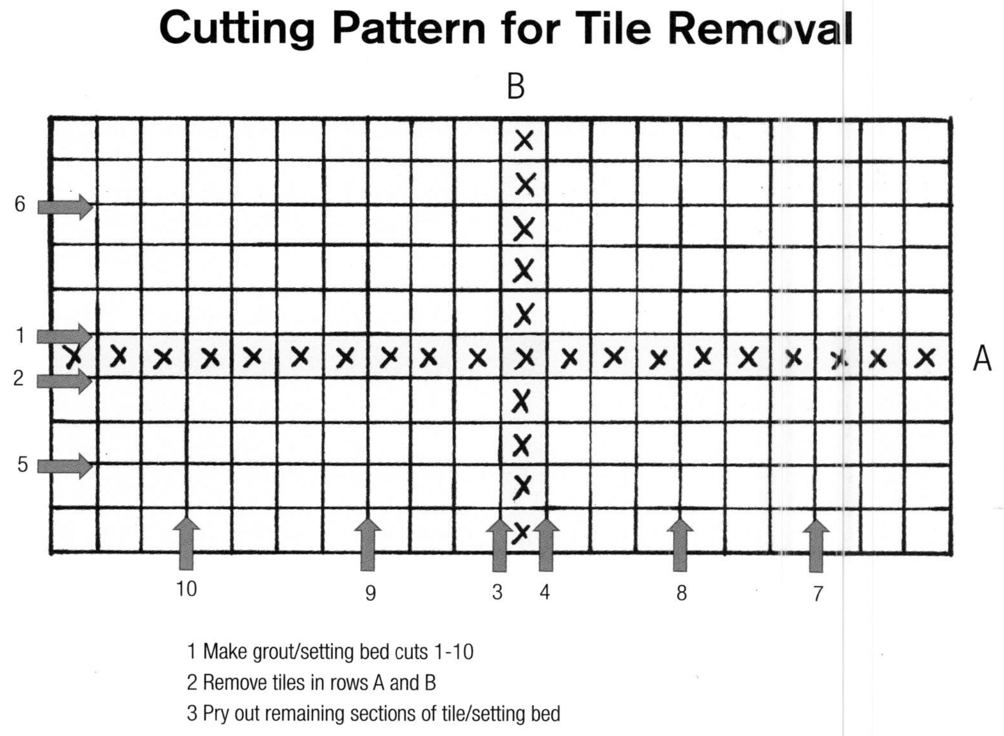

Cutting Pattern for Tile Removal

Figure 6-10.
Removing two rows that cross a field of tiles makes the demolition of an entire floor much easier, regardless of the setting bed.

1 Make grout/setting bed cuts 1-10
2 Remove tiles in rows A and B
3 Pry out remaining sections of tile/setting bed

Suspended Concrete Slabs

Suspended concrete slabs (supported only at the perimeter), whether cast in place or pre-cast, can be tiled using the same surface-prep techniques used for slabs-on-grade. The only real difference between the two is movement. A properly constructed on-grade concrete slab should exhibit no movement or deflection under normal conditions, while a suspended slab—under normal loading conditions—should be in almost constant (though limited) motion and deflection.

To accommodate this motion and deflection, all thinbed floor installations over suspended concrete floors need special treatment that includes a crack-isolation membrane system paired with a network of movement joints. This will prevent normal building movement from "pinching" the perimeter edges of all fields of tile and minimize shearing, tenting, and other conditions that can break the tile bond.

Post-Tensioned Concrete Slabs

Post-tensioned concrete slabs are something of a gamble when installing hard tiles without a crack-isolation membrane. Even under the best of conditions, they require very careful planning and detailing. Individual planks are sometimes very rough, and the joint transitions between neighboring planks can also be quite irregular and beyond the accepted tolerances for tiling—and for most other finishing materials, too. Because of that, this type of construction includes a level topping appropriate for whatever finish material is specified. Cracks in underlayment materials poured or floated over post-tensioned concrete planks are to be expected where planks meet. The tiles should be separated from the underlayment with a crack-isolation membrane system and a network of movement joints (Figure 6-11).

Renovating Concrete With a Self-Leveling Underlayment

Abrading or blasting concrete and finishing the slab with self-leveling compound has become one of the most effective ways to renovate concrete for tiling. Self-leveling underlayments (SLUs) are used to level concrete slabs or floors that have the appropriate

---

Tip: Not All SLUs Are Right for Tile

Not all self-leveling compounds or underlayments are suitable for use with tile! Before contracting with an SLU pumping service, verify that the material to be used is approved for ceramic tile. If the pumper cannot provide a tile-approved mix, he may be willing to pump material that you provide. The setup and movement joint requirements for tiles are different than for other finishing materials (such as carpet or vinyl) using an SLU. Make certain the pumping contractor follows the ANSI A108 tile installation specifications when setting up a pour for tile.

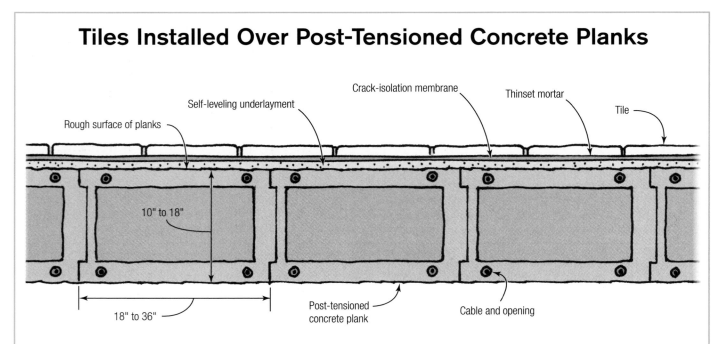

Tiles Installed Over Post-Tensioned Concrete Planks

Rough surface of planks

Self-leveling underlayment

Crack-isolation membrane

Thinset mortar

Tile

10" to 18"

18" to 36"

Post-tensioned concrete plank

Cable and opening

Figure 6-11. Tiles installed over post-tensioned planks require special construction so the joints between planks do not telegraph through as cracks in the tiled surface.

structural strength, but that are not level. Unfortunately, not all SLUs are suitable for use with ceramic and other hard tiles. *Note*: Some products are marketed as SLUs and others as SLCs (self-leveling compounds), but these are essentially the same material.

The following example, used in Project 3 in Chapter 1 (page 24), illustrates a typical SLU installation. The job began with a concrete slab that had been previously patched for some plumbing renovations. The installation, about 58 square feet, was small enough that two people could handle the work of pouring the SLU. Typically, I use buckets and mixing paddles for SLU pours smaller than 100 square feet and contract with a flooring pumper for larger installations. Unlike traditional mortar-bed materials that are relatively slow to set up and somewhat forgiving, SLU's are very fast setting, very unforgiving. This means that all prep work must be completed, and all tools and materials

must be in place prior to mixing. Some manufacturers offer SLUs with extended working time. If you do not have experience with rapid-setting formulas, a mix with extended working time is recommended.

Like any other setting-bed material, SLUs must have a network of movement joints. For a project this size, all that was required was a perimeter joint. To establish that, I affixed a strip of 1¼-inch-wide camper-shell mounting tape (¼ inch thick) to the surrounding walls. To ensure that none of the SLU flowed out one of the two entry doors (a raised threshold on the other door will block the SLU), I positioned a temporary dam made of a 2x4 and sealed with caulk between the door jambs (Figure 6-12).

After this slab was bush hammered, the surface was deep vacuumed to remove as much dust as possible. Over this clean but rough surface, I used a garden sprayer to apply the SLU's companion primer (Figure 6-13). The primer increases the bond between the slab and the SLU, but it needs to dry to the touch—about two hours for this particular primer—before pouring. Many brands of SLU require a reinforcing mesh when pouring over plywood subfloors, but not when placed over reinforced

Figure 6-12. Foam tape prevents the SLU from encroaching on the movement joint area, and the tar paper collar protects the bolt slots of the closet flange (top). A 2x4 dam will contain the SLU, and the foam-wrapped door jamb and wall ensure a continuous movement joint slot (bottom).

Determining Approximate Volume

According to the label information (and my math), it would take approximately three 50-pound sacks of dry SLU to complete the slab. My best guess was computed by packing all the debris from the bush hammer operation into 5-gallon buckets, then topping off all the buckets with water poured from a large measuring cup. The measure of water needed to fill in the voids and top off the bucket is then subtracted from the volume of the bucket to get the volume of material. A gallon of water contains 231 cubic inches; a five-gallon bucket contains 1,155 cubic inches. According to my math, bush hammering removed approximately 2,200 cubic inches of material. Adding 10% for error adds up to approximately 2,400 cubic inches removed. With each sack of material containing approximately 900 cubic inches of SLU material, and with the manufacturer's requirement that only full sacks be mixed, I arrived at three 50-pound sacks of SLU mix. Another way to estimate the amount of material needed is to consult the coverage chart printed on the bags of most brands of SLU. (Note: the 6.5 quarts of mixing water required for each sack does not significantly increase the volume of the finished mix and can be ignored in this computation.)

concrete, as on this project. (The SLU specified for this project was LevelQuik RS and the primer was LevelQuik Latex Primer, both from Custom Building Products.)

Before purchasing or using an SLU, I always double-check the production tag to make certain that each sack carries the same lot number. SLU materials are highly reactive, so mixing sacks from different batches is not recommended because it can lead to an incomplete cure, "plateauing," and other problems. Plateauing occurs when two incompatible batches of SLU meet. The SLU material at the batch interface rises $\frac{1}{4}$ to $\frac{1}{2}$ inch above the remainder of the pour, and this plateau has a significantly lower compressive strength than the rest of the floor. The wet-to-dry mixing ratio is impor-tant, and even more so when more than one sack is required. To ensure the ratios are the same from one bucket to the next (an entire 50-pound sack of SLU can usually be mixed in one 5-gallon bucket), I use a smart bucket (see page 280) set for the SLU manufacturer's recommended liquid amount: $6\frac{1}{2}$ quarts of water per 50-pound sack. I even use the smart bucket when using a larger mixing container (Figure 6-14).

To save time and steps, I staged all the tools and materials needed for the pour a few feet away from one of the floor's entry doors. In place were:

- one 15+ gallon mixing container, filled with the required measure of water

Figure 6-13. To ensure an even coat over the rough concrete surface, the author uses a garden sprayer to apply the primer.

Figure 6-15. At the end of the mixing cycle, the SLU should be lump free with a smooth consistency (top). As soon as mixing is complete, the SLU mix is distributed more or less evenly around the prepared concrete slab (bottom).

Figure 6-14. The author fills the mixing container with three measures of water from the smart bucket for the three sacks of SLU.

- three sacks of mix, opened and ready to add to the container

- a low-speed (less than 300 rpm) paddle designed for mixing SLU materials

- a half-filled bucket of water for cleaning the mixing paddle

- a watch with a second hand (since the manufacturer requires a two-minute mixing period)

The plan was for me to mix all three sacks and have my helper gradually pour the SLU powder into the mixing container. I mixed for the prescribed amount of time, then dumped 75% of the mix on the floor, in three more or less equal piles to help distribute the mix (Figure 6-15). Distributing fresh SLU material can be done with a raking tool, a trowel, or any other tool capable of pushing the material around the floor.

At this stage of the process, the trick is not to get the mix perfectly flat, but—especially for this very rough concrete surface—to make sure all areas of the floor have been "wetted" by the SLU mix, with no obvious piles or depressions (Figure 6-16). The important thing is how quickly the material can be distributed—not how pretty it looks. If most rapid-setting SLU mixes are distributed within 3 or 4 minutes, there should be plenty of time for them to achieve a highly accurate, level pour.

A quick glance told me that there was not enough SLU material on the floor, so I poured the rest of the mix still in the mixing container, quickly troweled over the floor to distribute the added mix (Figure 6-17), and allowed the floor to sit, undisturbed, for several hours. With this particular brand of SLU, I could begin tile or membrane work in four hours. However, because I was planning to install an impermeable membrane to provide crack and waterproofing protection, I let the SLU dry for at least 48 hours before covering it with the membrane.

It is very important when using any type of membrane or large-format porcelain or porcelain-like tiles to allow extra time for materials to cure and for excess moisture to dissipate. Trapped moisture is a major consideration on many surface preparation projects. If not dealt with properly, it can lead to inadequate or incomplete curing of adhesive or membrane materials, leaking membrane joints, loss of bond, discoloration of tiles, and other problems.

Figure 6-16. Although called self-leveling, all SLU mixes need help. Here, the author uses a trowel to ensure the entire surface of the concrete is wetted with SLU mix.

Figure 6-17. The author distributes the added SLU mix and looks for any obvious high or low spots and stray lumps of unmixed material. Lumps are simply flattened against the concrete.

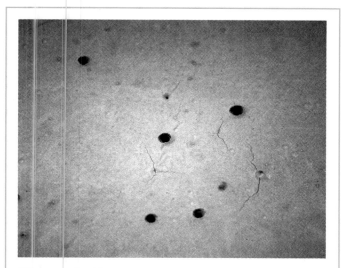

Figure 6-18. Surface bubbles often appear as an SLU pour is just setting up. Unless excessive, the mini craters should not be a problem.

After two hours, when the SLU was hard and dry to the touch, I checked its surface with a straightedge for flatness and slit through the foam edging flush with the floor's surface. With that done, I shut the doors to prevent dust and other contaminants from reaching the floor. After curing, the floor will be ready for membrane or tile, with no additional preparation.

Two common problems when using SLU mixes are the appearance of bubbles as the SLU mix is just setting up (Figure 6-18) and small shrinkage cracks that appear once the mix has dried (Figure 6-19). Neither the bubbles nor shrinkage cracks present any structural problem unless their number is excessive (more than a dozen per square foot). For insurance, though, any cracked surface should be covered with a crack-isolation membrane. Before applying membrane or tile, the surface should be sanded and vacuumed (Figure 6-20).

Fixing Slab High Spots and Depressions

Unless properly specified and produced, few concrete slabs in the U.S. meet the minimum ANSI A108 specifications. Unless they are specified with the correct finished height and a steel-troweled, fine-broom finish, most will require some remedial work before they can be covered with a membrane system or tile. When faced with only a few high or low spots on an otherwise ready-for-tile slab, I prefer spot repairs over whole-area renovations, mostly for reasons of time and cost. Minor high spots can be flattened flush with a diamond cup wheel while a bush hammer or other concrete surfacing tool can be used to make repairs on larger areas. An SLU should only be used if the entire floor needs help. Otherwise, a featheredge or patching compound should be used.

Patching materials (nonself-leveling), made with fine aggregate grains to allow featheredging, are available from many grout and tile mortar manufacturers. You can also make your own concrete patching materials by mixing 2 or 3 parts fine sand (60- to 100-mesh sand is available in 100-pound sacks) and 1 part portland cement with a latex or acrylic additive to a stiff, workable paste. This is the filler. (The exact recipe and cement/sand proportions will depend on the brand of latex or acrylic additive you use.) To bond the filler to the concrete, use a thin layer—$3/32$ to $3/16$ inch thick—of compatible latex thinset spread with a margin trowel or daubed on with a barely damp sponge (Figure 6-21). To fill in a depression, first cover the area with thinset. While this is still wet and tacky, trowel on the mortar filler and screed off the excess (Figure 6-22).

Wood Framing

Unlike wall-to-wall carpet, whose many thousands of threads can tolerate a moving or unstable substrate, ceramic tile requires a rigid subfloor, a strong supporting structure beneath it, and limited movement—even less for stone tiles. While concrete and masonry structures have a long, successful history as a substrate for tile, wood structures have been more problematic. Because they expand and contract with changes in humidity, and because they are inherently more flexible than concrete, wood structures must be carefully designed and built to support tile.

Also, the way we build wood structures has changed over the past few decades. One significant change that affects tiles—especially floor installations—is the increase in joist and stud spacing from 16- to 19.2- or

Figure 6-19. Small shrinkage cracks in the cured SLU are common and usually not a problem. However, excessive cracking (about 4 sq. ft. are shown) indicate that the floor should be covered with a crack-isolation membrane.

Figure 6-20. The author uses a carbide sanding block to flatten crater rims and other surface imperfections.

24-inch centers. At one time, the standard was 12-inch centers, but by the time I entered the trade, the standard had become fixed at 16 inches. Today, some installation systems allow tiles to be installed over joists and studs spaced up to 24 inches, which seems to be the limit for now. But who knows? With increasing resource scarcity, 36- or even 48-inch spacing may be next if a new generation of flooring and wall panels reaches the market.

Regardless of what joist or stud spacing the tile industry accepts as adequate, the laws of physics remain the same regarding wood structures. Increase the spacing by 50%, from 16 to 24 inches, and you increase the amount of deflection by roughly 200 percent! Modern thinset tile installations using tiles smaller than 10x10 inches are generally designed to withstand a certain amount of deflection, referred to as L/360. L designates the span of the floor joists. This means that a 30-foot, or 360-inch, span can safely deflect 1 inch (360/360=1). But because the tile industry recognizes both uniform and concentrated loading, the L/360 deflection standard also applies to the amount of deflection in the subfloor between two joists (see "Uniform Versus Concentrated Deflection," page 154).

> *Note:* The L/360 criteria apply to walls and countertops as well, but for clarity and to reduce repetition, my discussion from here on will refer to floors only.

Many sawn or engineered floor systems claim to meet all the L/360 requirements necessary for tiling, but their claims are based on uniform deflection

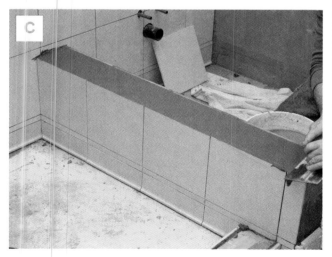

Figure 6-22. While the bond coat is still wet and tacky, the author trowels filler mortar onto the pony wall top (A), cleans the top edges of the tiles for an even screed (B), and finishes the top by removing the excess with a flat trowel (C).

Figure 6-21. The author applies a bond coat of thinset mortar, the first step to applying featheredge or other types of filler mortars.

only—not concentrated deflection of the subflooring between joists. For example, deflection between its joists installed at 24 inches on-center cannot exceed .067 inches, or a bit more than $\frac{1}{16}$ inch. Many sub-floors, even those made from $\frac{3}{4}$-inch (nominal) exterior-grade plywood cannot meet the L/360 deflection standard when installed over 24-inch joist spacing.

With some natural stone tiles, which do not have the same uniformity of strength as manufactured ceramic tiles, an even stiffer structure and subflooring are required. For most stone tiles the maximum allowable deflection is L/720 and even less for some types of stone.

Joist Selection and Blocking

There are too many different regional combinations of joist size, joist spacing, and joist spans in the U.S. to cover each adequately here. For that reason, I am going to focus on the use of 2x10 and 2x12 joists installed on 16-inch centers, with suspended spans no longer than 10 feet. If the building you are working in has a different configuration, you should consult with an architect or structural engineer regarding the load capacity and both concentrated and uniform deflection values. Many engineered flooring systems with 19.2- or 24-inch spacing claim to meet the L/360 deflection standard, but in fact, most meet the standard for uniform loading only, not for concentrated loading.

Although 24-inch spacing is now common, I prefer to rely on 16-inch spacing for most installations and specify 12-inch spacing for many stone installations. Examining the joist size, spacing, and span is the first step in determining whether a structural surface can be tiled. For either ceramic or stone tiles, I generally recommend that 2x12s be used in place of 2x10s and that the subfloor be constructed of nominal $\frac{3}{4}$-inch ($\frac{23}{32}$-inch) T&G exterior grade plywood (Figure 6-23). In new construction, these materials can be specified at the design phase with little effect on the budget and are simple to implement.

Reducing the spacing between joists is another way to stiffen a floor and also to reduce the deflection between joists. In new construction, for example, with joists on 24-inch centers, the most economical method of strengthening a floor is often to install additional joists between the existing, creating a floor with joists at 12-inch centers (required for many stone tiles).

On some remodeling projects, it may be possible to sister supplemental 2x10 or 2x12 joists to existing joists to increase the strength of the floor or center

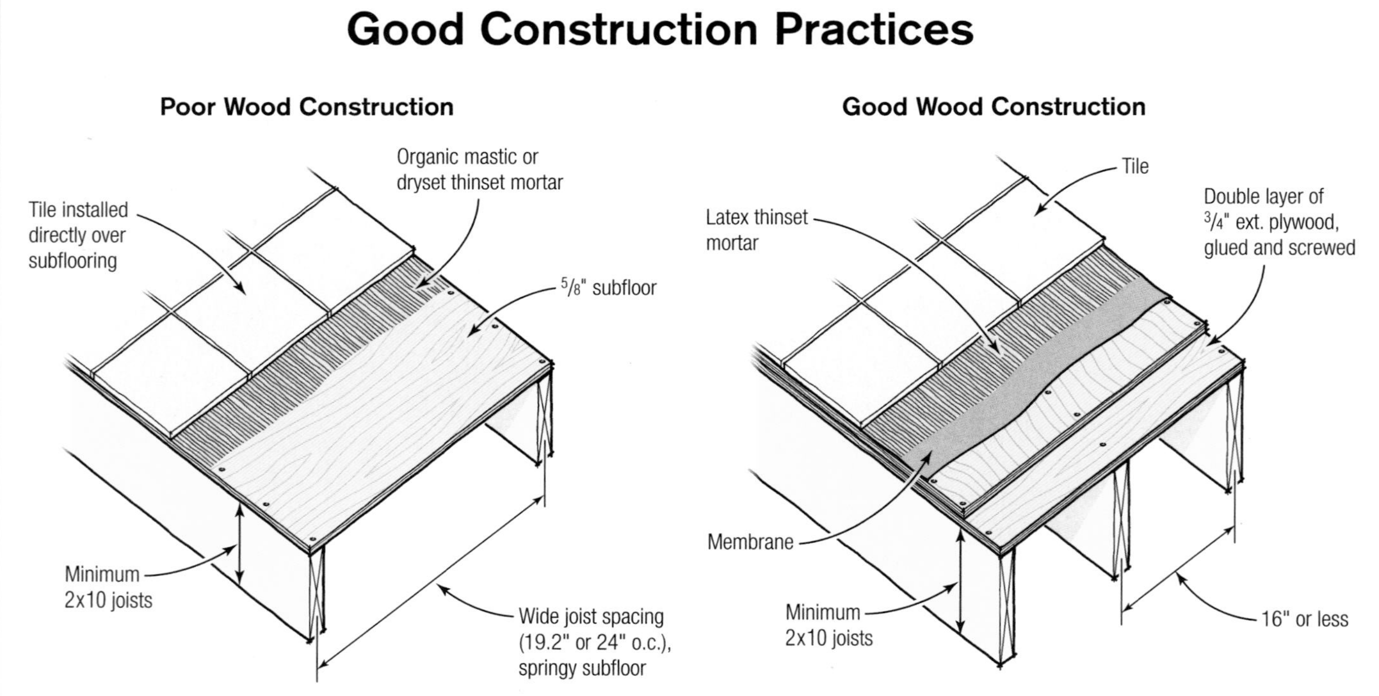

Good Construction Practices

Poor Wood Construction

Tile installed directly over subflooring

Organic mastic or dryset thinset mortar

$\frac{5}{8}$" subfloor

Minimum 2x10 joists

Wide joist spacing (19.2" or 24" o.c.), springy subfloor

Good Wood Construction

Tile

Latex thinset mortar

Double layer of $\frac{3}{4}$" ext. plywood, glued and screwed

Membrane

Minimum 2x10 joists

16" or less

Figure 6-23. All tile installations require a stable and rigid substrate. Because wood structures expand and contract with changes in humidity and are inherently flexible, they must be carefully designed and built to support tile. Movement joints are required and a membrane is highly recommended. Poor wood-frame details include widely spaced joists, thin subflooring, poor installation methods, and inferior materials. Good wood-frame practices include minimum 2x10 joists at 16 inches on center, sturdy subflooring and underlayment, attention to details, and quality materials.

additional joists between those installed on 16-, 19.2-, or 24-inch centers. Some structural deficiencies can be overcome through the use of a crack-isolation system. For best results, however, a strong structure—rather than a membrane—is the foundation that enables a tile installation to achieve long life.

Blocking or strapping has not been a requirement for floors made from dimensional or engineered joists for some time, but the practice is recommended under floors receiving ceramic or stone tiles and on any floor without supplemental supports where maximum performance is desired.

Subflooring and Underlayment Options

Subflooring is attached to joists and provides support for a floor's finish. The TCNA Handbook recognizes 23 different tile assemblies installed over wood framing and calls out either $^{19}/_{32}$ (nominal $^5/_8$-inch) or $^{19}/_{32}$ (nominal $^3/_4$-inch) OSB or plywood subflooring. Underlayment is a second layer atop the subflooring and can be used as a substrate for tile instead of backerboards or a mortar bed. The underlayment can be as thin as $^3/_8$ inch in some TCNA-approved assemblies.

Double-plywood setting bed. I have always been concerned about the minimum standards, and

although they have proved to give acceptable service for light-duty installations, this is one area where I have always upgraded to thicker subflooring and underlayment layers. When the height of the finished tilework is not an issue, I prefer to install two layers of $^3/_4$-inch plywood to serve as the subflooring and underlayment, giving my customers a floor that sounds and feels solid with no deflection problems (see "Subfloor and Underlayment Details", next page). Use plywood with an APA rating of Exterior or Exposure 1, typically designated EGP (exterior glue plywood) by the tile industry (see "Plywood Minimum Standards," page 175).

For extra strength and rigidity on stone-tile installations and where deflection may be an issue, I also prefer to glue and screw the plywood underlayment to the subfloor with Type 1 or Type 2 water-resistant carpenter's glue and corrosion-resistant screws (see "Laminate Underlayment Correctly," page 176). Also, I always cover the double-layer plywood "sandwich" with a crack-isolation membrane because the differential of movement between wood and tile is so great (Figure 6-24). The membrane should be made for use with ceramic tile and designed with waterproofing capabilities if used in wet-area installations.

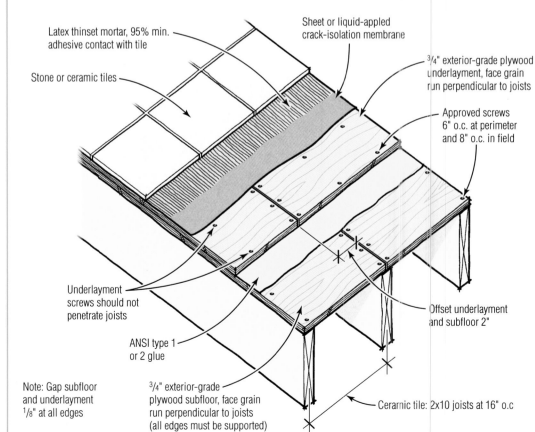

Laminated Plywood Setting Bed

Latex thinset mortar, 95% min. adhesive contact with tile

Sheet or liquid-applied crack-isolation membrane

Stone or ceramic tiles

$^3/_4$" exterior-grade plywood underlayment, face grain run perpendicular to joists

Approved screws 6" o.c. at perimeter and 8" o.c. in field

Underlayment screws should not penetrate joists

Offset underlayment and subfloor 2"

ANSI type 1 or 2 glue

Note: Gap subfloor and underlayment $^1/_8$" at all edges

$^3/_4$" exterior-grade plywood subfloor, face grain run perpendicular to joists (all edges must be supported)

Ceramic tile: 2x10 joists at 16" o.c

Figure 6-24. For extra strength and rigidity on stone/tile installations or where deflection is an issue, the author recommends a membrane over two layers of $^3/_4$-inch ply, glued and screwed. Stone tiles may require higher quality membrane systems, adhesives, and grouts.

Tip: Subfloor and Underlayment Details

Wood floor systems need careful detailing for ceramic and stone tiles. For maximum strength, the face grain of plywood used for both subflooring and underlayment should be oriented perpendicular to the joists. Also note that underlayment joints should be offset from subflooring joints, and that underlayment fasteners should fully penetrate the subflooring, but they should not penetrate into the joists.

A detail often overlooked on both subflooring and underlayment is a 1/8-inch minimum gap between plywood (or OSB) sheets. Also, around the perimeter of a tiled area, it is mandatory to leave a minimum 1/4-inch gap between the edges of the underlayment (plywood, backerboard, or SLU) and the wall, tub, or other restraining material.

Backerboard on floors. Where strength is an issue, plywood underlayment gives more load-carrying performance than any tile backerboard. However, plywood requires a membrane to isolate the tile from movement in the wood. An alternate to using a membrane in dry-area applications is to install a 1/4-inch-thick tile backerboard on top of a double layer of 3/4-inch plywood (Figure 6-25).

The only purpose of tile backerboard is to provide a stable, water-resistant attachment plane for tile (although some specialized boards provide built-in waterproofing). While water will not damage backerboard, it can readily pass through it and damage the building materials underneath. For that reason, membranes are essential for backerboard installations in wet areas.

Plywood is the number one choice for supporting backerboard, and some backerboard may allow for installation over OSB—but never over dimensional lumber. If the dimensional-lumber subflooring cannot be removed and/or height is not a problem, make certain the subflooring planks are firmly secured, apply a layer of 3/4-inch exterior-grade plywood over the planks, then install the tile backerboard or membrane system (Figure 6-26).

Dry Area Floor, Alternative Setting Bed

Top thinset coat
Reinforcing tape
Base thinset coat
1/4" cement backerboard
Fasteners
Support bed of thinset mortar
3/4" Exterior grade plywood underlayment
3/4" exterior grade subflooring
Joist

Figure 6-25. For dry-area floors, a 1/4-inch cement backerboard can be installed in place of a crack-isolation membrane.

OSB is sometimes specified for subflooring and underlayment beneath tile installations. However, many OSB panels are covered with wax or other moisture-resistant materials, making them useless as an underlayment for tile or membrane systems. OSB that has not been treated for moisture resistance can swell when it is exposed to the moisture in organic adhesives and thinset mortars, making this type of OSB unsuitable for either tile or membrane systems.

I have no problem with OSB as a subflooring (but not underlayment) material as long as it is ¾ inch, installed over 16-inch-on-center joists, and with a ⅛-inch gap between sheets. OSB technology is improving and at some point may replace plywood completely, but until all the bugs are out, I will continue to use and specify APA-rated Exterior or Exposure 1 plywood for both subflooring and underlayment.

Particleboard is used by many floor covering installers for sheet goods, but it is never recommended or approved for use with ceramic or stone tiles because it swells considerably when exposed to moisture found in latex-based organic adhesives and thinset mortar. When particleboard swells, it loses almost all of its compressive and cohesive strength; and once the swollen board dries out, it collapses, crumbles, and is unable to support any weight.

Plywood Minimum Standards

Note: All subflooring and underlayment supporting tile should meet tile industry standards. Each sheet of subflooring or underlayment should be identified with the trademark of a recognized quality assurance agency, such as APA.

Subflooring should be rated Exposure 1 or should be exterior plywood conforming to provisions of Voluntary Product Standards PS 1-95 for Construction and Industrial Plywood. Other acceptable products include plywood APA Rated Sheathing or plywood APA Rated Sturd-I-Floor conforming to provisions of APA PRP-108, Performance Standards and Policies for Structural-Use Panels or PS 2-92, Performance Standards for Wood-Based Structural-Use Panels.

Underlayment should be plywood underlayment, that is, plywood rated Exposure 1 or C-C Plugged Exterior. Other acceptable products include sanded plywood grades with special interply construction conforming to underlayment provisions of Voluntary Product Standard PS 1-95 for Construction and Industrial Plywood, or plywood APA Rated Sturd-I-Floor conforming to provisions of APA PRP-108, Performance Standards and Policies for Structural-Use Panels or PS 2-92, Performance Standards for Wood-Based Structural-Use Panels.

Dimensional Lumber Subflooring

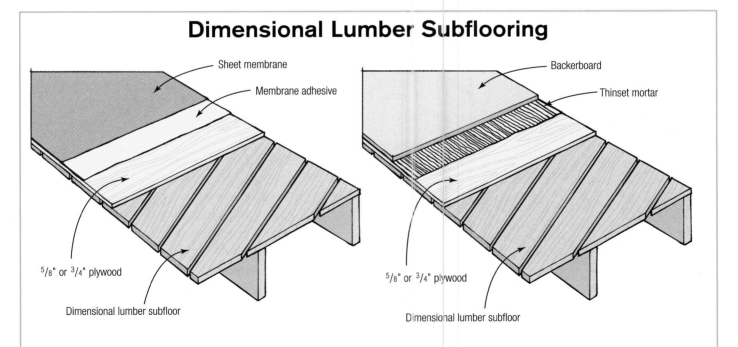

Sheet membrane
Membrane adhesive
Backerboard
Thinset mortar
⁵/₈" or ³/₄" plywood
Dimensional lumber subfloor
⁵/₈" or ³/₄" plywood
Dimensional lumber subfloor

Figure 6-26. If dimensional plank subflooring cannot be removed, it can be covered with plywood underlayment and membrane in wet- or dry-area floors (left) or with a combination plywood/backerboard underlayment in dry areas (right).

Remodeling solutions. On new construction, choosing the right subflooring is easy. Remodeling projects, however, often demand special construction methods, especially where access is restricted or impossible. For example, when I am faced with a subfloor that deflects, and the subflooring cannot be removed, I strengthen the subfloor by screw-and-glue laminating another layer of plywood with ANSI Type I or II glue spread over 100% of the existing subflooring and

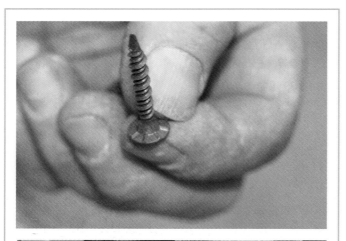

Figure 6-27. Only approved backerboard screws should be used to install backerboards—not drywall screws (top). Foam-core backerboards and accessories like this foam core shower pan (bottom) require a large washer nail for fastening.

secured with screws every 6 to 8 inches (see Figure 1-40, page 26) . Screws should only penetrate through to the subflooring—not the joists. With the subfloor strengthened, installation of the underlayment can proceed. I use this same method even on floors where deflection is not an issue because it produces a finished floor that feels and sounds more solid to customers. To overcome the differential of expansion and contraction between tiles and wood, I then cover the underlayment with a crack-isolation/waterproofing membrane.

Dimensional lumber, often positioned diagonally to the joists, was once very popular as a subflooring, but today it is rarely seen except on remodeling projects. It is possible to install a layer of plywood underlayment over such a plank subfloor, but tile backerboards can never be installed directly over dimensional lumber (or other strip flooring).

Cement Backerboard Installation

Over a suitable structural base, nominal ⅝-inch T&G plywood with APA rating Exterior or Exposure 1 can be used as the subflooring for most brands of backerboard. However, 2x12 joists plus ¾-inch subflooring will add significant stiffness and superior performance. They are what I recommend for most ceramic tile floor applications over wood construction. It is important that the subfloor meet the flatness criteria for the tile to be installed, as any imperfection in the surface of the subfloor will telescope through the backerboard.

The most important thing to remember with any type of screw-on or nail-on setting bed material—whether backerboard or plywood—is to eliminate air pockets that might collapse or otherwise create a

Caution: Laminate Underlayment Correctly

Plywood less than ½ inch thick should never be used as an underlayment for tile over any type of subflooring, regardless of its thickness. Always use a continuous layer of laminating glue (ANSI Type I or II) —not ribbons of panel adhesive squeezed from a tube —to laminate plywood to plywood. Ribbons of adhesive raise only a portion of the plywood sheet and result in numerous air pockets between plywood panels that can severely reduce a floor's compressive strength.

Also, never use panel adhesive to install backerboard on a subfloor or anywhere else. This practice is not allowed by any backerboard manufacturer.

weakness in an installation. When installing non-structural tile backerboard on floors, this means bedding each board in a support plane of thinset mortar. This is a requirement for all tile backerboards used on floors. In wet areas, most backerboards still need additional waterproofing material, unless the backerboard is specifically designed for wet applications and is installed properly.

Attachment plane only. Backerboards are merely attachment planes for securing tiles to an otherwise sound and capable structure. Most backerboard materials do not add strength to a building but, in fact,

contribute to its dead load. While it might seem at first like a good idea to use 1/2-inch backerboard on a floor instead of 1/4-inch backerboard to help stiffen the floor, the 100% increase in the weight of the setting bed may have the opposite effect. With the added weight, the floor system will probably flex and react more than if it was covered with lighter 1/4-inch backerboards. The solution to flexing is to fix the floor structurally—not to install a thicker backerboard! Generally, 1/4-inch backerboard is installed on floors, and 1/2-inch backerboard is used for wall installations.

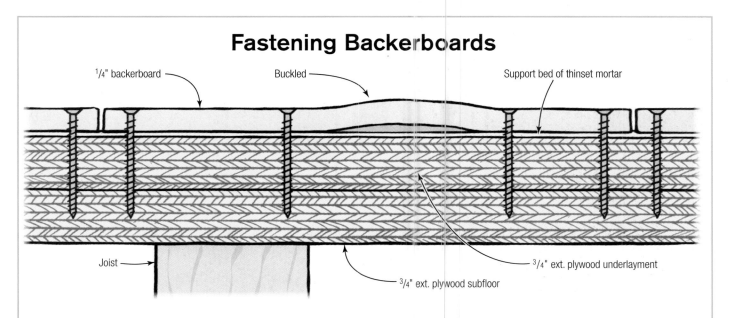

Fastening Backerboards

1/4" backerboard

Buckled

Support bed of thinset mortar

Joist

3/4" ext. plywood subfloor

3/4" ext. plywood underlayment

Figure 6-28. Backerboards and other types of underlayment should be fastened from one side to the other or from the middle out. Working from both ends toward the middle causes the board to arch.

Figure 6-29. To reduce dust, the author uses score-and-snap techniques with cement backerboard. A clamped straightedge and multiple passes of the scoring tool ensure a straight cut (left). A pair of tile biters helps clean up the rough edge (right).

Thinset support. The support plane of thinset mortar is designed to provide uniform support to the backerboard panels by eliminating pockets of air. It's not the job of the thinset to make them level or to laminate them to the floor. To ensure that cement boards sit as snugly as possible against the subflooring, I use specially treated and coated backerboard screws instead of hot-dipped roofing nails. I prefer the Simpson Strong-Tie Quick Drive system (www.strongtie.com) and the stand-up capability it gives to this otherwise slow and repetitive task. The auto-feed system, using magazine strips of 1⅝-inch square-drive screws, allows me to install plywood or backerboard on floors in minutes and with greater safety compared with driving individual screws with a regular gun (this tool's extension can be quickly removed to convert it to a mag-feed wall gun).

As with other materials, each brand of tile backerboard has its own mixing and application requirements, but most specify regular, unmodified thinset mortar. This allows the backerboard to remain stable by sliding against the subflooring (should the floor become overloaded or stressed) and "riding out" the structural movement without causing any damage to the tiles.

Approved fasteners. Hot-dipped galvanized roofing

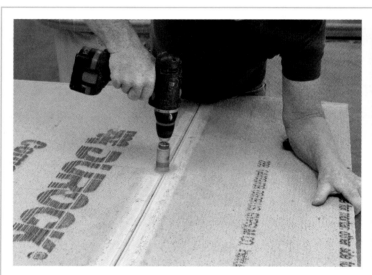

Figure 6-30. Openings should be made cleanly. Here, the author uses a carbide core bit to drill a small showerhead pipe opening (left). To make larger openings, he uses a jigsaw fitted with a carbide blade (right).

Figure 6-31. Pre-drilling three backerboards to be installed on one wall saves time.

Figure 6-32. Pre-countersinking with a large diameter carbide-tipped drill takes only a few seconds per hole.

nails (HDG) are found on most manufacturers' lists of approved fasteners. Collated HDG roofers for installing cement backerboard are available from Maze (www.mazenails.com) for use in stand-up guns. Water-resistant gypsum backerboards, which are installed over a support layer of thinset mortar, can be fastened with galvanized roofing nails. Ring-shank and other types of traditional underlayment fasteners cannot be used for attaching these or cement backerboards.

Although specific roofing nails can be used, I prefer to install backerboards with approved screws because of their more powerful and reliable holding power. Other types of board, such as those with an expanded foam core, may require fasteners with large-diameter washers (Figure 6-27). Regardless of the board or the fastener, the fasteners must be installed from one side to the other, or from the inside out—never from both ends towards the center, as this will cause any board to bunch and arch above the subfloor (Figure 6-28).

Cutting and drilling. To reduce dust when fabricating boards, I use power shears for cutting fiber-cement backerboards and use the score-and-snap method for cement backerboards (Figure 6-29). To make small openings for pipes, instead of banging an irregular hole with a hammer, which is difficult to seal, I use a carbide or diamond core bit. For larger holes, I use a jigsaw fitted with a carbide blade (Figure 6-30). When installing backerboards on walls, I prefer to pre-drill and countersink backerboards. To do this, I align and clamp the boards for one wall together, lay out the position of the studs and blocking, drill through with a 3/16-inch carbide bit, and countersink (Figures 6-31 and 6-32). Rather than purchase an expensive, solid carbide countersink from a machine shop supplier, I use an inexpensive carbide-tipped drill available at the local hardware store for under $20.

Installation. To conserve materials, I start by installing all the full-size boards and then fill in the remainder of the floor with cut pieces, working from the largest down to the smallest. Always maintain a 1/8- to 1/4-inch gap between boards and a minimum 1/4-inch gap around the perimeter of a floor or wall area to provide space for a continuous movement joint. Fasteners should go 6 inches on-center on the perimeter of the boards and 8 inches on-center in the field, and should not penetrate into the joists.

Figure 6-33 illustrates a typical backerboard layout that staggers the joints in 3x5-foot backerboards between the joints in the plywood subflooring. It is important to avoid stacking joints. By this, I mean that a backerboard joint should not sit directly over a joint in the subflooring. Most brands require a 3- or

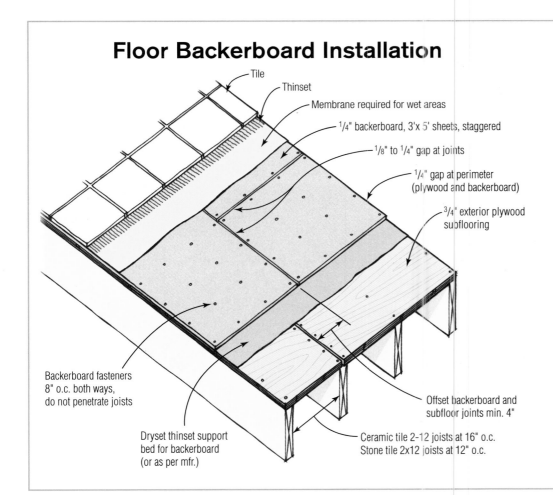

Floor Backerboard Installation

Tile
Thinset
Membrane required for wet areas
1/4" backerboard, 3'x 5' sheets, staggered
1/8" to 1/4" gap at joints
1/4" gap at perimeter (plywood and backerboard)
3/4" exterior plywood subflooring
Backerboard fasteners 8" o.c. both ways, do not penetrate joists
Offset backerboard and subfloor joints min. 4"
Dryset thinset support bed for backerboard (or as per mfr.)
Ceramic tile 2-12 joists at 16" o.c.
Stone tile 2x12 joists at 12" o.c.

Figure 6-33. On floors, backerboards serve as an attachment plane only and provide no structural support. Backerboard joints should be staggered and offset from subfloor joints. A support layer of thinset mortar provides uniform support for the board with no air pockets.

4-inch offset, but 12 inches is better, and a 50% offset is the ideal.

It is essential for the integrity of the membrane and tile that all backerboard edges be firmly supported by the subflooring and by full-width (1½-inch) framing on the wall. It is also critical that the installation include carefully detailed movement joints so that the structure can move normally without harming any parts of the installation.

Taping joints. If the boards are installed in a dry area and no membrane is to be installed, I wait until moments before the tiles are installed to fill and pack the board joints with thinset mortar and to strengthen the joints with a strip of alkali-resistant mesh tape made for use with thinset mortar. Because tile backerboards do not have tapered edges like drywall, waiting to reinforce the joints until just before the tiles are installed produces the smoothest finish. Taping the joints prior to tiling results in a slight hump over the joint. Remember not to pack thinset in the perimeter gap, which must be left open for a movement joint!

Wall-mounted backerboards do not need thinset mortar, but they do require ⅛- to ¼-inch gaps between boards and ¼-inch gaps at inside corners and between the boards and tub or shower receptor (Figure 6-34). When I cannot use the Quik Drive on walls, I prefer to pre-drill and countersink cement backerboards (Figure 6-35) for an easier installation.

Tiling Over Existing Floor Finishes

It is possible to install ceramic tiles directly over some sheet goods, such as vinyl flooring, but only if the floor covering is securely fastened and only if the underlayment (along with the subflooring and joists) is sized and matched for tile. For example, a vinyl floor securely fastened to ½-inch-thick particleboard secured to a ¾-inch plywood subfloor cannot be directly tiled because of the particleboard. In this case, the old sheet goods and all the particleboard must be removed and replaced with a suitable backing, such as another layer of plywood or backerboard (covered with a membrane system).

Particleboard is one of a list of materials considered problematic by the tile industry. This list includes (but is not limited to) particleboard, composite panels, nonveneer panels, lauan plywood, and pine plywood. Because of these materials' high rate of expansion from moisture; their tendency to stain thinset mortar, grout, and porous tiles (lauan); their ability to exude bond-breaking wood resins (softwood plywood); and their lack of tile-related strengths, they are not recommended as substrates for tile—whether or not they are covered with sheet goods (see "Caution, Notes, and Definitions" in the TCNA Handbook for additional details).

Tiling directly over sheet goods, such as vinyl flooring, without first abrading the surface is risky since the same properties that allow sheet goods to shed water and stains also interfere with bonding. Unfortunately, abrading the surface of some older sheet goods releases potentially harmful asbestos. If the sheet goods are soundly installed over underlayment, subflooring, and joists that are compatible with tile, and the budget does not allow for a full removal of the material according to asbestos abatement procedures, the preferred tiling method is to install ¼-inch-thick tile backerboard with thinset and fasteners over the suspicious sheet goods and set the tiles on the backerboard (Figure 6-36). A membrane should be installed over the backerboard in wet areas.

Sheet-type tile underlayments, such as NobleSeal TS, and crack-isolation/waterproofing membrane systems

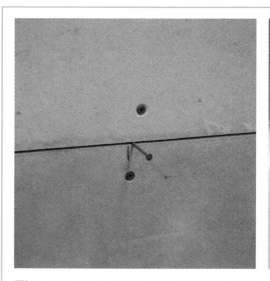

Figure 6-34. Nails tapped lightly into the studs provide ⅛- to ¼-inch spacing at backerboard joints (left). Framing shims work well to space backerboards off tubs and shower receptors (right).

rely solely on a good adhesive bond for attachment. Therefore, they should not be installed directly over vinyl flooring or similar sheet goods. Instead, if a waterproofing or crack-isolation membrane is required, install backerboard first and surface apply the membrane to the backerboard. This method can only be used over a single layer of sheet goods, which should be solid material—never on cushioned sheet goods! If the sheet goods are cracked, disbonded, or installed over an underlayment not rated for tile, another method of floor covering should be used.

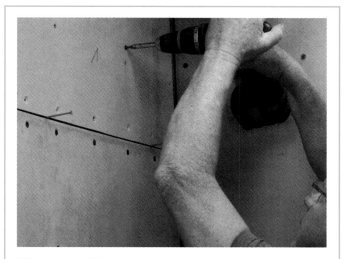

Figure 6-35. Pre-drilling and countersinking wall backerboards is recommended for an easier installation if the Quik Drive is not available.

Strip flooring, floating floors, and perimeter-bonded sheet goods cannot be tiled over directly or covered with backerboard or a tile membrane system. Keep in mind that regardless of the setting bed or conditions, all tilework—even that done over existing tilework or other finished goods—requires a network of movement joints to prevent damage from occurring to the new tiles.

Wall, Countertop, and Ceiling Structures

Although walls, ceilings and countertops do not carry the weight that is normally supported by a floor, these areas need to be properly detailed according to tile industry standards to receive tile. They must be structurally sound, level or plumb, and flat to within ¼ inch in 10 feet. In the past, when all tiles were installed over thick beds of mortar that were floated to correct any "out-of" conditions, the level, flat, or plumb of a structure was not critical. With thinbed installation methods, however, the trueness of a structure is vitally important because it determines, to a large extent, what the finished tiles will look like.

Will cuts facing inside or outside corners be consistent and unobtrusive, or will they be tapered and obvious? Will the floor/wall junction look balanced, or will tapering cuts make one of the surfaces appear askew? Because the tiles are directly applied to rigid setting beds with a thin bed of adhesive, much better results can be obtained if the setting bed surface is flat to within ⅛ inch in 10 feet—or less for large-format tiles (see Table 6-1, page 155).

Tiling Over Existing Sheet Goods

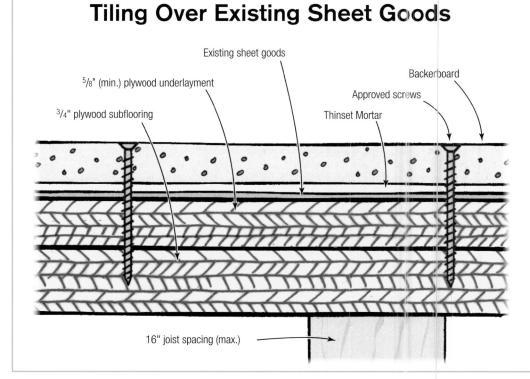

Existing sheet goods

⁵⁄₈" (min.) plywood underlayment

³⁄₄" plywood subflooring

Backerboard

Approved screws

Thinset Mortar

16" joist spacing (max.)

Figure 6-36. Bonding tiles or membranes directly to sheet goods, such as vinyl flooring, is risky. A better approach is to install backerboard first, as long as the vinyl is in good shape and fully bonded (not perimeter bonded only). The framing system, including subfloor and underlayment, must be approved for tile work.

Walls. Tile installations in new construction should be planned at the framing stage so that construction tolerances are guided by tile installation specifications. To help achieve the desired standards and tolerances, framers are advised to search for the straightest studs and reserve them for the surfaces to receive tile. The tile industry has developed materials and details for installations over floor joists spaced 19.2 and 24 inches, but the industry standard for wall studs receiving tile remains at 16 inches on-center.

Ceilings. For ceilings receiving tile, ceiling joists should be on 12-inch centers as an extra measure of safety, especially when installing heavy tiles. In addition, there should be ample, full-face structural support available around the entire perimeter of the ceiling. By full-face I mean that backerboard or plywood setting beds should sit on the full width ($1\frac{1}{2}$ inches) of the studs and joists to which they are attached (Figure 6-37). Flat, level ceilings tend to produce small brown spots from an accumulation of minerals precipitating from steam and hot water vapors. By sloping the ceiling, water drains quicker, and these spots can be eliminated. A slope of 2 inches per foot is the minimum industry standard for steam showers. The slope should be designed and executed so that drips do not land on people using the shower.

The ceiling details discussed in this section are intended for small ceilings found within the typical shower or steam shower environment. Tile installations on full-size ceilings involve significant amounts of weight (10 pounds or more per square foot) and significantly increase the structural load beyond that of a painted, $\frac{5}{8}$-inch gypsum board ceiling. This applies to both single- and multi-story structures. Make certain, if you are going to tile a large ceiling (larger than 4x4 feet), that an architect, structural engineer, or qualified general contractor has approved the installation of the structure.

Because moisture penetration can cause extensive damage to the structure and other finishing materials, all ceiling tile installations in showers and steam rooms need the protection of a waterproof membrane system. Ideally, waterproofing membranes should sit on the setting-bed surface, but not all brands allow this practice. Some require, instead, that the membrane be mounted behind the board, with tiles adhered directly to the board surface. Follow instructions for the membrane you select and make certain the board selected is approved for wet-area conditions (Figure 6-38).

Countertops are something of a problem since many of the supporting members—the side panels of individual cabinets—are spaced beyond 16 inches, and flexing can sometimes be excessive. To counter excess flexing, once all the cabinets are leveled and the side rails flush with each other, I add 2x4 supports where I can, especially around sink or stove top openings (see Figure 4-6, page 108) As a base for tile, I use a double-layer, glued-and-screwed sandwich of ¾-inch exterior-grade plywood sheets covered with a waterproofing/

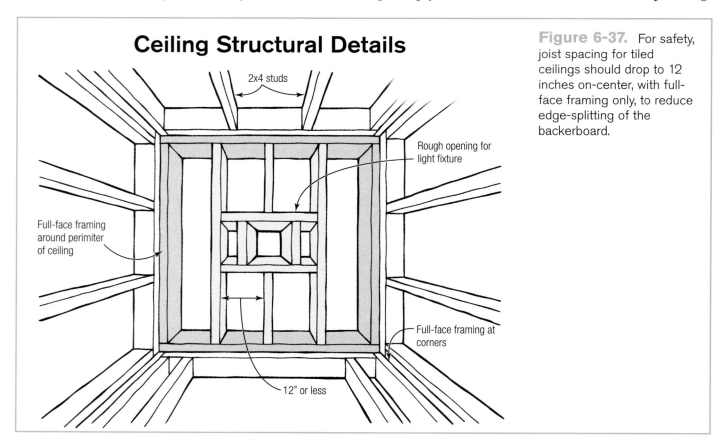

Ceiling Structural Details

2x4 studs

Rough opening for light fixture

Full-face framing around perimeter of ceiling

Full-face framing at corners

12" or less

Figure 6-37. For safety, joist spacing for tiled ceilings should drop to 12 inches on-center, with full-face framing only, to reduce edge-splitting of the backerboard.

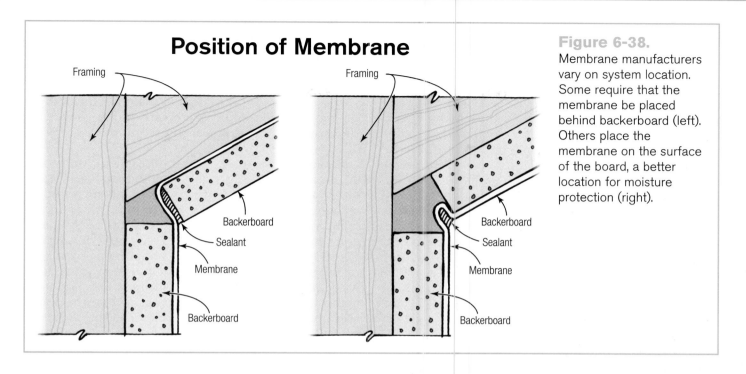

Position of Membrane

Framing

Framing

Backerboard

Sealant

Membrane

Backerboard

Backerboard

Sealant

Membrane

Backerboard

Figure 6-38.
Membrane manufacturers vary on system location. Some require that the membrane be placed behind backerboard (left). Others place the membrane on the surface of the board, a better location for moisture protection (right).

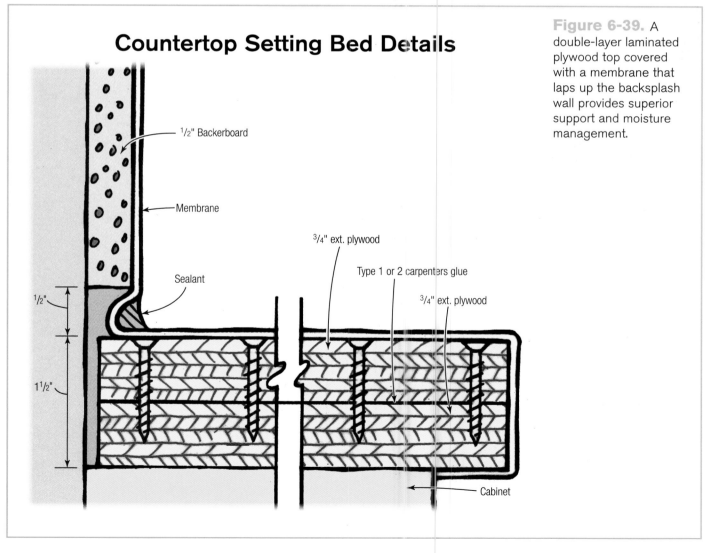

Countertop Setting Bed Details

1/2" Backerboard

Membrane

Sealant

3/4" ext. plywood

Type 1 or 2 carpenters glue

3/4" ext. plywood

1/2"

1 1/2"

Cabinet

Figure 6-39. A double-layer laminated plywood top covered with a membrane that laps up the backsplash wall provides superior support and moisture management.

crack-isolation membrane system (Figure 6-39). For best results, I use a sheet membrane cut wide enough to lap down over the countertop's front edge and lap up to cover the backsplash.

It is also possible to use certain brands of self-leveling compound (SLU) over a ¾-inch-thick exterior-grade plywood base, although damming the edges, openings, and cutouts found in the typical countertop requires time and patience. This type of installation requires 2.5-lb. or greater galvanized expanded metal mesh to reinforce the top, with the mesh fitted closely to the openings and edges. After curing and drying, the SLU will need to be protected with a surface-applied waterproofing membrane system. Since thin areas around sink, stove, and other cutouts are prone to cracking, I provide further reinforcing in the form of 9-gauge galvanized wire. To keep the heavy wire centered in the pour, I secure the 9-gauge wire to hot-dipped galvanized roofing nails with galvanized tie wire (Figure 6-40).

My approach to wall, countertop, and ceiling structures is the same as for floors:

• assume the setting bed will move

• assume that in wet areas the structure may be

damaged by moisture that penetrates the tile, grout, and adhesive

• assume that mold and undesirable pathogens will always find refuge in porous tiles, porous grouts, all other porous installation materials including tile adhesives and backerboard, and in voids located within grout or thinset mortar

Movement joints. As always, movement joints play an important role in every long-lasting tile installation. Wall, countertop, and ceiling planes must be separated from each other with a network of movement joints. By network I mean that the perimeter of each vertical, horizontal, or curved plane that carries tile should be isolated from neighboring planes of tile or other finish materials by a movement joint filled with sealant instead of grout. Although walls, ceilings, and countertops do not carry the same loads as floors, tiles installed on these surfaces are nevertheless just as susceptible to damage caused by normal structural movement as tiles installed on floors.

Tile Over Existing Wall, Ceiling, and Countertop Materials

While it is possible to tile over many existing floor tile

Figure 6-40. Careful damming of edges and openings ensures that none of the SLU "drains" into the cabinets. The author supplements the required metal mesh with 9-gauge galvanized wire (A). Extra care is required to evenly distribute the SLU into the narrow sections of this countertop (B). Once the forms are stripped away, a hardened featheredge caused by splashing and any other surface imperfections needs to be removed with 80-grit carbide paper or a grinding block (C).

installations as long as they are sound, tiling over existing wall, ceiling, and countertop tiles, or other hard surface materials, entails additional risks. First, if there are deficiencies in the original installation (cracks, leaks, mold, etc.), tiling over the original installation without a protective membrane system may cause cracked tiles or problems that will continue to threaten the structure. Yes, it can be done, but you will get better results by removing damaged materials first, making any needed structural repairs, and rebuilding over sound materials.

Even when there is no visible structural, leakage, or bonding problem, adding upwards of 10 pounds per square foot of additional weight may be enough to strain other finish materials that may not be able to carry the extra weight. Tiling over laminate countertops is an example. When adequately roughened to increase adhesive bond, it would appear that such surfaces (Formica, for example) would make ideal setting beds for tile, but because these materials are often used over particleboard and usually lack the support required for tiles, they make a relatively poor base for ceramic or stone tiles.

Tiling over an existing tiled ceiling—even one in good structural shape with no visible cracks or other signs of distress—is a calculated risk. Because tiles cover the installation materials, it may be difficult or impossible to determine if the original tile installation is capable of easily supporting another layer of membrane system, tile, or both. As with walls and countertops, yes, you can install new tiles over existing tiles, but is it worth the risk? A floor tile disbonding is one thing; a ceiling letting go is far more serious. Better to remove the existing ceiling tilework, assess the structure, and rebuild the ceiling tile installation from scratch.

Tiling "Out-of" Framing

On new construction, out-of-level and out-of-plumb conditions may not be so difficult to fix. If caught in time, the entire structure may still be exposed and only require shimming or repositioning. Replacement of one or more joists, studs, or rafters is not a big problem if everything is exposed. Once a structure is finished, though, "out-of" repairs for walls, ceilings, and countertops can be tedious, difficult, and time consuming.

For example, the ceiling of a typical enclosed shower stall generally is easily accessible if changes in the structure to create a sloped ceiling are required. In such installations, it's easy to lower or add new joists. For best results, all shower stall framing should be straight, square, plumb, and level to within 1/8 inch in

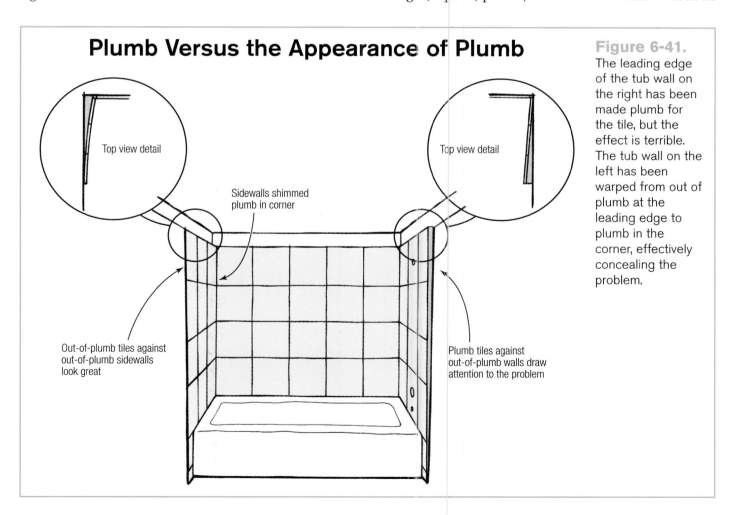

Plumb Versus the Appearance of Plumb

Top view detail

Top view detail

Sidewalls shimmed plumb in corner

Out-of-plumb tiles against out-of-plumb sidewalls look great

Plumb tiles against out-of-plumb walls draw attention to the problem

Figure 6-41. The leading edge of the tub wall on the right has been made plumb for the tile, but the effect is terrible. The tub wall on the left has been warped from out of plumb at the leading edge to plumb in the corner, effectively concealing the problem.

10 feet or better.

When studs fall outside this standard and cannot be replaced, for example on a remodeling job, it is still possible to make corrections. You can sandwich 1x4s on either side of a stud that is tipped back or in, or sister another 2x4 or 2x6 to the errant studs. This method can be used on installations where the walls are not enclosed by drywall or backerboard. If existing walls are falling in at the top, it is easy to make a smooth transition at the top of the field of tiles. But if the walls are falling back, a wide joint will be created

Figure 6-42. To avoid standing water or moisture at the top of this wall, the author uses the grout trowel to slope grout, behind the surface bullnose trim, toward the tub or shower.

at the top of that field of tiles when using the above methods to plumb or straighten a wall. To minimize the appearance that something is amiss, it is important to use restraint when "trueing" a stud.

For example, on a tub or shower surround whose walls are all out of plumb but in plane with surrounding, nontiled wall areas, "correcting" the leading tile edge would create a completely unacceptable, exposed tapered edge (at right in Figure 6-41). Instead, to create the illusion that all surfaces are plumb, only the studs indicated (at left in Figure 6-41) need to be corrected. This drawing shows the warping in the tiled surface required to get from an out-of-plumb leading edge to a dead-plumb corner—where tapering tile cuts would immediately announce that something is wrong with the setting bed and framing. Figure 6-42 shows how the upper edge—out of sight for most—can be beautifully finished with grout that is slightly sloped toward the face of the tiles.

Since the weight of the setting bed and tiles will be supported by the original stud, I run backerboard or plywood fasteners into the original stud instead of the materials that have been sistered or added on. I prefer using a pair of 1x4 "cleats" because this method allows the setting-bed material (backerboard or plywood) to sit flatter (Figure 6-43). Sistering a single 1x4 or 2x4 to an existing stud tends to warp the backerboard slightly when fasteners are cinched home.

Another important requirement of this method is to provide blocking for full support at all backerboard edges and to provide a tight fit when replacing any fire blocking removed during the process of correcting the wall.

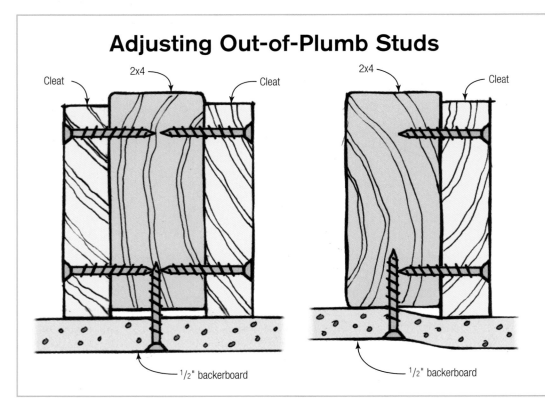

Adjusting Out-of-Plumb Studs

Cleat · 2x4 · Cleat

2x4 · Cleat

½" backerboard

½" backerboard

Figure 6-43. Cleating both sides of the stud with adjustment boards results in a firm, square foundation for the backerboard (left), while single-board methods may result in a warped surface (right). Always secure the board to the original stud for best support.

Leveling Wood-Frame Floors With SLUs

The advent of self-leveling underlayments (SLU) made for tile has simplified the renovation of out-of-level floors whose structure is covered with subflooring that cannot be easily removed.

Depending on the brand, SLUs (also marketed as self-leveling compounds or SLCs) can be used as an underlayment or patching material on either concrete or wood. While most SLU brands permit very thick installations, most limit each pour to about 1 inch, with additional pours, as needed, to achieve the desired height. Multi-pour SLU applications require special preparation, close timing, and attention to detail (a primer may be required between pours, for example). One brand of SLU can be applied up to 6 inches thick, requiring six separate, 1-inch pours. While this may be OK for the manufacturer, the cost of materials for such a project may push you to look for a less expensive alternative.

Most brands of SLU have a companion primer that prevents moisture required by the SLU from being suctioned out of freshly poured material (see Figure 1-27, page 18). For all my SLU projects over wood, I use reinforcing mesh stapled or nailed snugly against the floor to maintain the lowest floor height. Synthetic, rubberized-fabric-type mesh is available, but for best performance, I prefer to use galvanized, expanded metal mesh (2.5 pounds per square foot or heavier) instead, and secure it to the subfloor with galvanized roofing nails or staples as soon as the floor primer has dried (see Figure 1-28, page 18). All holes in the floor— even small nail holes—need to be sealed off with

caulk, tape, or plugging to prevent SLU seepage and runoff.

When installing any brand of SLU, it is recommended to have some material in reserve in case the original estimated height is too low. With a competent helper and a few simple tools, I can handle an eight-sack installation. However, when the project exceeds eight sacks, I hire a pumper to speed the mixing and delivery process.

Since no two SLUs are alike, specific installation instructions must be followed to the letter. However, there are general guidelines that apply to all. In particular, the wet-to-dry ratio is critical, especially where more than one sack of SLU mix is needed to complete the work—there should be no variation between batches. To ensure that, I use a smart bucket to measure the liquid. When mixing SLU materials, I use a 5-gallon bucket for a single sack application and a 15-gallon party bucket for larger pours. Also, I ensure that any residue in the bucket is thoroughly cleaned to prevent spiking (accelerating) subsequent batches and reducing their open time. The use of extended-setting mixtures is recommended for first-time users and veterans who prefer a more relaxed pace of work. Some rapid-setting brands can begin setting up within 8 to 10 minutes after mixing, while extended mixtures may allow 20 to 30 minutes or longer, depending on the brand.

The important issue with any brand of SLU, rapid set or slow set, is preparation. All surfaces must be 100% prepared, plugged, dammed, isolated, primed, and staged before adding any liquid to powder. All tools needed to distribute or smooth the SLU should be at hand, all mixing materials should be staged as close as possible to the application site, and all nonessential personnel escorted off the site. (Spectators always get in the way—and don't forget roaming dogs and cats, a particular problem!) As material is dumped and you work your way out of the installation area, all traffic needs to be restricted from the application areas. Just as important, the SLU will achieve a much better set and cure if all construction vibrations cease within the structure until the materials have cured. With some brands, this can occur in as little as an hour or two.

Featheredge Compound

When only a portion of a floor, wall, ceiling, or countertop substrate is depressed or out of plane, a featheredge compound (FEC), so-called because its rather fine aggregates allow smoothing to a feather-thin edge, can be used instead of more expensive self-leveling compound. Depending on the specific product, FECs can be used on concrete, wood, drywall, and other finishes. Featheredge compounds for tiling can be purchased in sacks, or they can be site-mixed by combining portland cement, fine sand (kiln-dried 60 to 100-mesh), and latex in the proportions determined by the latex manufacturer's mixing instructions.

Tip: Lump-Free SLUs

It is almost impossible to mix an SLU without any lumps, which tend to float to the top after the pour. Lumps are dry clumps of powder within the SLU mixture that become weak spots once the mix cures. To prevent this, I use a trowel to mash the lumps into the reinforcing mesh, breaking up the powder and incorporating it into the rest of the mix.

One of the tools I keep handy is a garden rake. It allows me to re-distribute the SLU mix and mash out lumps that are out of reach. Another improvised tool for SLU work is scrap 2x6 cut 12 inches long. I keep a dozen of these blocks handy in case a problem is beyond the reach of the rake and use them as stepping stones that allow me to walk onto the wet floor. After taking care of the problem, I retreat, taking the blocks with me as I go. Within a minute, the SLU flows back into the depressions, and the floor is level once again.

Applying Featheredge Compound

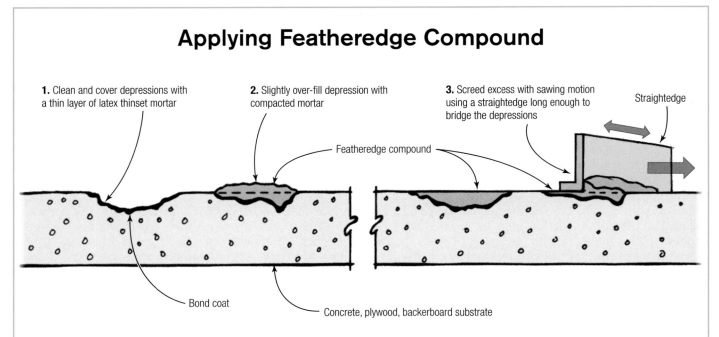

1. Clean and cover depressions with a thin layer of latex thinset mortar

2. Slightly over-fill depression with compacted mortar

3. Screed excess with sawing motion using a straightedge long enough to bridge the depressions

Straightedge

Featheredge compound

Bond coat

Concrete, plywood, backerboard substrate

Figure 6-44. Depressions in concrete and wood can be filled with featheredge compound. Use a gentle sawing motion to screed the compound flush with the surrounding surface.

Packaged FECs may require the application of a companion primer. For a site-mixed FEC, I spread a thin ($3/32$-inch minimum) layer of latex thinset mortar as the primer coat and trowel the FEC over the thinset mortar while it is still wet and tacky. While manufactured brands differ in overall strength or application thickness, most can be built up in layers or single applications of up to an inch thick. Thick applications of FECs on wall or ceiling surfaces may need to be built up of several thinner layers. All applications follow the same general principles: start with a clean substrate, apply an appropriate primer, pack and slightly overfill the depression, then screed off with a straightedge.

Wet-to-dry ratios should be measured precisely; and each brand's mixing, installing, and cleaning instructions should be followed closely for best results. This includes using wet and dry ingredients that are properly acclimated to normal room temperatures (never below 50°F or above 90°F). To assure consistency when more than one batch is required, I use a smart bucket for measuring liquids, time the mixing cycle, and clean and rinse the mixing paddle between batches. Cleaning the mixing paddle for each batch helps prevent material from a previous batch contaminating the next batch (this also applies to SLUs, rapid-setting thinset mortars, and tile installation epoxies).

The first step in applying featheredge is to identify the depressed area. This is done with a straightedge (the longer the better) and a marking pencil. Placing a light source opposite the straightedge, I slowly reposition the edge at roughly 6-inch intervals and mark the limits of

the depressed area with the pencil. Gradually, a dotted outline of the affected area develops, which serves as a guideline for applying the primer and FEC filler.

After mixing the FEC according to the latex additive instructions (one part portland cement, two parts fine sand, and enough latex to produce a smooth, spreadable mix), I mix enough latex thinset mortar to cover the depression. I spread the thinset mortar primer with a $3/16$-inch V-notch trowel, and flatten the uniform ridges with the smooth edge of the trowel. Then, while the thinset is still moist and tacky, I trowel the FEC filler into the primed depression and compress it against the thinset mortar primer coat. For best results, the depression should be slightly overfilled to prevent "bird-baths" after screeding.

Once the depression has been filled, I allow the FEC to rest for 10 to 20 minutes, depending on brand instructions, and then screed away the excess with a light, reciprocating motion of a straightedge held firmly against the substrate surrounding the depressed zone (Figure 6-44). If the FEC has been mixed to the right consistency, compacted thoroughly, and screeded gently, there should be minimal voids, divots, and tear outs that require backfilling and re-screeding. For best results, the straightedge should be regularly scraped free of accumulating mortar deposits that can cause unwanted surface voids.

After screeding, I allow the FEC to harden and cure 72 hours (at about 78°F) before applying membrane or tile. Whether the FEC is factory made or site mixed, I generally cover it with a membrane, rather than cover a membrane with an FEC.

NOTES

NOTES

Chapter 7
PROTECTIVE MEMBRANE SYSTEMS

Membrane systems have been a part of tile installation for thousands of years. In fact, one ancient version of this system, building a tile installation over a bed of sand, is still used in many parts of the world. There are three types of membrane systems used for thinbed tile installations: crack isolation, waterproofing, and sound reduction.

Each of these three types has two options for installation: 1) a manufactured sheet requiring an adhesive and 2) a liquid-applied membrane that is site-built with a gel, liquid, or paste and a reinforcing fabric. Whatever approach is used, all thinbed membranes are designed to be applied between the tiles and their setting bed. Some do double or even triple duty. For example, the Noble Company (www.noblecompany.com) makes a membrane system for sound reduction that also acts as a crack-isolation and waterproofing membrane (NobleSeal SIS).

Many membrane systems offer both waterproofing and crack-isolation protection, but no two membrane systems offer exactly the same type or level of protection, and each system has its own installation requirements.

There is a new additional approach to installing membranes, which I will not discuss in detail in this book, that deserves to be mentioned. In reality, this new type is a material property rather than an actual membrane. I am referring to the property of crack isolation or sound reduction now incorporated into several thinset mortars. No doubt, brands with waterproofing properties are just around the corner. One example of this new approach is Custom Building Products's Megalite Rapid Set (custombuildingproducts.com) crack-prevention mortar, a lightweight polymer thinset that offers protection against cracks up to $\frac{1}{8}$ inch wide when applied according to manufacturer's instructions (this material requires no reinforcing fabric).

This new approach is a viable option for some types of tile installation projects. Their higher square-foot costs compared with regular thinset should be balanced against the cost of adding a membrane. As with any emerging technology, early users should exercise caution and follow the manufacturer's instructions closely.

Use the Right Materials

Numerous membrane systems have been tested specifically for use on thinbed tile applications. When reasonably specified and installed according to manufacturer's instructions, most give dependable service. Problems arise, however, when light-duty systems are specified for heavy-duty applications or when the installer fails to accurately follow label directions. These are the leading causes of tile installation failure!

Problems may also develop if inappropriate or untested materials or coatings are used as waterproofing. For example, some installers may apply one or more coats of a "waterproofing liquid," such as Thompson's WaterSeal, thinking that it will stop the transmission of water or moisture through backerboards, plywood, or other substrate material. Unfortunately, such products at best protect the treated material and do nothing to stop water penetration through the structure.

Scribing felt, tar paper, and other types of construction papers, glued to a substrate with mastic, are sometimes used as crack-isolation membranes under thinset mortar and tile. The idea for this may have come from the tile showroom practice of setting display tiles on an easily removable surface. Nevertheless, the materials have proved to be ineffective for thinbed crack-isolation applications, and not a single thinset mortar manufacturer recommends their use. Rather than use untested or unapproved materials and methods that place responsibility and liability in the hands of the installer, use membrane systems made specifically for use on tile installations.

Exterior Tile Installations

Exterior tiles subject to water exposure require a sloping substrate (a crowned walkway or a sloping deck) and a membrane rated for exterior use. Depending on the application and materials used, some may also require a drainage layer. The installation also needs to have positive slope so that rain or snowmelt runs off the surface of the tiles quickly. This can be done with a system of drainpipes or by simply allowing excess water to run off the surface away from the structure.

One major difference between interior and exterior tile installations is the size, placement, and frequency of movement joints. Because exterior installations are subject to temperature cycling and extremes, they require wider and more frequent movement joints. Many tiles, tile installation materials, and tile membrane systems are suitable for exterior use. Make certain that the materials you plan to use are approved for exteriors and that the manufacturer can provide appropriate test data and installation specifications.

Sheet and Liquid Membrane Systems

Sheet membrane systems are composed of a core made of plastic, asphalt, or other materials bonded to one or more layers of fabric reinforcing. The sheet is cut, fabricated, and installed with an adhesive (Figure 7-1). Normally, the adhesive is thinset mortar or a contact-type organic adhesive. A major advantage of sheet membranes is that their performance (whether for waterproofing, crack isolation, or sound reduction) is guaranteed by the manufacturer.

With liquid-applied systems, the membrane is com-

Figure 7-1. For an accurate fit, the author lays out a cut line on the sheet membrane. The cut section will be bonded to the setting bed with an adhesive.

Figure 7-2. Liquid-applied membranes are composed of a reinforcing fabric embedded in liquid, paste, or gel. Here, the author is embedding the reinforcing fabric in the first coat of liquid.

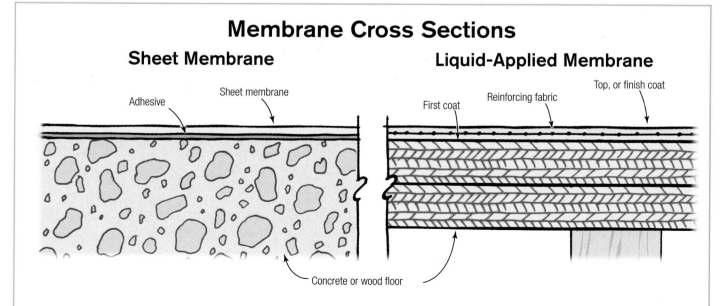

Membrane Cross Sections

Sheet Membrane

Adhesive

Sheet membrane

Concrete or wood floor

Liquid-Applied Membrane

First coat

Reinforcing fabric

Top, or finish coat

Figure 7-3. Sheet membranes install with an adhesive (left), while trowel-applied systems require two layers of the liquid component, which acts as the adhesive (right).

posed of a gel, liquid, or paste, plus a reinforcing fabric (Figure 7-2). Reinforcing fabrics may vary in strength and composition from one brand to another, but most are some variation of a porous spun-polyester fiber that is either woven or nonwoven. To install a liquid-applied system, a thick layer of liquid or gel—enough to bleed through the fabric—is applied to a setting bed, followed by the fabric. The fabric is then pressed into the liquid layer, followed by one or more top-coatings of liquid or gel (Figure 7-3).

Some applications—tub shower walls and bathroom floors, for example—need a membrane system that only has to shed water or hold a small amount of standing water. Another type of waterproofing membrane, commonly referred to as a shower pan, must be able to contain and hold standing water and be able to channel it to a drainpipe. Shower pans are usually found at the base of a shower stall, but with a few slight variations, they can also serve as waterproof liners for tiled sunken tubs, pools, and fountains. However, not all tile waterproofing membrane systems are rated for use in applications that are subject to continuous immersion in water.

Shower pans are usually associated with mortar-bed installations, but special drains and flashing now permit thinbed membranes to be used for many shower pan applications that require little or no mortar. This eliminates one of the biggest problems with traditional shower stall installations—saturation of the mortar bed floor. A wet mortar bed in a shower stall is the perfect environment for mold, mildew, unwanted smells, and potential wicking into the walls and underlying structure. Fitting a traditional shower stall

floor with a surface-applied membrane can eliminate saturation of the sloped floor, the growth of mold and mildew, and other moisture-related problems. Projects 2 and 3 in Chapter 3 provide two examples of how to build all-tile thinbed shower stalls.

Crack-Isolation Membranes

Crack-isolation (CI) systems are sometimes referred to as crack-retarder or uncoupling membranes, or whatever the marketing people want to call it. To me, it's all crack isolation. Probably the most important aspect of crack-isolation membranes to remember is that none of the systems available for tiling can guarantee a crack-free installation. They are designed to reduce the incidence of cracked tiles and grout joints—not completely eliminate them. CI systems are not designed to deal with structural cracks in wood or concrete construction.

For concrete slabs, only shrinkage cracks $\frac{1}{8}$ inch wide or less can be covered by most brands (Figure 6-3 page 158). Structural problems in wood construction may not be readily apparent, but installers should at least inspect the floor system for any conditions that might be detrimental to tile. At a minimum, check the joist dimensions, spacing, and spans, and the thickness of the subflooring. Crack-isolation membranes are usually applied to wood underlayments to resolve the difference in expansion and contraction between wood and tile.

Cracks in a structure are always accompanied by movement. Crack-isolation membrane systems remove the tiles from direct contact with a shrinking or expanding setting bed around the area of the crack,

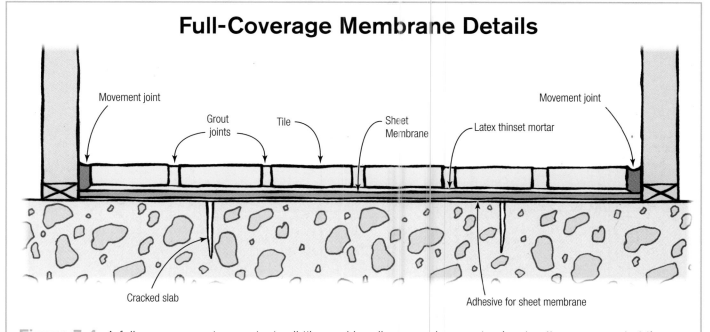

Full-Coverage Membrane Details

Movement joint

Grout joints

Tile

Sheet Membrane

Latex thinset mortar

Movement joint

Cracked slab

Adhesive for sheet membrane

Figure 7-4. A full-coverage system protects all tiles and handles normal expansion/contraction movement at the perimeter of the floor.

resulting in fewer cracked tiles. Selling crack isolation to the customer can be difficult, but one of the tools I use to get a CI system specified for an existing (old or new) slab is to indicate the ends of the crack(s) with an indelible marker and add a date and signature. I do this on my first site visit, making sure the building owner is with me to witness and understand the marking process. Along with an indelible marker, I bring a camera to record my identification marks.

If the concrete is less than a year old, by the time I am ready to return and install the tiles, the crack usually will have advanced beyond the mark, a sure indication that the slab is moving and requires a membrane. When I present a bid to a customer, the cost of the installation is noted up front, while the cost of a membrane installation—if needed—is spelled out toward the end of the contract.

Full coverage versus bandage method. Conventional crack-isolation membranes, consisting of either a manufactured sheet or a liquid-applied system, may be applied in one of two ways: full coverage or bandage. Full-coverage membranes cover an entire floor or wall surface, while bandage systems cover only the area immediately surrounding a crack. In general, bandages are only used in large commercial spaces as a cost-saving measure.

With full coverage, the entire area to be tiled is covered with membrane, and the perimeter joint is filled with resilient sealant instead of hard grout (Figure 7-6). With the bandage method, the membrane is installed only over the cracks, and a movement joint must be placed closely encircling the original crack (Figure 7-5). The width of the bandage is determined by the size of the tile, with most systems requiring a sheet or fabric width equal to three or four times the size of the tile. As with the full-coverage method, a movement joint around the perimeter of the floor also is required.

I am not a big fan of crack-isolation bandages for several reasons: They do not protect all the tiles on a floor; they typically raise the level of the floor in the area of the crack (Figure 7-6); and as shown in Figure 7-5, they require an awkward network of movement joints. When the customer specifies the bandage method, I take several precautions to guard against future problems.

First, I recommend a crack location map be included in the project specs, with the appropriate signatures and waivers required on any cracked or problem substrate, to further reduce an installer's liability. In addi-

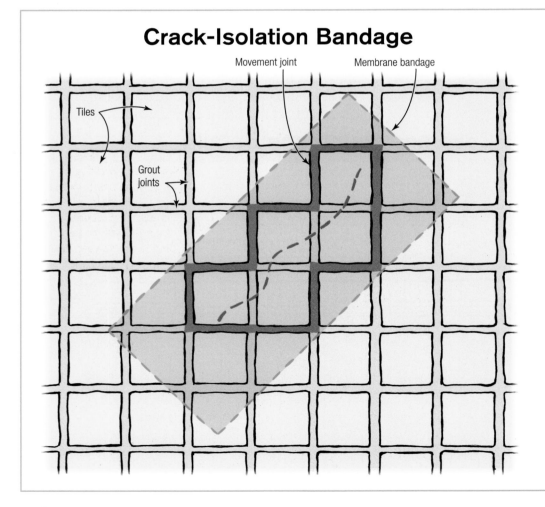

Crack-Isolation Bandage

Movement joint   Membrane bandage

Tiles

Grout joints

Figure 7-5. A crack-isolation bandage protects the tiles only in a small area of a floor. Its conspicuous, irregular perimeter movement joint will require constant maintenance and more frequent replacement because of its mid-floor location.

tion, I also inform the customer, in writing, that the bandage system will create a hump in the treated area(s) and negatively affect the finished appearance of tiles installed over it. A crack-location map does not have to be precise (Figure 7-7), but it is an essential tool that reduces finger pointing should cracks appear after the installation has been put into service. An installer should not have to warranty the installation against future cracks appearing in unprotected areas of the floor.

It's possible to install a crack-isolation bandage without a hump, but the process is labor intensive as it requires lowering the concrete surface under the area of the patch (Figure 7-8). Because of the expense of grinding the concrete slab, such a repair only makes sense on a big-budget restoration of a vintage tile floor; otherwise, the cost of concrete work may exceed the cost of covering the entire floor with membrane.

Regardless of the brand or type of application, all

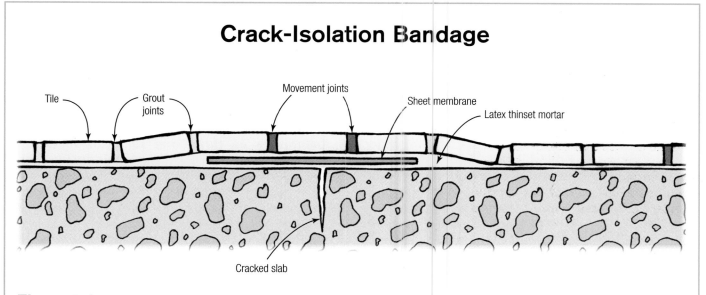

Crack-Isolation Bandage

Tile — Grout joints — Movement joints — Sheet membrane — Latex thinset mortar

Cracked slab

Figure 7-6. The bandage method can save money on large jobs, but it creates a hump that will show in the finished floor, especially if the tiles are 8 inches or larger.

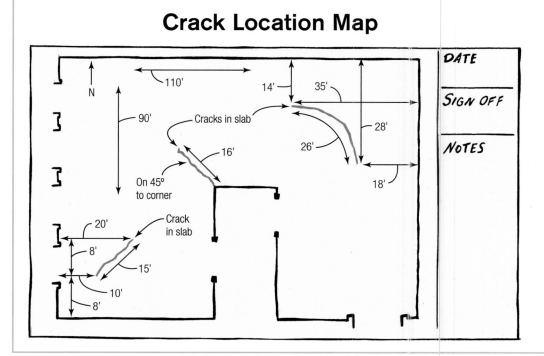

Crack Location Map

110'
N
90'
14' — 35'
Cracks in slab
28'
16'
26'
On 45° to corner
18'
20'
Crack in slab
8'
15'
10'
8'

DATE

SIGN OFF

NOTES

Figure 7-7. When the bandage method is specified, a crack location map should be made part of the specifications. Bandages are for large commercial spaces—not residential-size floor layouts.

membrane systems require a protective network of movement joints to remain intact and effective. This is true whether you install an irregular joint around a bandage system or an unobtrusive joint around the perimeter of a floor.

Curing. A final precaution involves curing. This applies to both sheet and liquid-applied systems. As a marketing feature, manufacturers of sheet systems say that tiling can proceed immediately after the sheet is installed. This is true when the sheet is installed with a contact-type cement, but there are caveats when the bonding adhesive is thinset mortar. When I use latex thinset mortar to bond the sheet membrane, I usually use NobleSeal TS and prefer to wait 48 hours or more before tiling. This ensures that the thinset mortar and the bond between the sheet and the setting bed are not disturbed or diminished. For best results, closely follow sheet membrane manufacturer's recommendations regarding adhesives above and below the sheet.

Is it possible to install tiles over a fresh membrane bonded with thinset? Yes, but unless the tiling work can begin as soon as the sheet is down, and proceed quickly and only during the thinset mortar's plastic stage, the disturbance to the membrane is often great enough to cause bonding problems with the membrane. For best results, wait a day or two (or whatever the manufacturer's instructions indicate) before installing the tiles and an additional day if the tiles are particularly heavy, ½-inch-thick tiles, for example.

The liquid component of some liquid-applied systems, as well the adhesive used to install a sheet membrane, may also be harmed if they are exposed to water or portland cement products before properly curing. All brands are different and have specific instructions regarding drying times and time between coats. Curing times are particularly critical with liquid-applied systems when they must be water tested, for example, when a liquid-applied system is used to construct a shower pan or when the installation will be submerged in water, as in a pool or fountain. If it is a pool or fountain you are tiling, keep in mind that some membrane materials were not designed for constant immersion in water.

Waterproofing Membranes

Waterproofing membranes are installed using the same methods, materials, and techniques as crack-isolation systems, except you must take greater care in detailing seams, corners, and terminations (where the membrane meets the top of a bathtub, for example) to reduce the incidence of leaks. Waterproofing membranes need to flex and yield to normal structural movement without disintegrating, and all must be installed in conjunction with a network of movement joints so that movement won't harm the membrane.

Reinforcing at turns and joints. Manufactured sheet systems contain an integral reinforcing fabric, while liquid-applied systems rely on reinforcing fabric installed on site, where it is embedded in liquid or paste. The membrane reinforcing must be continuous at upturns and at other changes in direction. Without a reinforcing fabric, cracks are likely to occur when movement tugs at the membrane. There are several systems on the market that do not require reinforcing fabric at upturns and movement joints, but until they have established a good track record over time, I prefer to stick with those systems that use reinforcing fabric for strength. Should new materials, such as crack-isolation or waterproofing thinset mortar, prove their worth, their use could substantially reduce

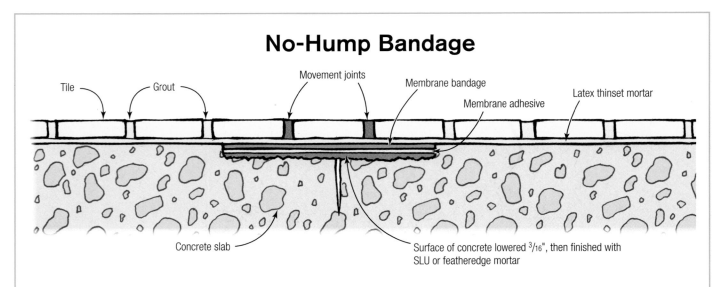

No-Hump Bandage

Tile · Grout · Movement joints · Membrane bandage · Membrane adhesive · Latex thinset mortar · Concrete slab · Surface of concrete lowered 3/16", then finished with SLU or featheredge mortar

Figure 7-8. For an optimal installation of a crack-isolation bandage with no unsightly hump, a small amount of concrete (equal to the thickness of the cured membrane) must be removed on either side of the crack using a bush hammer or shotblaster.

Movement and Termination Joints

To get the longest life from any type of membrane, I use special detailing where the membrane turns a corner (Figure 7-9) or terminates at a bathtub or shower receptor (Figure 7-10). Membranes that form a sharp crease at inside corners are frequently damaged from normal structural movement that is focused on the crease or the abrupt termination. To provide extra membrane to absorb the corner movement, I space the

Membrane Corner Details

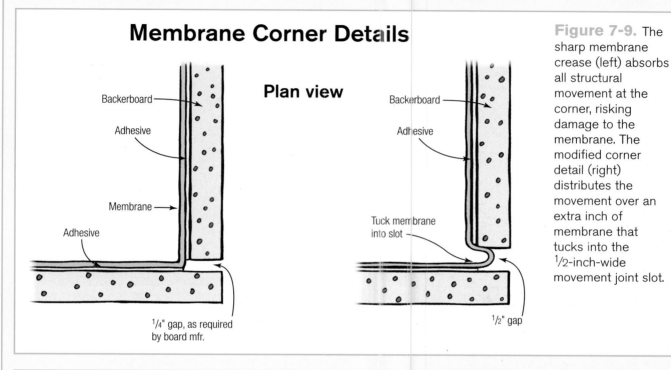

Figure 7-9. The sharp membrane crease (left) absorbs all structural movement at the corner, risking damage to the membrane. The modified corner detail (right) distributes the movement over an extra inch of membrane that tucks into the 1/2-inch-wide movement joint slot.

Membrane-to-Tub Detail

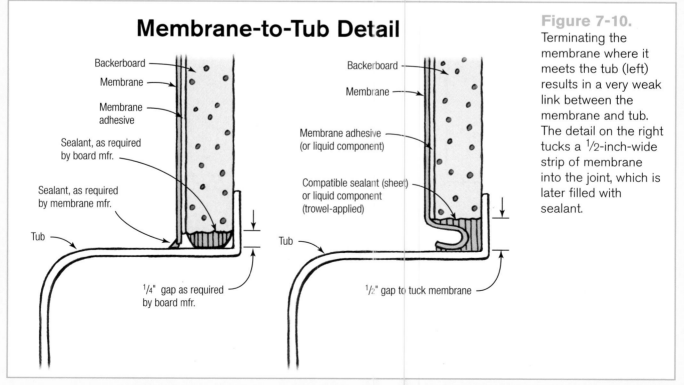

Figure 7-10. Terminating the membrane where it meets the tub (left) results in a very weak link between the membrane and tub. The detail on the right tucks a 1/2-inch-wide strip of membrane into the joint, which is later filled with sealant.

backerboards to leave a $^1/_2$x$^1/_2$-inch gap at the inside corners and a similar gap wherever a membrane meets a bathtub or shower receptor. This gives me enough room to tuck an extra amount of sheet membrane or reinforcing fabric (for a liquid-applied system) into the gap. I do not attempt to laminate the membrane to the gap, but rather give it a somewhat circular, loose-fitting bend that provides about 1 inch of extra membrane to absorb movement. This results in less stress on the membrane, protecting it from damage.

For maximum strength and durability with liquid-applied systems, corners and terminations should have three layers of liquid, two layers of fabric, and one or more

topping coats, or as specified by the membrane manufacturer's printed instructions (Figure 7-11). The same double-fabric flashing detail applies to floor/wall tile junctions, curbs, plumbing penetrations and openings, and wall/ceiling junctions. To be effective, though, all movement joints must continue from the structure through to the tiles. If the tiles are butted against the tub or receptor, normal structural movement

Figure 7-12. This section of fabric was cut wide enough to cover the side wall, plus overlap the flashing. The resulting two-ply corner, with an extra inch of fabric tucked into the corner, outperforms a membrane that is sharply creased in this critical movement joint.

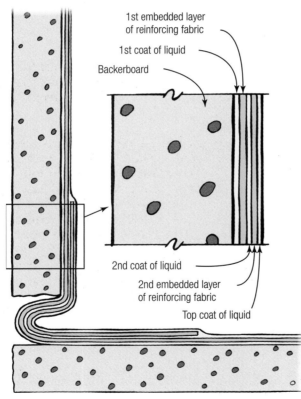

Liquid-Applied Membrane Corner Detail

1st embedded layer of reinforcing fabric

1st coat of liquid

Backerboard

2nd coat of liquid

2nd embedded layer of reinforcing fabric

Top coat of liquid

Plan view

Figure 7-11. For maximum performance, the author prefers to build corners and terminations with two laminations of fabric, three coats of laminating liquid, and one or two additional topping coats, as allowed by the manufacturer.

Figure 7-13. If left unfilled, this cavity would fill with moisture and become a maintenance problem. Filling the void with silicone locks out moisture, yet allows free movement within the joint.

will cause the membrane materials to shear off. Movement joints eliminate the leverage created by direct contact.

To waterproof corner joints, I begin by flashing the corner with 6-inch-wide fabric and overlap the flashing with the edge of a full-width section of fabric (Figure 7-12). As soon as the membrane has cured, I fill the resulting cavity with silicone sealant. If left open, this cavity would fill with moisture and be a potential source of mold or mildew. The sealant fills the void (Figure 7-13) but still allows for plenty of movement within the joint.

Where the membrane meets a tub or shower receptor, the backerboard setting bed should be held ½ inch away so there is enough room for the membrane to continue around the board's lower edge. It is essential that the fabric continue completely through the termination gap. I provide extra fabric and trim away excess after the liquid has cured. Figure 7-14 shows an obvious downside to working with liquid

Figure 7-14. The author uses a stiff paint brush to force the fabric into the movement joint. Excess fabric, where it meets the tub, should be trimmed after the liquid has cured.

systems over a tub. Drips and splashes are a part of the job and, for easiest cleanup, should be removed promptly.

installation costs.

Avoid membranes behind setting bed. In inspecting numerous failed membrane installations, it's clear to me that inside corners and where a membrane meets a bathtub or shower are problem areas for waterproofing, regardless of the setting bed. Part of this is due to the practice of locating a membrane behind the setting bed, as is traditionally done with 15-pound roofing felt or 4-mil plastic film. Originally conceived as light protection for the structure, these two materials —and the detailing they require—actually contribute to the problem, in my opinion. Each backerboard fastener punctures the membrane, unsealed overlapping seams promote capillary action, and locating these materials behind the backerboards means that, even if the membrane is working effectively, the setting bed can become waterlogged. This condition is conducive to the growth of mold and mildew, and aside from being unsanitary, it is a siphon waiting to pump moisture into the framing, causing structural damage. I do not recommend any membrane systems located on the structural side of the tile setting bed. In my opinion, only systems that are applied to the surface, and made specifically for use with tiles, should be used to waterproof wet-area tile installations.

Movement joints. One thing that will render any tile waterproofing membrane useless is a lack of movement joints. With no soft joints to absorb normal building movement, tiles and hard grout work against each other at inside corners and create enough leveraged movement to cause rips in the membrane. To my knowledge, all manufacturers of waterproofing, crack-isolation, and sound-reduction membranes for tiling specify movement joints as part of the installation (see "Movement and Termination Joints," above).

Sound-Reduction Membranes

Sound-reduction membrane (SRM) systems are available in sheet or liquid-applied form and are installed using the same basic techniques as waterproofing and crack-isolation systems, with each brand having its own material and installation instructions. When designed and installed properly, SRM systems reduce sound in two ways: by isolating tiles from direct contact with the substrate and by blocking airways through which sound waves can travel. In some ways, they are installed like waterproofing membranes: The membrane must be continuous, so lapping the membrane at any change in direction is a common installation feature. For example, a typical floor installation spec will call for an upturn of a specific height wherever the floor meets a wall surface.

Sound-reduction membranes require installation that is as patient and detailed as that of waterproofing membranes. In fact, the result of a poor installation is that this type of membrane system can leak sound. This is especially true of applications where the correct membrane was used, but a less expensive latex or silicone caulk was substituted for the system's acoustical sealant. The result is that sound transmitted through the air can leak through an otherwise waterproof joint. Different brands of SRM systems provide different levels of performance, installation ease, and cost. It is beyond the scope of this book to determine a system's performance levels. For more information on wall and floor sound-reduction systems, refer to TCA Handbook RW800 for detailed information.

Figure 7-15. The author uses a straightedge to flatten the sheet membrane against the cured liquid membrane used under the shower floor. The two beads of sealant bond effectively with both materials.

Basic Application Techniques.

I use a variety of membrane systems, both sheet and liquid applied, and find that each type is well suited for certain kinds of tile work. For example, I like using NobleSeal TS sheet membrane, but it is particularly suited for large open areas that lack detail. The greater the detail, the more I tend to use liquid-applied systems. When performance is critical, I tend to use a sheet type, but in some applications, the spec may call for both. Compatibility is always an issue, and whenever you attempt to join one system to another, contact both manufacturers for written approval. In Project 1 in Chapter 1, I was able to join the sheet membrane I prefer to a liquid system without any compatibility issues (Figure 7-15).

Surfaces receiving a membrane should be prepared as carefully as a setting bed is prepared for tile. The first step, after ensuring that the structure is rated for its intended use (and for the demands of stone tiles, if they are specified), is to prepare the setting bed to a ⅛-inch-in-10-foot standard for plumb, level, and flat or sloped (this tolerance needs to be tightened for large-format tiles). The next step is to ensure the set-

Warning: Follow Substrate Requirements

Caution! Membrane systems made for use with ceramic tile are meant to be used over a specific type of plywood recommended by the tile industry: APA-rated exterior grade plywood. OSB, particleboard, flake boards, lauan, and pressure-treated lumber should not be used as a substrate for either sheet or liquid-applied membrane systems.

When installing any type of membrane system over concrete, pay particular attention to the slab's moisture content and pH level, both of which can have a significant negative effect on the bond between the membrane and slab. Primers can sometimes be used to overcome a slab that is too wet, and some membrane components and adhesives can tolerate concrete that is outside the ideal pH zone. If the problem is caused by insufficient curing, however, the best thing to do is to give the concrete enough time to cure properly.

Unfortunately, problems with concrete are sometimes caused by excessive moisture trapped within the concrete by a surface-applied curing compound. In that case, the only way to release the trapped moisture is to remove the surface concrete affected by the compound through mechanical means such as bush hammering and shot blasting, allow the slab to dry out and lose the excess moisture, rehab the floor's surface, and install

membrane or tile. (Examples of rehabbing concrete surfaces for tiling can be found in Chapter 1, pages 24, and Chapter 6, page163).

The tile industry has been slow to adopt the floor covering industry's concerns about the negative effects of high moisture and pH imbalance in concrete slabs. An informal test I use to determine if more accurate testing is required involves a 12-inch square of household plastic wrap (such as Saran) taped to the clean surface of the concrete: If condensation appears on the plastic film within 72 hours, more precise testing is warranted. The most accurate way to test for excess moisture is with ASTM F-1869, more commonly known as the Anhydrous Calcium Chloride Test. For pH testing, I use a pH pencil. The cost of testing materials for both tests is under $10 (for more information, see Chapter 6, pages 157).

If the moisture content is high, the age of the concrete will determine what course of action to take. To reduce moisture content in new concrete that was not finished with a curing compound, simply allow the concrete more time to cure. For new or old concrete finished with a surface-applied curing compound, only mechanical removal of that portion of the concrete affected by the curing compound—plus time for the excess moisture to evaporate—will release the moisture.

ting bed materials have cured. Covering uncured materials with a membrane may significantly delay or permanently suspend curing. All surfaces receiving a membrane must be clean and dust free (see "Warning: Follow Substrate Requirements," above).

Up to this point, surface preparation for either type of system is the same. As a residential or light-commercial installer, I need to be fluent with both systems and with the variety of sheets, liquids, fabrics, accessories, and sealants that are part of each system's materials list. Although it takes extra time up front, careful preparation and staging of sheets and fabric before applying any laminating adhesives or liquids to the setting bed actually save time in the long run. I use different techniques and methods for each system and for floor, wall, and countertop installations. Many application details can be found in the projects in Chapters 1 through 4, but the basic methods I use are found here, beginning with liquid systems.

How to Install Liquid Membrane Systems

In this book, *liquid membrane systems* refers to applications that use gels, ready-to-use liquids, and site-mixed pastes used to embed a reinforcing fabric. Fabrics are always water resistant and may be either woven or

nonwoven. I use different methods for floors, walls, and countertops, but the goals are always the same. Make sure that:

- the base coat of liquid is wet and tacky enough for instant transfer to the fabric

- the base coat is thick enough to fully bleed through the fabric

- all fabric overlaps are minimum 2 inches

- all upturns and corners are reinforced with two layers of fabric and three layers of liquid

Where to begin applying and how far to extend the membrane depends on the application. For example, if I am tiling a floor in a wet area, even with a baseboard other than tile, I don't consider the floor membrane complete without continuing it up the wall a suitable amount to protect the entire structure. Sometimes I may continue the wall membrane down onto the floor to provide the same level of protection (as shown in Figure 7-22, page 204). When waterproofing bathroom walls, I use special detailing at inside corners and where the membrane terminates against a tub or other such fixture to reduce stress on liquid systems (see "Movement

Figure 7-16. The author uses a small-diameter paint roller (A) or paint brush (B) to spread some types of liquid membrane. With thicker gels, a $1/8$-inch V-notch trowel helps spread an even layer (C). He generally uses the same tool to spread the liquid component and embed the reinforcing fabric (D).

And Termination Joints," page 197).

When I waterproof a bathroom with tiled walls and floor (and countertop), I arrange the work so that the membrane is continuous, even though I may install only a portion of the overall system. For example, when tiling both walls and floors, I generally install the wall portion of the membrane first, lap it 3 to 6 inches onto the floor, and hold off installing the floor portion until after all the wall (and cove) tiles have been installed. At that point, I tie into the wall downturns with more fabric and liquid to complete the membrane, and after it cures, I cover it with tile.

Depending on the viscosity of the liquid and the complexity and size of the installation, I may use a paint roller, a paint brush, or a notched trowel to apply the base coat of liquid and generally use the same tool to embed the fabric (Figure 7-16).

Flashing First

Some liquid systems call for two layers of fabric in the corners and at upturns and downturns. This may be accomplished by overlapping sections of fabric, using factory-cut flashing, or both. The first step is to lay out the location of the membrane and cut all the fabric needed for the installation (Figure 7-17). To install flashing, I begin by coating the affected area with liquid. Working quickly, I position the fabric, use a brush

Figure 7-17. To save steps and time, the author cuts all fabric sections to size before spreading any liquid.

Figure 7-18. After coating the inside corner with liquid, the author carefully positions the flashing strip (A). He uses a stiff brush to force the fabric into the corner (B) and a paint roller to efficiently embed the material (C). Where the flashing occasionally buckles, the author slits through the fabric to re-flatten it (D).

to help force it into the corner, and a paint roller to embed the fabric into the liquid (Figure 7-18). Sometimes flashing will buckle as I work it into the corner, and when this happens, I slit through the fabric and re-flatten it. When installing flashing, I cover all corners and upturns before applying full-width fabric.

Covering Walls

When installing full-width fabric sections, I begin spreading liquid at the top and work down. To ensure the fabric goes where I want it to, I stake it in place with a couple of staples located 18 to 24 inches below the top of the fabric, apply the liquid, and press the fabric into the liquid (Figure 7-19). Then I add more liquid, as needed, to ensure the fabric is completely wetted and encapsulated by the liquid. I begin the section chest high, where it is easiest to work, then embed the fabric above that. With the upper section embedded, I use my fingers to work the fabric into the corner and a brush to embed it in liquid (Figure 7-20).

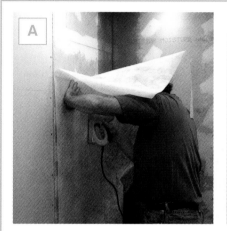

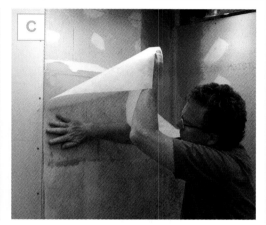

Figure 7-19. To simplify wall installations, the author temporarily staples the fabric into position (A). Next, he spreads liquid with a roller to the upper portion of the wall (B) and uses his hands to gently lay the fabric into the liquid (C).

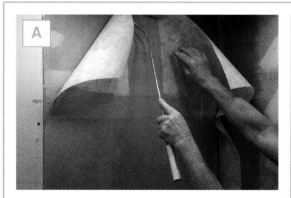

Figure 7-20. With a chest-high band of fabric embedded, the author works to embed the top section (A). He uses his fingers and a stiff brush to ease the fabric into the corner (B). To complete the lower section, he rolls up the loose fabric and stakes it temporarily with staples, then works down the wall, spreading liquid and embedding fabric (C).

To finish the wall, I roll up and stake the lower end of the fabric, and then work downward until the entire wall is covered.

Plumbing and Other Wall Penetrations

Holes made for plumbing and other penetrations need special attention since the edge of the hole or opening must be as waterproof as the surface of the wall, floor, or ceiling. For best results, openings should be detailed as the work proceeds and while the liquid around the hole's inner curved edge is still wet. Sometimes, when there is an obstruction, such as a mixing valve within an opening, I slit through the fabric roughly so that it sits flat around the opening. To finish this opening, first I make a half dozen slits across the opening, add liquid to the inside of the opening if it has skinned over, and then fold the fabric tabs over the edge and into the liquid (Figure 7-21).

Finishing the Lower Edge

When covering a wall with liquid membrane, there are two ways to finish the lower wall. If the wall installation is a tub surround or shower walls over a shower receptor, I use a termination joint described in "Movement and Termination Joints" (page 197) to join the membrane to the tub or receptor. I also use narrow strips of fabric to protect the tub or receptor doglegs. If the wall installation joins with a tile floor, I always lap the wall membrane 3 to 6 inches onto the floor (Figure 7-22). This allows me to work on the walls without having to worry about damaging the floor membrane. After the wall tiles are installed, I unmask the down lap and use more liquid and fabric to extend the membrane over the floor.

Floor Installations

Because gravity works with you, liquid membrane systems are easier to install on floors than on walls and ceilings. Junctions with walls are simplified by the fact that I install the wall membrane first with 3 to 6 inch downturns. The corner detail is usually simple and straightforward, requiring one layer of fabric to lap over the downturn and one or two layers of liquid.

Countertops

Without proper waterproofing and good tile installation practices, a tile countertop can be a maintenance and sanitation problem. With a liquid membrane system, I cut the fabric long enough to cover the back-

Figure 7-21. At openings for plumbing, the author slits through the fabric, leaving tabs to fold down over the edge. For maximum protection, he brushes liquid onto the fabric tabs and their mating surface and presses the tabs into place.

Figure 7-22. The author embeds a narrow strip of fabric under the last tile course next to the tub (above). In cases where the floor will also be tiled, he extends fabric strips to overlap the floor by 4 inches (right).

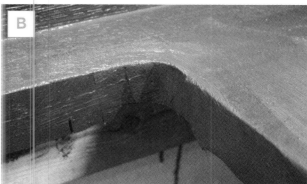

Figure 7-23. To ensure continuous waterproofing, the author uses a single section of fabric to cover the splash, top, and edges of the counter (A), including the edges of cutouts (B). Once the fabric is embedded, a sharp knife is used to cut off the excess at the apron and sink openings (C).

splash, the top, and the apron edge with a single piece of fabric. At stove and sink cut-outs, I trim the fabric at the opening, but leave enough material to lap down and completely cover the edge (Figure 7-23). Cut-out and apron edges are easier to complete if there is enough fabric to grab onto. So I cut fabric that is a few inches wider than what is required to cover the edge and cut off the excess once the fabric section is embedded and the liquid hardens.

Ceilings

Ceilings are the most difficult, and since I don't need to waterproof my head, I prefer to use a gel, which is applied with a trowel and tends to drip far less than some liquids. A hard hat with visor is required on commercial installations but is sensible for any ceiling project. In addition, I make sure all fabric sections are pre-cut and ready. To keep my clothes from getting permanently fouled with membrane, I cut three holes in the bottom of a large garbage bag, and wear it as a throw-away shirt.

More important than a clean shirt is the cohesive strength of a membrane, which will determine how much load it can safely carry in the ceiling area. Check your brand's application information to see if there are any limitations or prohibitions against direct ceiling applications. Some manufacturers instruct installers to place the membrane behind a cement backerboard. If this is the case, I pre-drill the backer-

Figure 7-24. The author applies a final topping coat of gel. When finished, this shower membrane will have three coats of gel, with the reinforcing fabric doubled at seams and upturns.

board, plot fastener locations on the ceiling, and shoot a quarter-sized dollop of sealant on each mark to help seal around the screw fasteners. Don't use nails to install backerboard ceilings!

Finishing the Membrane

While in the same general class, all liquid membrane systems have their own application and installation instructions that must be followed. Depending on the brand and the application, liquid systems may require one, two, or more coats of liquid. For example, one brand may specify only one coat of liquid for a wall installation, two coats where the membrane is protecting a wet-area floor, and three or more coats for a shower pan liner. For the shower floor application shown in Figure 7-24, for example, I follow the manufacturer's spec of two coats of gel applied one hour apart. For an upgrade, I wait four hours (manufacturer's instructions) and give the entire shower membrane a third coat of liquid.

Gauges to determine the wet-film thickness are often taped to the lids of liquid systems. For spreading gels, I rely on a notched trowel to lay down the right amount. Applying the right amount is critical to meeting warranty and spec requirements. One way to help myself, an inspector, or a building owner to further determine the thickness of each individual layer as well as the aggregate thickness of the application is to apply liquid waterproofing materials to a 3x3 section of scrap backerboard—layer for layer—as the full-size installation is being worked. By stepping back the layers along the edge of the sample, a micrometer or caliper can be used to measure the system's layers. On some commercial applications, this kind of measuring may be a part of the installation spec.

Figure 7-25. Starting with the accessory pieces, the author works the inside corner (left) and outside corner pieces (right) into the contact cement with his fingers.

Figure 7-26. To speed up sheet membrane installation, the author cuts, dry-fits, and folds all sections before applying adhesive. First, he positions the cut sheet (A), secures the back of the sheet with weighted buckets, and lifts it out of the way (B). He folds the loose end back, weighing it down with tiles (C) while he prepares to spread adhesive.

How to Install Sheet Membrane Systems

Sheet membrane systems available for tiling are made from a variety of materials. Some are made of polyvinyl chloride (PVC), while others have a PVC core. The sheet membrane used for this section is the brand I prefer, NobleSeal TS (NSTS), is made from chlorinated polyethylene (CPE). Like other sheet membranes, both sides of NSTS are covered with a reinforcing fabric that anchors the sheet to a substrate and allows tiles to be installed directly on the installed sheet.

As with other tile installation materials, each brand has its own application limitations and installation instructions that must be followed (in particular, the type of adhesive used to install the sheet and install tiles over the sheet), but the information below should help you plan and execute a solid sheet membrane installation.

Surface Prep

As with liquid systems, no work should begin until the setting bed surface meets all the surface prep requirements for flatness and surface texture. For tiles up to 8 inches (long or wide), the setting bed should be flat to within ¼ inch in 10 feet and have a smooth, but

Figure 7-27. Once the contact cement becomes tacky, the author unfolds the loose end of the membrane (left) and laminates the sheet with a straightedge (right).

Figure 7-28. With the front of the sheet laminated, the author pulls the back portion forward and weights it down while he spreads contact cement on the rear portion of the floor (left). When the cement is tacky, he carefully eases the remainder of the sheet into position and laminates it to the floor (right).

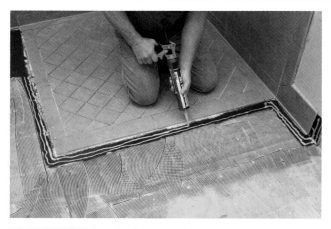

Figure 7-29. For a flat and leakproof seam in the sheet membrane, the author lays down two beads of manufacturer-supplied sealant (top) and flattens the seam with a straightedge. Sealant squeeze out indicates the seam is closed (bottom).

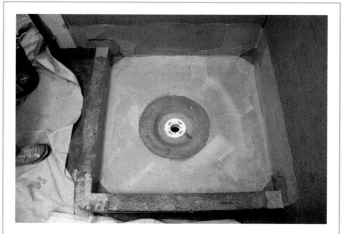

Figure 7-30. To begin this shower floor and curb installation, the author installs a drain flashing (at center in photo), four inside corners (the orange pieces), and five dam corners (two overlapping at each end of the curb and another for the curb's inside corner) before installing the sheet.

granular, finish.

Larger tiles require a flatter setting bed. For 24-inch tiles, I prefer a setting bed tolerance of flat to within $\frac{1}{16}$ inch in 10 feet. Manufacturers of most sheet membranes require the $\frac{1}{4}$-inch-in-10-feet tolerance, which is also the industry's minimum standard.

When working over a wood structure, I prefer to install a sheet membrane over a double layer of $\frac{3}{4}$-inch AC exterior plywood. Two layers of $\frac{3}{4}$ plywood over minimum 2x10 joists on 16-inch centers provides the level of stiffness required for ceramic tile and most stone tiles. I prefer to use AC plywood because CC grade, the industry minimum standard, is usually hard to find and often riddled with interior voids. If height is an issue, I may use $\frac{3}{4}$-inch subflooring and $\frac{5}{8}$-inch underlayment, but generally, I stay away from a thinner underlayment layer because of flexing. One critical step when installing over plywood is to ensure all fastener heads are flush or slightly below the surface.

Concrete can be an incredibly stable base for membrane and tile, but excess moisture or extreme pH levels can harm any membrane system. So when tiling over fresh concrete, I test for both moisture levels and pH. Whenever I inspect a concrete slab prior to submitting a bid proposal, I sprinkle drops of water on at least half a dozen sections of the floor to see if it is readily absorbed. If not, I know a curing compound or other bond breaker has been used and that extra surface prep steps are required. Chapter 8 provides information on how to test for excess moisture, pH levels, and the presence of curing compounds.

To help demonstrate the techniques and methods I use, photos in this section were taken from three different installations: a double-layer plywood floor with a three-room layout, a stall shower with cement backerboard walls, and a concrete floor. The basic techniques used to complete these installations should enable you to cover practically any surface with a sheet membrane. For information on how to use these techniques to construct a thinbed shower pan, refer to Project 3 in Chapter 3.

Layout

Because liquid systems are more or less continuous, I usually rely on perimeter layout lines only. However, since sheet membranes extend their coverage by 2-inch overlapping seams, I pay more attention to how the sheet will flow across a floor, wall, or countertop than I do when I am working with the fabric from a liquid system.

Flashing Up or Down?

When working with sheet membrane systems, I use a strategy that is very different from the one I use for liquid systems. For instance, while I delay installing the floor portion of a liquid membrane for a tile bathroom where both floors and walls will be tiled, I generally install 100% of a sheet membrane installation before beginning to tile. The reason? I prefer to have the wall portion of the membrane lap over the floor section for an extra measure of protection when waterproofing is required.

Floor Installations

The sheet membrane featured in this section, Nobleseal TS, can be laminated to a setting bed surface with either latex thinset mortar or a proprietary contact-type cement (NobleBond EXT). I prefer to use the contact cement because I can begin tiling as soon as the membrane is in place. I also prefer contact cement because it is stickier than thinset mortar. To apply an even amount of the cement, I spread it with a ⅛-inch V-notch trowel. The sheet measures 5 feet wide and comes in 100-foot rolls. Accessory pieces (dam and inside corners) are available to ensure complete waterproofing.

Figure 7-31. With the right side laminated and staked out of the way, the author spreads contact cement over the rest of the wall. As soon as the cement is tacky, he applies beads of sealant around the showerhead and valve flashing and to the lower seaming edge (left), and laminates the rest of the sheet. Any staple or nail holes are sealed with small patches secured with beads of sealant (right).

Figure 7-32. To heat form a small hole in the CPE patch, the author uses a pipe with a rounded end and a cardboard mask (A) to direct the heat provided by a 300-watt light bulb (B). After a minute or so of heating, the author presses the CPE patch over the end of the pipe. In a few seconds, the patch is cool enough to remove and retain its shape (C).

On any installation requiring dams or inside corners, I generally install the accessory pieces first, using contact cement to install them (Figure 7-25). To speed up the installation process, I cut, fold, dry-fit, and stage all the sheet sections needed to complete an installation before I spread any adhesive. The first step involves positioning the sheet. With this done, I weigh down the back of the sheet, drape the front part of the sheet out of the way, and use more weight to secure the loose end while I spread contact cement (Figure 7-26). After waiting 10 to 20 minutes for the contact cement to become tacky, I carefully unfurl the loose end over the adhesive and laminate it to the floor with a short straightedge (Figure 7-27). A trowel or a heavy floor roller can also be used for this task.

Once the front of the sheet has been laminated, I pull the back portion forward and weigh it down while I spread contact cement on the rear portion of the floor. When the cement is tacky, I carefully ease the remainder of the sheet into position and laminate it to the floor (Figure 7-28). When more than one section of this sheet is required, I use the system's sealant to join the two sheets. For both waterproofing and crack isolation, the seam should be leakproof as well as sit flat against the surface. To do this, I follow the manufacturer's instructions and lay down two $\frac{1}{8}$-inch beads of sealant, use a short straightedge to flatten the seam, and rely on a small amount of sealant squeeze-out to tell me that the seam is closed (Figure 7-29).

When an installation calls for this system's accessory pieces (inside and dam corners), I install them first,

before tackling the sheet sections, with the contact cement. To simplify this task, I use a small notched hand spreader to lay down the contact cement and press each piece into position. Wherever two (or more) accessories overlap, I use sealant, instead of contact cement, to keep the seams waterproof. Figure 7-30 illustrates how this system's three accessory pieces are used.

Wall Installations

Walls require the same thinset mortar or contact cement to laminate the sheet. To overcome gravity and assure correct positioning, I cut the sheet to size and position it against the wall, using staples to temporarily hold it in place. Next I fold back one half of the sheet, spread contact cement, and laminate the first half with a short straightedge or hand roller. Then, I pull back the second half, apply contact cement (and sealant, if needed) and finish laminating the sheet (Figure 7-31). After the installation is finished, I use 2-inch-diameter patches, made from scrap sheet and sealed with beads of sealant, to close off the staple holes. Once laminated with contact cement, the sheet is fully capable of supporting tiles, but tiling should wait until any sealant used to close seams or accessories has cured at least 24 hours.

Plumbing and Other Wall Penetrations

With liquid systems, I waterproof the edges of all wall and floor openings (called penetrations in the trade) by cutting tabs and folding them into the liquid. When

Figure 7-33. A loose-fitting mold made from two pieces of scrap plywood is used to focus heat on the center of the membrane patch (A). Once the CPE is soft, the author presses the plug against the patch (B) until the piece has cooled. The accessory patch is then adhered to the setting bed with contact cement (C).

working with my favorite sheet membrane, I heat form patches on site for an easier and cleaner installation. (The patch for the valve opening is visible in Figure 7-31). Heat forming is not possible with asphalt or PVC sheet materials, but with a little work to produce simple forming molds, CPE materials like NobleSeal TS or Chloraloy 240 can easily be formed. I prefer to use Chloraloy 240 stock for this purpose because it is thicker (40 mils) than NobleSeal TS.

For smaller openings, such as a showerhead penetration, I use a short length of plastic pipe (slightly smaller in diameter than the opening) as a mold. I begin with a 6-inch diameter piece of Chloraloy 240, make a 1/2-inch diameter hole at the center, and mask it with scrap cardboard so only the affected area is heated. Heat is applied with a high wattage light bulb for a minute or so until the CPE is soft, and working quickly, I press the CPE down over the pipe. Usually, in less than 15 seconds the patch will cool enough to retain its new shape (Figure 7-32).

Larger openings require the use of a mold made from two pieces of scrap plywood, an appropriately sized cardboard shield, and the application of some heat. Once the CPE patch is soft, I press the plywood plug against the patch and into the female portion of the mold and hold it until the patch cools (Figure 7-33).

Countertops

The 5-foot width of NobleSeal TS enables me to waterproof and crack isolate most countertops with a single piece of sheet that stretches from the top of the backsplash, across the top, and down over the apron edge. When applying a liquid-applied membrane to a countertop, I cut reinforcing fabric wide enough to cover the apron, the top, and at least a portion of the backsplash (if the entire backsplash area will be tiled). To ensure positive waterproofing protection, I use the system's compatible sealant to join the sink rim to the membrane (see Figure 4-14C, page 113).

Ceilings

NobleSeal TS instructions call for installation of the membrane behind ceiling backerboards. To do this, I cut, fold, and fabricate a section of sheet that resembles a shower pan and whose downturned sections lap over the wall membrane. I secure the membrane with a few staples, cover the staples with a small amount of sealant, pre-drill the backerboard(s), and shoot dabs of sealant over each fastener hole (on the back of the board).

Joining a Sheet Membrane to a Liquid Membrane

It is not very common, but when a spec calls for a sheet and a liquid membrane on the same installation, the first step is to ensure that both systems are compatible. In the following example, I join a liquid applied system (Bonsal B-6000, the brown coating in

Figure 7-15 on page 200) with a sheet membrane (NobleSeal TS) using beads of NobleSealant 150, which is compatible with both systems. (I confirmed compatibility by contacting both manufacturers, the only way to be certain.)

Note: The liquid membrane must be fully cured before joining to the sheet membrane. To do this, I first apply contact cement to the setting bed surface. When the cement is tacky, I quickly apply a double bead of the sealant along the edge of the cured liquid membrane and the seaming edge of the previous section of membrane (Figure 7-34). Then I laminate the sheet into the contact cement and sealant.

Figure 7-34. The author spreads contact cement for the sheet membrane, leaving uncovered the 2-inch-wide edge of the cured liquid membrane used in the shower area (top). Just before the contact cement becomes tacky, he quickly shoots two beads of compatible sealant on the uncovered strip to seal the final piece of sheet membrane to the shower floor membrane (bottom).

NOTES

Chapter 8
MOVEMENT JOINTS

ovement joints are one of the most overlooked components of tile installations.
Leaving them out affects a tile installation's
looks, performance, and longevity. In addition, a lack
of movement joints invalidates the warranty of most
tiles, installation materials, and membrane systems.

What Is a Movement Joint?

A movement joint is an intentional interruption
between two hard surfaces that

- compensates for differences in expansion and
  contraction of building materials, and

- allows normal building movement to occur without causing damage to other parts of the building.

Movement joints are required for all dry- or wet-area
tile installations, and they are an essential component
of all tile membrane installations—especially crack
isolation systems. The visible part of a tile movement
joint is nothing more than a grout joint that has been

Figure 8-1. Look closely and you will see a faint
difference in color between the grout and the sanded
caulk used to create the movement joint where the
tiles meet the maple strip floor.

filled with an elastomeric caulk or sealant instead of
hard grout (Figure 8-1). Movement joints are required
on floor, wall, countertop, ceiling, and stair installations. Industry standards may be found under EJ171
in the TCA Handbook and under 108.1, 3.7 in the
ANSI A108 Handbook.

Movement joints need to be able to stretch and
compress in response to normal building movement.
Exterior tile installations, which are exposed to an
extreme range of temperatures, need wider and more
frequent movement joints than do interior installations. Interior tile work is located in a controlled environment with a much narrower range of high and low
temperatures. However, where interior tile work is
exposed to sunlight through windows and doors, the
movement joints must follow the TCA Handbook
requirements for exterior tile work.

On both wet- and dry-area tile installations, movement joints are needed to prevent cracks in grout
joints and to reduce the chance that normal building
movement will damage tiles or shear them off the
surface. In wet areas, using hard grout where movement joints belong results in cracked grout that will
allow water to penetrate into the setting bed, promot-
ing mold and mildew growth, maintenance problems,
and even structural damage.

A movement joint has two basic components: an
empty slot and soft material to fill it. For the installer,
the first task is to ensure that adequate space is left for
the required slots. Once that is done, and the tiles
installed and grouted, the next task is to fill the open
slot with a resilient material. There are two ways to
produce a movement joint. One method is to install
manufactured movement joints. The other is to create
the necessary slots during construction and fill them
with an appropriate sealant. Standard specifications
for movement joint sealants may be found in ASTM
C920 (www.astm.org) and are referenced in EJ171 in
the TCA Handbook.

Manufactured Movement Joints

Manufactured floor movement joints have a place on
large-scale commercial floors, but they can be cumber-

some in the smaller confines of residential work. Manufactured movement joints also are available for wall installations and are used to create a movement joint between two neighboring walls or between the walls and floor—especially important on wet-area installations.

Manufactured joints are extruded from plastic, aluminum, brass, and stainless steel. The anchor flanges on one or both sides of the joint are punched to key into the tile bond coat and have to be installed just ahead of the tiles. Manufactured joints can be effective, but they have two weak points created by the housing and anchor-flange extrusions. The first weak point is where the edges of the tiles abut the joint housing, an area normally supported by grout. When using a manufactured joint strip, it is important that the entire leading edge of each tile be in direct contact with the abutting edge of the strip. If the tiles do not have a straight edge, gaps must be filled with grout or sealant.

The other weak point is created where the anchor flanges of the joint are embedded in thinset mortar. Unless an adequate amount of thinset is placed underneath the manufactured joint and tile, the tiles are likely to crack along or near the edge of the embedded joint flange (Figure 8-2). As required by industry standards, there must be at least $3/32$ inch of thinset mortar between the setting bed surface and the bottom of the flange and another $3/32$ inch of thinset between the top of the manufactured joint flange and the bottom of the tile. To prevent creating a bump in the tiles bordering the movement joint, a thicker layer of medium-bed

thinset is usually required for the surrounding tiles. If you plan to install manufactured movement joints, make sure they are deep enough to accommodate the tile and the required thinset mortar.

One final consideration is that manufactured movement joints that are damaged cannot be removed and replaced without removing the tiles located on either side of the joint. With tile designs and colors always changing, obtaining suitable replacements for the tiles could be a problem, not to mention the significant expense if repairs are needed.

Movement Joints Over Concrete Slabs

Depending on the type of construction, a movement joint may need to go beyond the tile and extend into the setting bed, underlayment, or even deeper. For example, if tiles are installed over a concrete slab that was built with movement joints, those joints must extend upwards and be incorporated into the tile installation. This can be done either by laying out the tiles so that grout joints will fall directly above existing slab joints or by cutting any tiles that fall over the slab joints and leaving a space for a movement joint. If a mortar bed or self-leveling compound is placed over the slab, the movement joint must continue through these materials, too.

In addition to movement joints within the field of a slab, a tile floor also will need movement joints between the floor and the surrounding walls. Movement joints also are recommended at thresholds on multi-room installations.

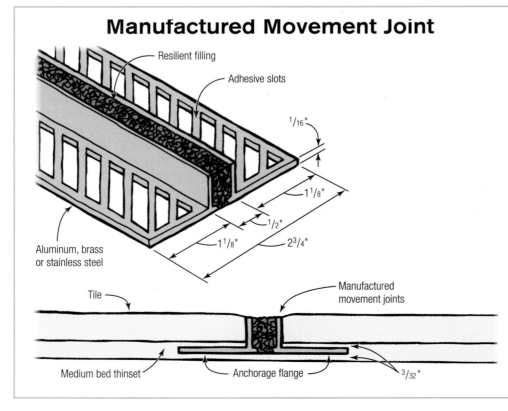

Manufactured Movement Joint

Resilient filling
Adhesive slots
$1/16$"
$1/8$"
$1/2$"
$1/8$"
$2^3/4$"
Aluminum, brass or stainless steel

Tile
Manufactured movement joints
Medium bed thinset
Anchorage flange
$3/32$"

Figure 8-2. Manufactured movement joints for floors and walls are composed of punched metal or plastic strips extruded with flanges for anchoring under tiles and a resilient center that absorbs motion (top). If too little tile adhesive is used, it will thin out at the anchor flange, reduce tile support near the joint, and may cause tiles to crack.

Concrete slabs are often partially cut to create control joints. If this is part of the project specifications, the contractor cutting the control joints and the tile installation contractor should agree—before the joints are cut—on the right locations. When a waterproofing membrane is specified for a concrete slab cut with control joints, the membrane should not bridge over the control joints, but rather be tucked into the control joint (Figure 8-3). This reduces the stresses on the membrane.

> **Note:** Some membrane systems allow the movement joints for tile to be offset from control joints, but not all do. Refer to each brand's instructions.

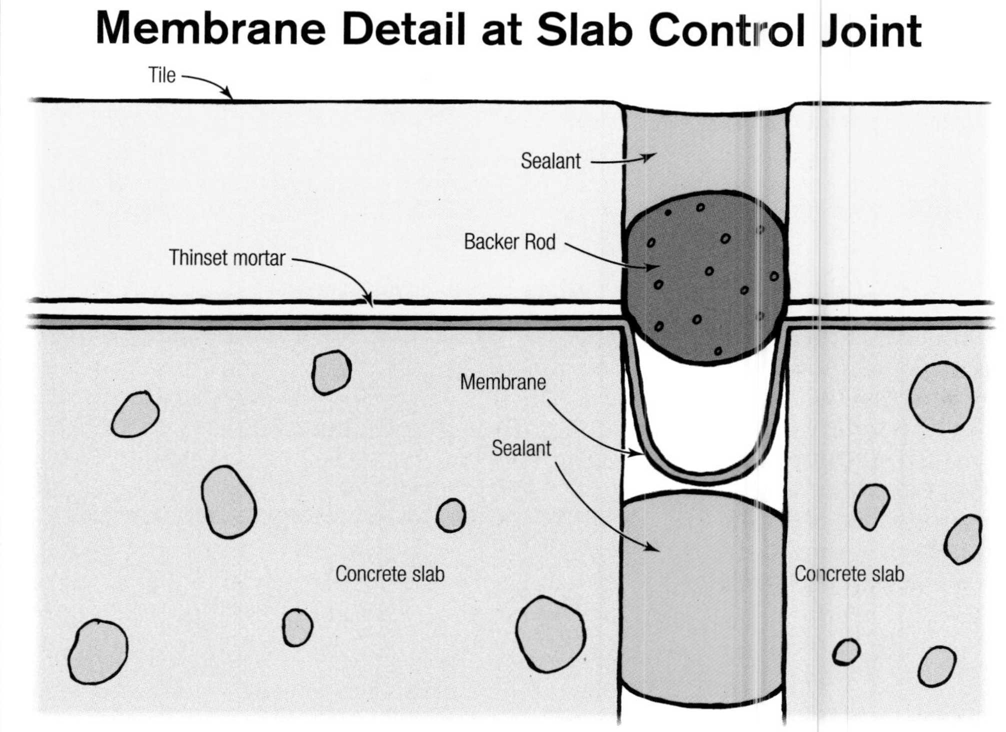

Membrane Detail at Slab Control Joint

Tile

Sealant

Backer Rod

Thinset mortar

Membrane

Sealant

Concrete slab

Concrete slab

Figure 8-3. If a waterproofing membrane is used over control joints cut in a concrete slab, the membrane should tuck into the control joint to reduce stress on the membrane.

Movement Joint at Change of Setting Bed

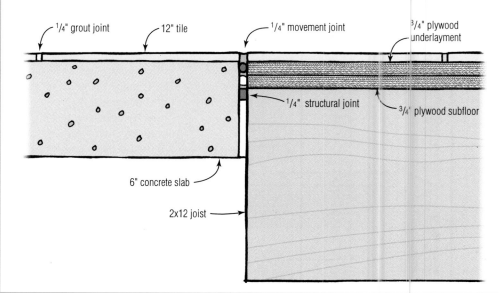

1/4" grout joint

12" tile

1/4" movement joint

3/4" plywood underlayment

1/4" structural joint

3/4" plywood subfloor

6" concrete slab

2x12 joist

Figure 8-4. A movement joint is required where wood construction meets a concrete slab and at other transitions between different setting bed materials.

Movement Joints Over Wood Construction

In wood framed floors, the most common movement joints are around floor perimeters. Other typical locations for movement joints are at changes of plane, wherever setting-bed materials change (Figure 8-4), and within the field of large floors or floors exposed to direct sunlight. However, such field movement joints (those found in the center of a floor or wall) are rarely seen in residential projects. Nevertheless, movement joints are still required when tiles are installed over wood-framed floors, walls, and ceilings. Whether the setting bed is plywood, backerboard, or self-leveling underlayment, movement joints on wood construction must begin at the underlayment level and continue through to the tiles (Figure 8-5).

Movement Joints on Ceilings and Countertops

Movement occurs everywhere in a modern house, so movement joints are required on all surfaces, including ceilings and countertops. Ceiling tiles, unless they are isolated from normal building movement, risk shearing and falling without movement joints. Although you needn't worry about tiles falling from a countertop, a lack of movement joints will cause grout to crack and allow water to penetrate into the base of the counter or into the structure supporting the cabinets and countertop. This is especially true behind the faucet, at the joint between the countertop and backsplash (see Figure 8-6).

Industrial Versus Commercial Versus Residential

Many installers believe that movement joints are required only on industrial and commercial installations. However, the laws of physics operate every-where, and most tile installation material warranties are null and void if movement joints are not built into the installation. Movement joints are especially important in wet areas. For example, if the movement joint between a tub and the first row of tiles is filled with grout instead of an elastomeric sealant, a crack may appear even before the tub surround is put into use.

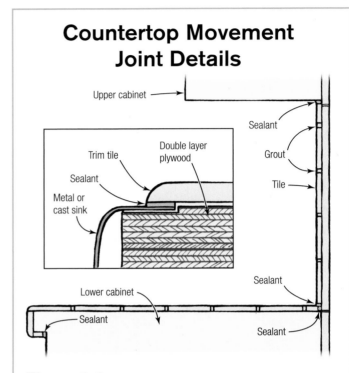

Countertop Movement Joint Details

Upper cabinet

Sealant

Grout

Tile

Trim tile

Double layer plywood

Sealant

Metal or cast sink

Lower cabinet

Sealant

Sealant

Sealant

Figure 8-6. The joint between the countertop tiles and backsplash is notorious for cracking, allowing water absorption to create unsanitary conditions. Instead of grout, the joint needs to be filled with a resilient caulk or sealant.

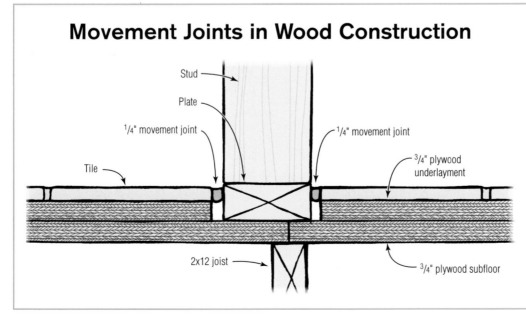

Movement Joints in Wood Construction

Stud

Plate

1/4" movement joint

1/4" movement joint

3/4" plywood underlayment

Tile

2x12 joist

3/4" plywood subfloor

Figure 8-5. To prevent normal building movement from damaging tiles, all movement joints must begin at the underlayment level. Specifically in this case, the gap between the underlayment and the immovable wall framing should be the same width as the gap between the tile and the wall framing.

Typical Locations for Movement Joints

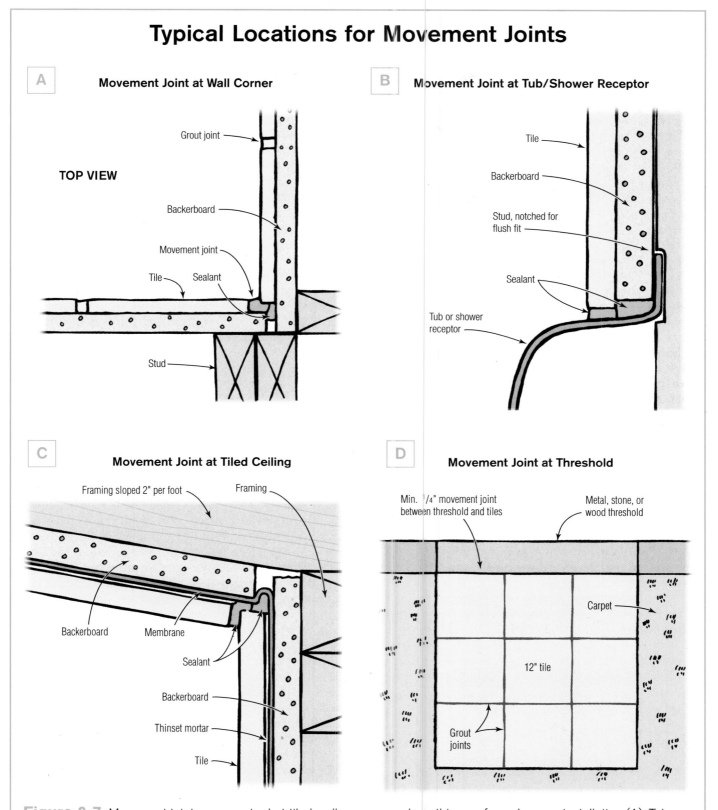

A   Movement Joint at Wall Corner

TOP VIEW

- Grout joint
- Backerboard
- Movement joint
- Tile
- Sealant
- Stud

B   Movement Joint at Tub/Shower Receptor

- Tile
- Backerboard
- Stud, notched for flush fit
- Sealant
- Tub or shower receptor

C   Movement Joint at Tiled Ceiling

- Framing sloped 2" per foot
- Framing
- Backerboard
- Membrane
- Sealant
- Backerboard
- Thinset mortar
- Tile

D   Movement Joint at Threshold

- Min. 1/4" movement joint between threshold and tiles
- Metal, stone, or wood threshold
- Carpet
- 12" tile
- Grout joints

Figure 8-7. Movement joints are required at tiled wall corners, such as this one for a dry-area installation (A). Tub surrounds and shower stalls built over receptors have similar requirements because of the different rates of expansion and contraction (B). To prevent normal building movement from shearing them off, ceiling tiles need to be isolated from surrounding hard surfaces with movement joints (C). Even if a tiled entry is surrounded by carpet, a movement joint is required between the tiles and the threshold, especially in wet climates (D).

With a crack between the tub and tiles, there is nothing to prevent moisture penetration into the setting bed or deeper into the structure (Figure 8-7B).

Where to Locate Movement Joints

All tile installations require movement joints. Ideally, movement joints should be located in areas where movement is likely to be concentrated. The joint separating a tub and tile is a typical location because the two materials expand and contract at such different rates. Other typical locations for movement joints are the joints

- between floor and wall tiles
- between wall and ceiling tiles
- between countertop and backsplash tiles
- at the corner between two tiled walls
- where entry-hall tiles meet the entry-door threshold

I mention these examples because they are the most visible locations in residential work, but they certainly make up only a portion of the complete list found under TCA Handbook EJ-171:

- wherever tiles abut hard surfaces, such as perimeter walls, curbs, risers, columns, ceilings, pipes or other plumbing penetrations
- wherever changes occur in backing materials
- over existing expansion, control, cold, construction, and seismic joints
- every 20 to 25 feet, in two directions, for interior tile work
- every 8 to 12 feet, in two directions, for exterior tile work
- every 8 to 12 feet, in two directions, for interior tile work exposed to direct sunlight or moisture.

Trade Tip:

I prefer the look of 1/8-inch-wide joints and use that size on most residential interior installations for walls, floors, and other tiled surfaces. However, when I encounter conditions such as interior tile exposed to direct sunlight, I increase the joint width to the appropriate dimension (see "Residential Movement Joints," page 222).

Typical movement joint locations and details are shown for wall corners, shower receptors and bathtubs, tiled ceilings, and mud and entry room floors (Figure 8-7).

Width of Movement Joints

Movement joints positioned directly over existing structural joints, such as concrete control joints, should never be narrower than the structural joint. Movement joints for interior floor tiles should be the same width as the grout joints. For interior installations using ceramic mosaic tile or glazed wall tiles, the tile industry's preferred movement joint width is 1/4 inch and never less than 1/8 inch. When an interior floor or wall receives direct sunlight, movement joint widths and spacing are the same as for exterior joints, discussed below.

For exterior tile work, movement joints need to be significantly wider. For movement joints laid out at 8-foot centers, the minimum width is 3/8 inch; for 12-foot centers, the minimum width is 1/2 inch. In addition, minimum widths must increase 1/16 inch for every 15°F change in tile surface temperature greater than 100°F (between summer high temperatures and winter lows). Exterior movement joint width for tile work in Miami and Los Angeles, where joints are located every 12 feet, is 1/2 inch minimum; in northern sections of the U.S., the same installation would require 3/4-inch movement joints on 12-foot centers.

Movement Joint Materials

Caulks and sealants play a critical role in tile installation as movement joint fillers. On a shopping mall floor, movement joints are out in full view, crossing the tiles every 20 to 25 feet, while on most residential tile floors, the movement joints are located primarily around the perimeter of a floor, where they are less noticeable or completely hidden by baseboard trim. Not all caulks or sealants are identical, so it is important to match the material you select to the demands of the installation.

For example, field-movement joints on a shopping mall floor must be able to stretch and compress to compensate for normal building movement; withstand daily, heavy-duty cleaning materials and routines; and be able to support wheeled traffic and high-heel shoes. To meet these demands, the material list for commercial jobs must include commercial sealants, backer rod, backup strips, and bond-breaking tape. In comparison, the perimeter movement joints found on a typical residential dry-area floor never receive any foot traffic and need only the ability to stretch and compress. Because they face fewer demands and are primarily located at the perimeter of floor and walls, I typically use a simplified approach with residential movement joints. In many cases, these simplified movement joints consist of nothing more than a clean movement joint slot filled with an appropriate caulk or sealant.

Caulks

The science of construction caulks and sealants is too vast to explore fully here, but we will examine how the tile industry classifies these materials, as well as my own approach to selecting and using them. In this book, I use the term *caulk* to refer to latex-based, water-cleanable, elastomeric compounds sold in standard 10-ounce caulking tubes and also packaged in smaller amounts. These caulks are available in white, black, gray, and in colors to match grout.

When made by grout manufacturers, this type of caulk is often available in either plain or sanded form to match the texture of either unsanded or sanded grout. The properties of latex caulks vary widely (see "Types of Caulks & Sealants," next page). High quality caulk is fine for all dry-area residential tile installations and should provide adequate service in most properly installed wet-area residential applications. This type of latex-based caulk should not be used

- where continuously immersed in water

- to fill field joints that are wider than ⅛ inch if exposed to foot traffic

- wherever harsh, daily cleaning methods are used

In other words, caulks are suitable for most residential applications. However, you should switch to sealants for most commercial applications and on demanding residential applications (such as water immersion or wide joints exposed to foot traffic).

Sealants

Sealants are generally more robust than caulks and usually cost more. They are usually not water-cleanable and take more skill to install and finish than caulks. For commercial as well as a growing number of residential applications, sealants include silicone, urethane, and polysulfide, but like latex caulks, the properties of sealants vary widely.

In residential work, I use sealants where joints wider than ⅛ inch are exposed to foot traffic, in outdoor applications, in applications that will be immersed in water, and in locations where preventing water intrusion is critical, such as shower or steam room plumbing penetrations. Joints exposed to excessive moisture, heavy wear, or significant building movement are also candidates for high-performance sealant (Figure 8-8). Standardized specifications for tiling sealants may be found in ASTM C920, which references ASTM tests for sealants and classifies them according to type, grade, class, and use (www.astm.org).

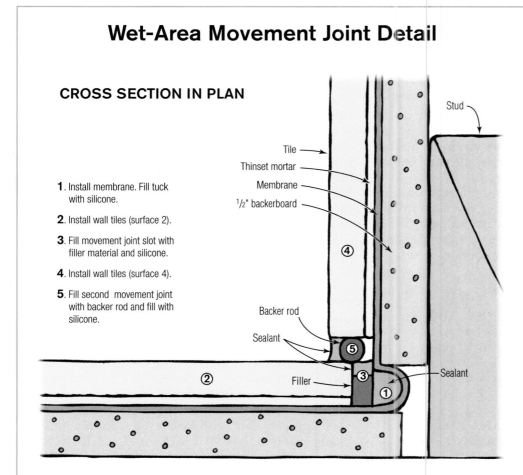

Wet-Area Movement Joint Detail

CROSS SECTION IN PLAN

1. Install membrane. Fill tuck with silicone.

2. Install wall tiles (surface 2).

3. Fill movement joint slot with filler material and silicone.

4. Install wall tiles (surface 4).

5. Fill second movement joint with backer rod and fill with silicone.

Tile
Thinset mortar
Membrane
½" backerboard
Stud
Backer rod
Sealant
Filler
Sealant

Figure 8-8. To be effective, movement joints must be continuous from the structure to the tile surface. Where the edge of one field of tiles (Surface 2) is covered by another (Surface 4), movement joint slot 3 should be filled prior to the installation of the second field of tiles.

Types of Caulks and Sealants

There are hundreds of different construction sealants, but for tiling, only a few are commonly used—typically silicone, siliconized latex, and latex. Selecting the right material should be based on a realistic assessment of the level of abuse the installation will receive, with special consideration given to any sealant joints that will be continuously immersed in water. The main designations for sealant types used with tile are shown below. A list of the primary ASTM tests related to the properties of sealants is found in "Sealant Standards and Testing," on page XX.

Sealant Types
- Type S – a single-component sealant, such as silicone
- Type M – a multi-component sealant, such as polysulfide or urethane

Sealant Grades
- Grade P – a self-leveling, pourable sealant used to fill horizontal movement joints
- Grade NS – nonsagging sealant used to fill vertical joints

Sealant Classes
- Class 25 – a sealant that can stretch and compress to withstand 25% increase and decrease in the width of the movement joint*

- Class 12 ½ – a sealant that can withstand 12½% increase and decrease in the width of the movement joint*

Sealant Uses
- Use T – a sealant designed for use in areas open to both pedestrian and vehicular traffic**
- Use NT – a sealant designed for non-traffic areas***
- Use I – a sealant designed for continuous immersion in water****
- Use M – a sealant designed for use with portland cement mortars.
- Use G – a sealant designed for use with glass
- Use A – a sealer designed for use with aluminum

* Class 12½ is the lowest permissible rate of joint elasticity. The values extend to 25, 35, 50, and 100/50, with the latter representing sealant that can stretch 100% in width and compress to 50% of its width.

** The hardness reading from ASTM C661 testing should be not less than 25 or more than 50.

*** The hardness reading from ASTM C661 testing should not be less than 15 or more than 50.

**** There are two sub-classifications for Use-I sealants: Class 1 sealants are ASTM C1247 tested for 6 weeks, while Class 2 sealants are tested for 10 weeks.

Other Movement Joint Materials

Hidden components of movement joints include bond-breaking tape, backer rod, and compressible backup strips. These are required to construct the field and perimeter joints specified on many commercial installations. They are especially important on wide field movement joints required to withstand heavy, continuous foot or wheeled traffic. In addition to improving the performance and longevity of the sealant, bond-breaking materials make it much easier to remove and replace the sealant when the time comes.

Note: I often omit bond breakers (backer rod or bond-breaking tape) and backup strips on residential installations because they are not necessary in the ⅛-inch caulk joints I primarily use. Residential jobs usually have no wide field movement joints required to withstand heavy traffic. However, backer rod or bond-breaking tape should be used on residential jobs that include joints wider than ⅛ inch—especially field joints subject to foot traffic and sealant-filled joints required for waterproofing. Where a bond breaker is required with thin tiles, bond-breaking tape can be used instead of backer rod.

Backer rod is a circular foam extrusion whose surface should possess bond-breaking properties. It is available in a small number of diameters and is packed in wheels. Backer rod helps impart a bow-tie cross section to the sealant bead, which is essential to the durability and performance of the joint (Figure 8-10). The bow-tie shape of the sealant bead provides a wide area of good adhesion at the sides of the joint, while the middle, thinner section allows the sealant to stretch without straining the sides. Equally important, the thin middle section of sealant produces less bunching when the joint contracts.

Backer rod is used primarily on commercial jobs, which usually feature grout and movement joints ¼-inch or wider. Backer rod and backup strips are available for these in large quantities but are very difficult to find in smaller sizes and quantities for residential work. Backer rod is made in ¼, ⅜, ½, ⅝, ¾, ⅞ inch and larger diameters and should be sized for a snug fit. The recommended diameter is 25% to 40% larger than the width of the joint. Backer rod is not made for the ⅛-inch joints that I use on most residential jobs, but I have found that ¼-inch backer rod works fine in ⅛-inch joints when needed. Backer rod and installation tools are available through www.bestmaterials.com.

Sealant Standards and Testing

Installers may have to install sealant on commercial jobs and some residential jobs. The properties of a particular type of elastomeric sealant vary by brand. Not all sealants can be used in exterior, horizontal, or vertical applications. Ideally, a caulk or sealant should flow easily into a joint, adhere quickly and tenaciously to its side walls, and cure into a material that can stretch or compress to suit normal building movement.

In selecting a sealant, you will usually find listed on the container which specs the product meets. Descriptions of the most common specs, which are useful in choosing a sealant, are provided below. Test results may be available from a manufacturer (pass or fail) but not a description of the spec. By consulting TCA EJ171 and ASTM C920, a contractor can match the sealant properties to the installation requirements.

1. ASTM C510 – a test for staining and color change for both single and multi-component sealants. Sealants that pass will not stain a white cement mortar base.
2. ASTM C639 – a test of the flow properties of sealants.
3. ASTM C661 – a test of the relative hardness of Use-T sealants.

4. ASTM C679 – a measure of the working time of sealants. Samples must be tackfree after 72 hours.
5. ASTM C719 – a test of the adhesion and cohesion of freshly installed sealants. A measure of the loss of bond or cohesion when movement is applied to the test joint.
6. ASTM C794 – a test of adhesion-in-peel, performed on cured sealants. No more than 25% loss of bond is accepted with a minimum peel strength of 5 lb/ft.
7. ASTM C793 – a weathering test to gauge endurance. Measures crack resistance of sealant exposed to ultraviolet light.
8. ASTM C1183 – a test of the application life of sealants.
9. ASTM C1246 – a test of the effects of heat aging on sealants. A measure of the loss of weight of test samples.
10. ASTM C1247 – a test of the durability of sealants exposed to continuous immersion in water. Class 1 sealants are ASTM C1247 tested for 6 weeks, Class 2 sealants for 10 weeks.

Bond-breaking tape is used primarily in commercial work to prevent sealant from bonding to the setting bed. It is useful for joints that are too shallow to accommodate backer rod, which also creates a bond break. Sealant works best when it is bonded to only the two sides of a joint. If it also bonds to the setting bed, it is less able to expand and contract freely and is more prone to failure. For the easiest installation, bond-breaking tape should be installed prior to the installation of the tiles. Tape specifically made for this purpose is available in a variety of widths through specialty suppliers (www.dkhardware.com).

Compressible backup strips are sometimes specified on thick setting bed installations to position and support backer rod. With thinbed work, however, they are not commonly used and are not readily available in a range of useful sizes. However, they come in handy in residential and light-commercial work when pouring self-leveling underlayment (see Figure 1-41A, page 26, CH 1). I use ¼-inch-thick, self-adhesive foam tape, stuck to the surrounding walls, as a backup strip to create a perimeter movement joint slot. After the SLU cures, I trim the 1¼-inch-wide tape flush with the floor surface. The tape I use is sold as camper-shell mounting tape and is available at hardware and supply stores.

Specifying Movement Joints and Filler Materials

All tile installations require some type of movement joints, although not all movement joints are constructed or perform the same. The demands of each installation will determine the width and location of the joints (never less than the width of grout joints on an installation) and the type of filler materials. According to the ANSI A108 Standards and the TCNA Handbook, it is up to the architect or designer to specify the locations and widths of movement joints. If you are working from a set of blueprints, the locations, widths, and filler materials should be part of the plans. If not, request them in writing before starting the installation.

In commercial spaces, I adhere to the ANSI and TCNA standards and recommendations regarding the construction and placement of movement joints. Commercial installations usually feature grout and movement joints ¼ inch or wider. Backer rod and backup strips are available for these in large quantities, but very difficult to find in the small sizes and smaller quantities needed for residential-size applications. For residential installations, I stick to the fundamental principles but modify some of the details (see "Residential Movement Joints," above).

Residential Movement Joints

In most residential applications, I use a simplified movement joint that relies on a clean joint slot filled with caulk. The main issue of what to put in the joint revolves around the special requirements for movement joints that are walked on in the field of a large floor. Few residential floors are large enough to require field joints, and joints on the perimeter of residential floors and walls do not endure foot or wheeled traffic.

On most residential jobs, I use primarily $1/8$-inch-wide grout joints, matched by $1/8$-inch-wide movement joints. One-eighth inch is the minimum width allowed for a movement joint. I originally started using $1/8$-inch grout joints in residential work for aesthetic reasons, but have found that $1/8$-inch grout and movement joints are also highly functional. Narrow joints are easier to clean and maintain than larger joints, and they work well with latex caulk, my preferred movement joint filler on residential projects.

Even where the joints are exposed to foot traffic, weight-supporting sealants and backer rod are not required since $1/8$-inch joints are smaller than the spike of most high heels. Figure 8-9 shows the typical movement-joint detail I use for both wet and dry areas on most thinset installations in wood-framed residential projects.

For perimeter movement joints, I usually omit backer rod, backup strips, and bond-breaking tape, as I have found that these components are not critical in most residential work. However, where movement joints over $1/8$ inch wide are required in the field (within the visible floor area), I generally use backer rod or bond-breaking tape and pair them with a high-performance sealant.

The most important element of a movement joint, regardless of whether backer rod and bond-breaking tape are used, is its ability to stretch, compress, and stay attached to the tiles on either side of the joint. The industry minimum standard for movement requires that a movement joint be able to stretch or compress an amount equal to $12^1/2\%$ of the joint's width. When straying from the combination of filler, backer rod, and bond-breaking tape, I generally use a caulk or sealant that can stretch or compress at least 50% of the width of the joint (ASTM Class 50).

My usual choice of movement joint filler is color and texture matched caulk distributed by grout manufacturers. These latex (or "siliconized" latex) caulks come in a vast range of colors and are easy to install. In general, however, they do not perform as well as silicone, urethane, or polysulfide sealants and require more frequent replacement—every one to five years,

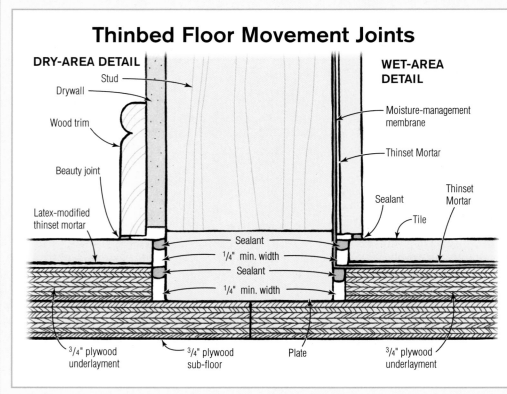

Thinbed Floor Movement Joints

DRY-AREA DETAIL

- Stud
- Drywall
- Wood trim
- Beauty joint
- Latex-modified thinset mortar

WET-AREA DETAIL

- Moisture-management membrane
- Thinset Mortar
- Sealant
- Thinset Mortar
- Tile

- Sealant
- $1/4$" min. width
- Sealant
- $1/4$" min. width

- $3/4$" plywood underlayment
- $3/4$" plywood sub-floor
- Plate
- $3/4$" plywood underlayment

Figure 8-9. On wood construction, all movement joints must extend from the top of the subflooring to the top of the tile.

depending on the tile installation's level of use. Still, the matched caulks are preferred by most customers since the color and texture almost perfectly match the grout.

When working with certain glossy tile colors—white, black, silver, gray, almond, or beige—I prefer to use silicone in wet-area movement joints, even though the color, texture, and light-reflecting properties will not perfectly match the grout. Silicone has fewer reactions with water and moisture, is more resistant to abrasion and wear, and is better suited to adverse conditions than latex caulk. Some brands of silicone sealants, in a limited range of colors, are available with 50-year performance warranties. By comparison, latex caulks may not carry any warranty, can be expected to provide one to five years of service in a wet area (longer in a dry area), and should not be used for exterior joints.

Installing Movement Joints

Since the purpose of a movement joint is to allow normal building movement to occur without damage to finishes, it must be designed properly and be carefully constructed to absorb the anticipated building movement.

Preparing for Installation of Movement Joints

The first step in installing a movement joint is to ensure that all movement joint slots are of minimum width and are free of all foreign materials, including construction debris, dirt, drywall compound, thinset mortar, and grout. Grout in surrounding joints should be cured enough for contact with the movement joint filler material. The only exception to this is when using 100% solids epoxy grout. Because 100% solids epoxy grout flows, the movement joints should actually be filled and allowed to cure prior to grouting (see "Movement Joints and Epoxy Grout," below).

Because movement joints stretch and compress and must prevent water from penetrating in wet-area installations, it is essential that the sealant or caulk used adheres to the side walls of the movement joint. For best results, contact edges must be clean and dry. To maximize adhesion, slick tile edges can be sanded or ground. Some sealants may require that

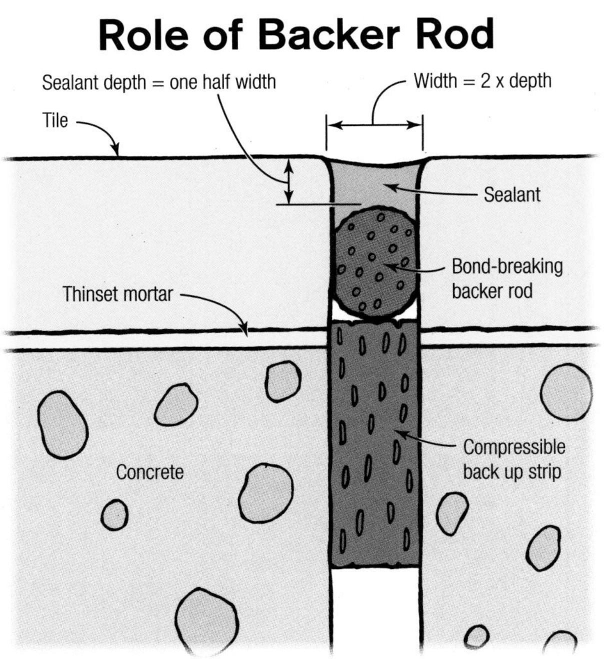

Role of Backer Rod

Sealant depth = one half width
Width = 2 x depth
Tile
Sealant
Bond-breaking backer rod
Thinset mortar
Compressible back up strip
Concrete

Figure 8-10. Backer rod helps give the sealant bead a "bow-tie" profile required for best performance. The shape provides ample bonding surfaces at the sides of the joint and a thin cross section that stretches and compresses easily.

Movement Joints and Epoxy Grout

When traditional portland cement grouts are used, most movement joint work is done after grouting. When tiles are grouted with 100% solids epoxy grout, however, movement joints are filled first to help contain the free-flowing epoxy material and prevent it from oozing into the empty movement joint slot. This applies whether you will be using a caulk or a sealant to fill the joints. With 100% solids epoxy grout:

- fill the movement joints first
- allow the caulk or sealant to cure and harden
- trim back the sealant, as required, to suit the grout
- fill the remaining joints with the epoxy grout

To avoid potential cross-contamination or damage to the sealant, do not install epoxy grout until the sealant has cured!

bonding surfaces be treated with a primer before the joint is filled.

When using elastomeric sealants, the installer must also maintain the room temperature and tile surface temperatures as recommended by the sealant manufacturer for timely setup and eventual curing. Low temperatures sometimes cause sagging, and freezing temperatures may ruin some sealants before they have properly cured. High temperatures may reduce open time, overheat and ruin the sealant, or cause other curing and finishing problems.

Installing Manufactured Movement Joints

With manufactured movement joints, it is essential to use enough thinset mortar to properly support both the tile and the movement joint anchored below it. There should be at least $3/32$ inch of thinset mortar between the setting bed and movement joint flange, and another $3/32$ inch of thinset between the top of the flange and the tile. If you use a trowel that spreads only enough thinset to provide 80% adhesive contact, there will not be enough adhesive to support either the tile or the joint and still maintain a smooth, even surface plane.

Whenever working with manufactured joints, deter-mine what notch size delivers the right coverage, then choose a trowel that will spread an additional $1/16$ inch of thinset mortar on the surface. One-sixteenth inch is the approximate thickness of most manufactured joint anchors, and the extra thinset will lift all the tiles to the plane of the joint strip, eliminating any bumps on the surface of the installation, as shown in Figure 8-2, page 214.

The next step is to double-check layout figures and marks and ensure that cut-to-fit sections of movement joints are staged and ready when needed by the tile installers.

The cut or mitered edge of any joint strips should be filed or sanded smooth. Also, to prevent the need for repositioning and the subsequent loss of adhesive support, a layout line or pencil mark should indicate the precise location of each joint strip. Tile edges that face and make contact with the body of the joint should be flat and smooth with no uneven glaze buildup.

It may be necessary to sand or grind the tile edges smooth. If hand-molded tiles with very uneven edges result in gaps between the tiles and the body of the movement joint, tiles facing the joint should be trimmed with a wet saw to create a uniform straight edge. Movement joint strips should be selected so that, after installation, they sit flush or slightly

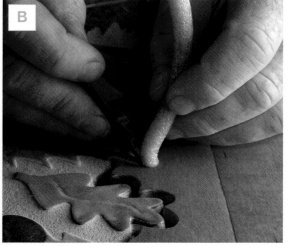

Figure 8-11. After waiting until the grout has lost all plasticity, but before it begins to harden, the author uses a ¼-inch tuck pointer to disturb and loosen grout in the movement joint slot (A). After vacuuming the slot, he carefully installs the backer rod (B). Since no backup strip is used to space the backer rod off the setting bed, patience is required to set the backer rod at the proper depth (C) so the sealant depth will equal approximately one half the width of the joint.

below the surface of the tiles.

Installing Water-Cleanable Caulk

In the example shown in Figures 8-11, 8-12, 8-13, and 8-14, I am installing a movement joint surrounding a mosaic tile floor that is inset into a residential wood strip floor. Grout between the tiles and wood flooring would quickly crack and erode from the constant movement of the surrounding wood. Another problem on this floor was the resident pet, a large dog whose claw marks were visible in the maple flooring at the time the mosaic was installed. To overcome the first problem, I used a matching, sanded latex caulk made by the grout manufacturer. To prevent the dog's sharp claws from mincing the caulk, I designed the installation with a ⅛-inch-wide movement joint—just narrow enough to keep the claws from dropping onto the surface of the cured caulk.

The first step in creating a functional movement joint, done during the tile installation, is to scrape off any fresh mortar or grout encroaching on the movement joint slot. Unwanted material should be scraped away before it hardens and becomes far more difficult to remove. After the grout cured on this job, I used a vacuum to remove any dirt or grit. The next step was to stuff the joint with backer rod (Figure 8-11) so that

Figure 8-12. Because of the winding nature of this joint, the author makes no attempt at producing a one-shot finished joint. Instead, he piles up caulk above the joint so there will be additional material to tool into the empty slot.

the depth of the sealant at the center of the joint, when finished and cured, equaled approximately one-half the width of the joint.

> *Note:* While I rarely use backer rod on residential jobs, I used it here because the joint was in the middle of the floor where it would be highly visible, subject to foot traffic, and subject to the movement of the surrounding wood floor. In short, the demands on the joint required a commercial-style joint.

Next, I began filling about 3 or 4 lineal feet of the joint with caulk, making sure I slightly overfilled the joint as it runs around the perimeter of the tile insert (Figure 8-12). Overfilling the joint is the best way to avoid a finished caulk surface that is too concave. After a bit of tooling with my finger to ensure each joint cavity was completely filled, I began gently washing the surface of the tiles and strip flooring with a barely damp grouting sponge.

Cleaning sanded latex caulk is similar to cleaning fresh grout, although a far lighter touch on the sponge is required. I applied the lightest possible pressure with the sponge, concentrating primarily on the areas on either side of the joint. After a second pass with the sponge, I can use my finger to scrub away a stubborn glob of caulk before giving the area a final wipe of the sponge (Figure 8-13).

The final wipe for latex caulk is similar to the final wipe for grout: single, parallel passes of the sponge, with a fresh sponge side for each pass and no reversing directions with the sponge (this dumps caulk residue back onto the tile). As soon as the caulk skinned over, about 40 minutes for this floor, I removed any visible latex haze with a light scrubbing pad, then allowed the caulk to harden off for three days. As you can tell from Figure 8-1 on page 213, the match is not exact but close enough that, at a glance, it is difficult to tell the caulk from the grout.

After seven years (at the time of this writing), the joints on this award-winning installation are still in good shape (Figure 8-14). Although the original joint was filled with a latex caulk, its useful life has been extended because the joints are ⅛ inch wide, the dog's claws have not been able to reach the surface of the caulk, and the installation is located in a protected area with little exposure to moisture.

Filling Nonvisible Joints With Caulk or Sealant.

There are numerous residential movement joints that are covered with tiles, baseboard trim, and plumbing fixtures. To fill these joints, I generally use leftover caulk: silicone for wet-area joints and silicone, latex, or siliconized latex for dry areas. Normally, I fill these

Figure 8-13. After tooling, the first pass with the sponge should be gentle and careful enough not to disturb too much of the caulk mounding the joint (A). For the second pass, the author goes back to the beginning of the joint and lightly scrubs the excess, with frequent rinsing to avoid spreading or gouging. Sometimes, the best tool for cleaning is a finger, used here to spot clean crusted-over caulk (B). After most of the visible, unwanted material has been removed, one-direction-only wipes—each with a freshly rinsed side of the sponge—remove most of the cement or latex haze (C).

joints with caulk or sealant only and omit bond-breaking tape, backup strips, and backer rod unless specified on a commercial job.

At the perimeter of floors, for example, there are two movement joints: one between the floor tiles and the abutting wall and another between the floor tiles and baseboard tiles (see Figure 1-2, page 2). The joint between the floor tiles and wall should be filled with caulk in dry-area applications so it does not become filled with dirt, sand, grit, and other material that could restrict free movement. In wet areas, this joint should be filled with silicone so that water will not collect and cause maintenance problems.

The gap between a tub and a waterproofing membrane should be filled with silicone to prevent it from becoming clogged with thinset mortar or filled with moisture once the tub is put into service (see Figure 8-7B, page 217, and 7-10, page 197).

The gaps around tub spouts and shower head pipes are well known for allowing water or steam vapor to penetrate into the wall cavity and cause structural damage. To prevent this, I fill these gaps with silicone and make sure there is enough room for a plumber to cut through in case repair or replacement of the spout or pipe is needed (Figure 8-15).

Filling Visible Joints With Silicone Sealant

I typically use silicone sealant in visible joints in the following applications: Commercial and industrial floors; residential and light-commercial floors with field movement joints larger than $\frac{1}{8}$ inch; joints that will be submerged in water; and joints where preventing water penetration is critical, such as steam showers and commercial food-preparation countertops.

Filling nonvisible joints with silicone is one thing, producing attractive visible joints is another. Some tradespeople are artists with a caulking gun. They can extrude perfect beads of sealant without breaking a sweat. Unfortunately, I am not one of them. So whenever possible, I avoid the issue altogether and hire a sealant contractor when I have to install non-water-cleanable sealants such as silicone (this is common on commercial work, less so on residential jobs).

Nevertheless, I still have to shoot a lot of silicone show joints, and over the years I have learned the hard way not to attempt it without the proper prep work. That means taking the time to mask off areas I don't want smeared with sealant, shaping the sealant tube nozzle, being careful about filling the joint (not just capping the top), tooling the silicone so it has a

Figure 8-14. A perimeter movement joint, encircling this mosaic insert and filled with a color-matched sanded caulk, masks the continuous movement between the wood strip floor and the tiles. Its relatively narrow width (1/8 inch) prevents the homeowner's dog from damaging the relatively soft caulk with its claws.

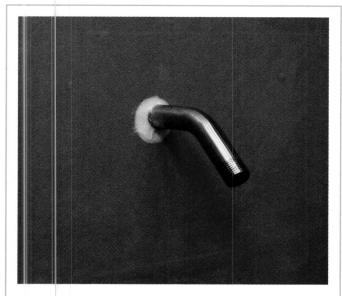

Figure 8-15. The openings around tub pipes and showerhead goosenecks should be sealed watertight, but made large enough for plumbing access in case a repair is needed.

Backer Rod Depth Gauge

Depth gauge

Backer rod

Adjustment stop

Thinset mortar

Tile

Concrete slab

Movement joint

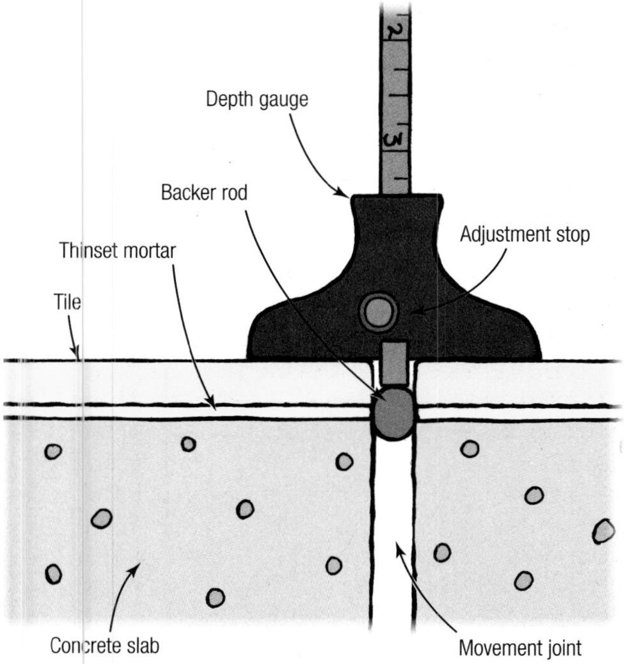

Figure 8-16. IThe author uses a depth gauge to ensure uniform height for the backer rod.

uniform profile, and removing the tape when the timing is right—after the surface of the fresh sealant has begun to harden over. This strategy creates the least amount of mess and minimizes cleaning with solvent. In spite of the precautions I take, though, the finished results are sometimes less than perfect, and finishing may require a bit of knife or razor-blade work after the silicone has cured.

Prepping and Masking the Joints

When I'm working with movement joints with a bond breaker specified, I generally use bond-breaking tape for shallow joints and backer rod for deep joints that can accommodate the thickness of the backer rod.

When installing backer rod, its diameter should be 25% to 50% larger than the width of the joint for a snug fit. Ideally, the height of the backerboard should be uniform enough to produce a sealant joint whose depth is one-half the joint width. With the relatively narrow 1/8-inch-wide joints I prefer for residential work, though, a 1/16-inch thickness is, in my opinion, too thin, so I set the backer rod to produce a joint depth (measured at the center of the joint) of 1/8-inch minimum and use a depth gauge to ensure the rod is properly positioned (Figure 8-16). Because the smallest available backer rod is 1/4-inch diameter, I stretch the rod slightly (to reduce its diameter a bit) as I press it into the movement joint slot. I use a closed-cell backer rod because it does not absorb water and because its surface is a bond-breaker.

Next, I use blue painter's tape to mask the tiles on either side of the movement joint (Figure 8-17). To do this accurately takes some time, but it also eliminates a lengthy, nasty cleaning job once the joints are filled with sealant. The tape will stay in place until after the

Figure 8-17. When using silicone sealant, the author uses blue painter's tape to mask tiles on either side of the joint.

surface of the sealant has been tooled but before it begins to skin over.

Filling the Movement Joint Slot With Silicone

Once the joint is prepared, I cut and squeeze the opening of the cartridge nozzle into a slanted oblong shape. This shape allows the maximum flow of sealant with the least pressure. This is especially important if you are not using power-driven equipment, but instead are pumping out sealant by hand. The wedge-shaped nozzle opening allows me to move the sealant tip more smoothly across the joint opening. With the tip of the nozzle positioned next to the movement joint slot, I begin filling it with sealant (Figure 8-18). Unlike water-cleanable materials that can be easily shaped and finished with a damp sponge, silicone must be tooled instead of washed. The trick is to fill the joint slot completely without overfilling it.

The ambient (room) temperature, plus the width and depth of the joint slot, determine how much sealant I can shoot before stopping to tool and finish. This takes a bit of experimentation and experience, but it is essential that whatever tooling is required gets done before the sealant begins to skin over. Once that happens, the tools are likely to snag the skin, deform the sealant profile, and require refilling. With straight runs and low temperatures, I may fill 50 feet of empty slot before going back to tool and finish the joint. With a lot of directional changes or with high temperatures, though, I may only shoot 10 feet or less before stopping to tool.

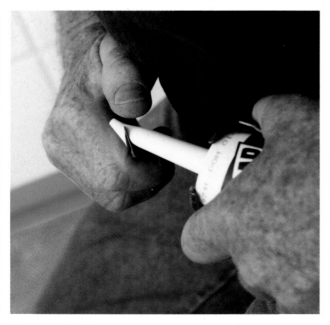

Figure 8-18. Cutting the cartridge tip on a slant allows more flow at less pressure, producing a smoother finish with less waste (left). To ensure that the caulk or sealant anchors itself to the sides of the tile, the joint needs to be filled—not just topped off (right).

Figure 8-19. A film of paint thinner on the trowel makes tooling the joint easier, but this work must be done before the sealant skins over.

Figure 8-20. To avoid damaging the surface of the joint, the tape should not be removed too soon. The author typically allows the sealant to cure overnight before stripping the tape.

Tooling Silicone Sealant

When tooling silicone sealant, I work mostly with narrow margin trowels, a variety of strikes, and a lubricating agent, such as paint thinner, to prevent the silicone from sticking to the tools. For the joint shown in Figures 8-17 to 8-20, I use a 2-inch margin trowel, some paper towels to clean the trowel, a container of paint thinner, and a small scrubbing sponge dampened with thinner. I begin by wiping the trowel with the sponge. Then, holding the trowel at a low angle to the joint with the tip of the blade held against the upper tile, I draw the trowel slowly and lightly along the length of the slot (Figure 8-19). I can usually tool each section with just one pass of the trowel, but sometimes a second pass (with the trowel cleaned and moistened with thinner) is needed, especially if there are any voids in the sealant bead. Voids should be filled with fresh silicone. The surface of the finished bead should be smooth with a uniform profile.

Removing the Masking Tape

Once a movement joint has been successfully tooled, there is a great temptation to strip off the masking tape. But, if possible, the tape should remain until the sealant has cured. Instead of stripping off the tape right away, I carefully scrape or paper-towel any blobs of sealant on the surface of the tape and then wait as long as required for a tack-free cure before removing the tape. Yes, it is possible to remove the tape immediately after tooling, but you must work with precision to avoid contaminating the tiles with hard-to-remove sealant or mucking up the finished bead.

For me, a more relaxed approach is to allow the sealant to cure, at least to a tack-free surface, while concentrating on removing any excess sealant from the tape that might interfere with its removal. After the sealant has skinned over, the tape can be removed without risk of harming the movement joint or marring tile surfaces (Figure 8-20). If the tape is applied with care, there should be no sealant residue once the tape is stripped off. If any cured blobs of silicone remain on the surface of the bead, I use a razor blade moistened with paint thinner to slice off the excess.

Repairing a Sealant Joint

Using bond-breaking materials not only increases the service life of sealants used in movement joints, but they also make the inevitable repairs rather simple compared with most other forms of tile repair. The first step in a repair is to clean the affected area of all wax, oil, soap film, grease, and other contaminants, and allow it to dry. Then slit through the cross section of sealant or caulk at each end of the problem area, while being careful to avoid cutting through the backer rod. If bond-breaking tape or backer rod was originally used, the unwanted section of caulk or sealant should simply lift away; if not, expect some tearing of the sealant bead when making this type of repair. Maintain clean conditions throughout the repair, use primers if required by the sealant manufacturer, replace any damaged backer rod, and duplicate the profile of the original joint as closely as possible.

NOTES

Chapter 9
TILE LAYOUT

For tile installation, I use the term layout to refer not just to a set of chalk lines plotted to guide the tile installation, but also to a systematic process that includes

- measuring a structure

- determining accurate sizes for tiles and tile trim

- plotting layout lines for tile and other installation materials

- estimating the amount of tile and installation materials, and

- staging materials for an efficient installation

My education in layout began in a large manufacturing and repair shop for machinery. For six months, I was apprenticed to a layout specialist who taught me

Figure 9-1. Layout lines do more than just guide tile placement. Here, they are used to stage tiles for a more efficient installation.

how to plot accurate layout and machining lines on rough iron castings. Almost 45 years later, I still use the skills I learned on rough castings and apply them to the not-so-perfect floors, walls, countertops, and ceilings I have to cover with tile.

Producing a tile layout is a three-step process for me.

1. measure the area being tiled (including flat, square, level, and plumb)

2. measure the tiles

3. snap the lines

Most layouts are rather simple, with only a few lines required to guide the tiles; but some are quite complex. They require a lot of thought, trial and error, and patience and can take considerable time to plot.

Whether simple or complicated, there are two main goals behind every layout. The first is to provide an accurate framework of chalk, pencil, or laser lines to guide placement of tiles. The second is to improve the efficiency of the installation by eliminating unnecessary steps.

Attaining these goals is the result of using numerous layout steps throughout the installation. These steps include measuring the dimensions of the work area, plotting cut lines on backerboards or sheet membranes, and plotting layout lines for the membrane system and placement of the tiles. On large floor installations (greater than 100 square feet), I also use the tile layout lines to stage tiles (Figure 9-1).

Checking Measurement Accuracy

Accurate tools are needed to plot accurate layouts. It is a good idea to check your layout tools before getting started. Plumb bobs do not need checking, but measuring tapes, squares, and lasers do. I keep a machinist-quality, 12-inch scale to check whether the hook end of a tape will yield accurate inside and outside measurements. To check outside dimensions, I hook the tape to the scale and compare inch marks. For inside measurements, I butt the tape and the scale against a flat, hard surface and compare inch marks (Figure 9-2).

To achieve accuracy for both inside and outside measurements, the hook at the beginning of a tape measure slides back and forth a total distance that is equal to the thickness of the hook. If the rivet slots that allow the hook to move are worn (Figure 9-3), the tape will not measure accurately, and it should be discarded.

Hint: Clearly mark a defective tape you want to continue to use for roughing work.

Figure 9-2. To check a measuring tape for accuracy, the author compares it to a machinist's scale for outside (top) and inside (bottom) measurements.

Is Your Tape Accurate?

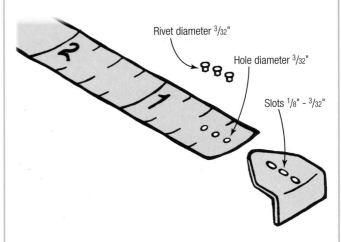

Rivet diameter $^3/_{32}$"

Hole diameter $^3/_{32}$"

Slots $^1/_8$" – $^3/_{32}$"

Figure 9-3. For accurate inside and outside measurements, the hooked end should slide only a distance equal to the thickness of the hook.

Fine-tuning a Carpenter's Square

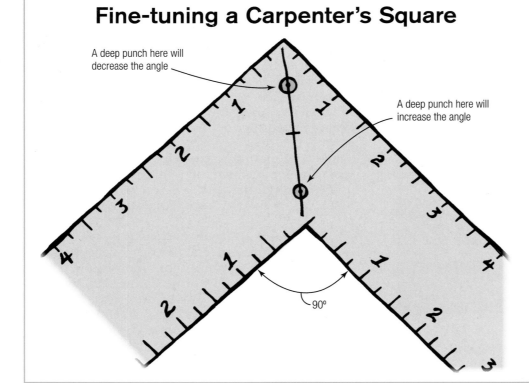

A deep punch here will decrease the angle

A deep punch here will increase the angle

90°

Figure 9-4. Tap a steel punch near the outside of the square to decrease the square's angle. A punch mark on the inner side will increase the angle.

To check my squares, I begin with the largest (a 3x4x5-foot folding square) and check it against a 3-4-5 triangle plotted on a flat surface. To do this, I trace around the perimeter of the square and measure each leg of the resulting triangle. If the folding square's pivots are worn, it will not give accurate results and should not be used to check for square. (Instead, dismantle the square, and you end up with usable 3-, 4-, and 5-foot straightedges.)

If the folding square is accurate, I sandwich the framing square against it and compare. An inaccurate framing square can be fixed with a hammer and center punch. First, scribe a line between the inner and outer corners of the square and use a prick punch to help make fine adjustments: Punch along the outer

Figure 9-5. The author checks the vertical beam of his cross-hair laser against a plumb line. He checks the horizontal beam against a second unit, both projected against a flat surface.

side of the line to make a square's angle smaller, along the inner side of the line to make the angle larger (Figure 9-4).

I check my laser square by aligning one of the beams against a straight line, marking the location of the second beam, then rotating the square 90 degrees, marking the resulting line, and repeating until I have reached the original line (or not). If the square is off tolerance, I send it back to the factory for adjustment.

The vertical beam of a cross-hair laser can be checked against a plumb line. To check the horizontal beam, I adjust the line against a flat surface and align the beam of a second unit for comparison (Figure 9-5). If either line is off factory tolerances, I check one of the lines against an accurate spirit level and send the inaccurate unit to the manufacturer for re-alignment.

Layout Basics: Flat, Level, Plumb, and Square

All layouts use the same basic tools and techniques, but applied differently depending on the shape and orientation of the work surface. The key concepts, tools, and techniques are described below.

Level and Flat

Spirit levels are important for both floor and wall work, and I still rely on them heavily during the installation phase. In the layout process, however, contractor-grade cross lasers (both horizontal and vertical beams) have taken a lead role in speeding up the work. Lasers can significantly reduce the amount of time an installer spends measuring a surface, plotting layout lines, and checking tile alignment.

Nevertheless, I still use spirit levels extensively to help keep the tiles aligned and prefer the positive contact of a good level. Plus, with a spirit level, I don't have to worry about my eyes catching laser beams. Accuracy is increased by using the longest possible level or level/

Checking Level and Flatness With a Laser

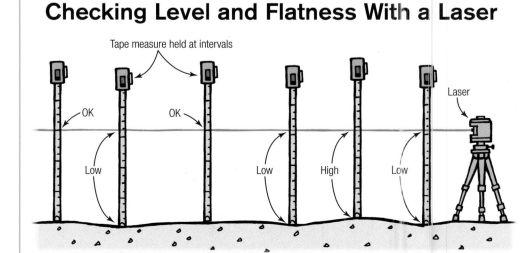

Figure 9-6. On large floors, a convenient technique for checking level and flatness is to position a horizontal laser beam at a convenient height, then use a tape measure to check for level and to locate high and low points.

The 3-4-5 Method

3-4-5 Triangle

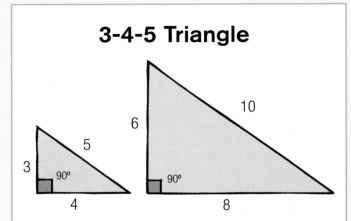

Figure 9-7. The 3-4-5 triangle, a simple expression of the Pythagorean theorem, is used by builders everywhere to establish or check right angles. Use larger multiples, such as 6-8-10, for larger areas.

Figure 9-8. This manufactured 3-4-5 folding square is ideal for laying out typical bathroom floors.

In high school, I had problems with the Pythagorean theorem. The first time I saw a builder use the 3-4-5 method, however, its simplicity swept away years of ignorance (Figure 9-7). The 3-4-5 method works, but it requires a high degree of measuring accuracy. In practice, I rarely plot a 3x4x5-foot triangle because I have a full-size 3-4-5 folding triangle, which is much easier to use than plotting distances with a ruler or large compass (Figure 9-8). On most residential projects, I need larger than a 3-4-5 triangle, so I lay out using multiples of 3-4-5, typically using 6-8-10, 9-12-15, 12-16-20, and 15-20-25 triangles. To ensure accurate measurements, I use a beam compass (made from clamp-on trammel points and a long straightedge) for 6-8-10 and 9-12-15 triangles, and measuring tapes for the larger sizes (Figure 9-9). For measuring lengths or setting the beam compass, measuring off the hook end of a tape is not nearly as accurate as measuring off one of the inch lines

straightedge combination. It is possible to accurately check small floors with a spirit level. For whole-floor residential and commercial layouts, however, layout with a level is a tedious, cumbersome, and inaccurate task. When I need to check a single- or multi-room floor layout for level and flatness, I use a laser and note changes in elevation by reading the laser's beam off a measuring tape. With minimal setups, I can assess several rooms in just a few minutes (Figure 9-6).

Using a combination of plumb bobs, spirit levels, squares, and lasers, it does not take long for me to assess a structure for level and square. With this information, I can adjust the tile layout to downplay any problem areas or determine if corrective measures are needed for surfaces that are off spec.

Plumb

The easiest way to produce a plumb line that is absolutely vertical is to use a plumb bob. Plumb bobs cost-ing $100 or more are common, but they are no more accurate for tiling than a heavy bolt on the end of a length of string. The earliest plumb bobs were mated to a right-angle square so that level or angled lines could be accurately plotted. I use plumb bobs for layout at the beginning of an installation to assess various parts of the structure I may be tiling or tiling against: door and window jambs, inside and outside corners, walls, and other vertical surfaces.

I sometimes use plumb bobs to help align tiles extending around an outside corner or to mark the end of a field of wall tiles. The only drawback to a plumb bob is that the two elements that make it such a valuable tool—a length of string stretched taut by the weight of the bob and the pointed end of the bob—are also the two things that always get in the way. For that reason, although I may use plumb bobs to assess a structure or plot layout lines, I generally use a spirit level or laser when installing tiles. Nevertheless,

Checking Reference Lines With a 3-4-5 Triangle

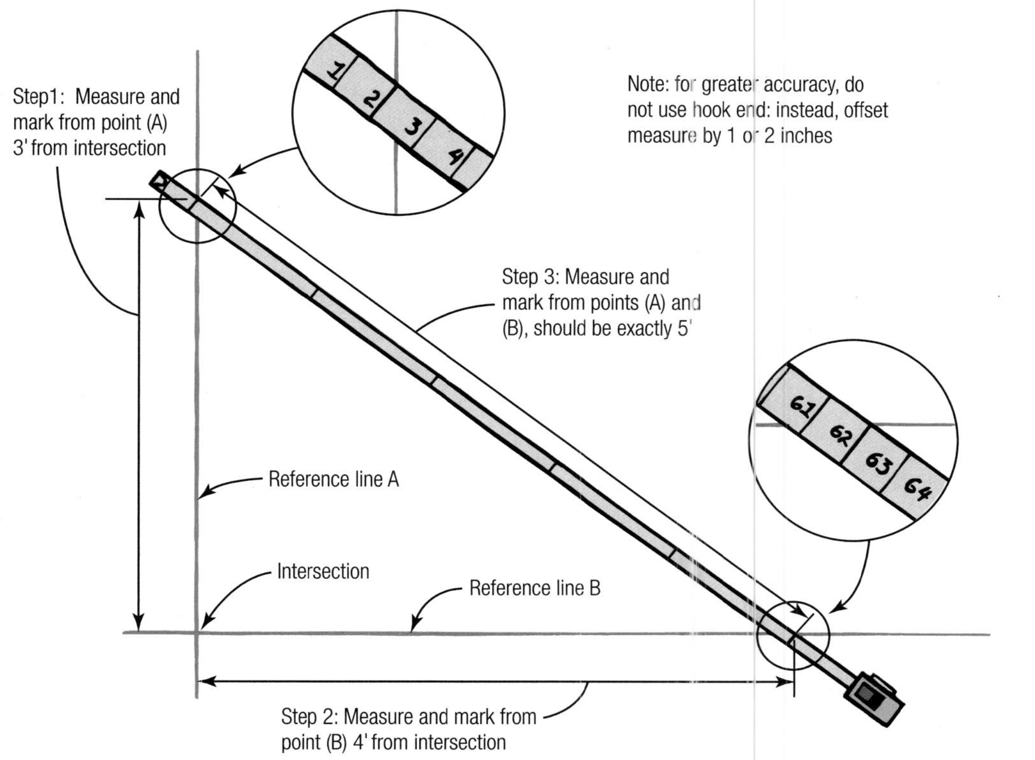

Figure 9-9.
The author checks intersecting reference lines A and B for square by carefully measuring out a 3-4-5 triangle with the tape precisely aligned with points on the reference lines. A large folding square or beam compass can simplify the procedure.

Step1: Measure and mark from point (A) 3' from intersection

Note: for greater accuracy, do not use hook end: instead, offset measure by 1 or 2 inches

Step 3: Measure and mark from points (A) and (B), should be exactly 5'

Reference line A

Intersection

Reference line B

Step 2: Measure and mark from point (B) 4' from intersection

on the straightedges.

While I primarily use lasers nowadays to establish layout lines, I still use the trusty 3-4-5 method discovered by Pythagoras around 500 B.C. to verify the accuracy of the laser beams before converting them to chalk or pencil reference lines.

to check for accuracy of any wall reference lines—and ultimately, the layout lines—I use a plumb bob as the last word.

Square Reference Lines and Layout Lines

The general method I use for most layouts starts with a set of two right-angle reference lines. These are two lines plotted at 90 degrees to each other and used to determine the dimensions of a floor, wall, countertop, etc. Where a floor tile layout extends into an adjoining room, I run the second reference line through the threshold between the two rooms. A third perpendicular reference would be added if needed to run across the threshold into another room.

The first use of reference lines is to provide an accurate benchmark for assessing the condition (level, plumb, square, etc.) of the area to be tiled. Reference lines also provide the basis for plotting a grid of layout

lines, which guides the installation of tile and other materials, such as membranes. Reference lines may also act as layout lines if they happen to be in the right place.

I base my layouts on reference lines because most structural surfaces are not perfectly straight and true, and thus produce misleading measurements. Plotting a highly accurate set of right-angle reference lines can be done with nothing more than a tape measure, a pencil, some string, and a few nails, employing the 3-4-5 triangle. Regardless of what tools you use to establish reference lines, including lasers, it is a good idea to check the accuracy of your lines using the 3-4-5 method (see "The 3-4-5 Method," above). This is a critical skill for an installer because most tiles, and most houses, have right-angle corners. Right angles are needed for floor, wall, countertop, and ceiling installations.

For all but the smallest jobs, the fastest way to plot layout lines is to first make perpendicular reference marks on the setting bed using a cross laser. Then use the laser to plot additional layout lines—or you can use the laser for directly aligning tile edges. With chalk layout lines replaced by a laser secured on an adjustable mount, time is saved, adhesive mortars can be spread quicker and more accurately, and tiles can be installed more precisely, without concern about obscuring the chalk lines as you work.

Extending reference lines. Along with, or in place of, laser squares, I use large, folding, 3-4-5 and 45-degree angle squares and straightedges to extend reference lines or plot layout lines (Figure 9-10). When converting laser beams, I use a sharp pencil to mark beam end points and fine chalk lines centered over those marks to "ink" in the line (Figure 9-11). If a line gets snapped in the wrong place, and it is not possible to remove it with a clean, damp sponge, I switch chalk lines and use one with another color to avoid confusion. I may also use additional colors to indicate trim locations and other details.

Working without a laser. When a laser is not available, I snap a chalk line over two measurement marks that are equidistant from the wall (distance "x" as shown in Figure 9-19, page 242). Then I add a second perpendicular chalk line with the help of my framing square (or large folding square) and check the two lines with a 3-4-5 triangle. This method can also be applied to wall surfaces.

Wall reference lines. Reference lines for wall installations differ from floor layouts in that the horizontal and vertical references must remain true. Skewing a wall layout produces unsightly results between tiles and doors or enclosures and at any inside or outside corner wrapped with tile. Wall reference lines should always be based on a true plumb line, with a ⅛-inch-in-10-foot surface tolerance or better. With patience, any plumb bob can easily produce plumb lines accurate to within the thickness of the plumb bob line in 100 feet.

The Layout Process

Approaching a new job, the layout process proceeds in a logical and systematic fashion. I approach all jobs in the following order:

1. check the surface to be tiled for flatness

2. assess horizontal surfaces for level and vertical surfaces for plumb

3. evaluate the tiled area for square

4. measure the tiles

With this information, I am able to plot my reference lines and then plot all other layout lines from

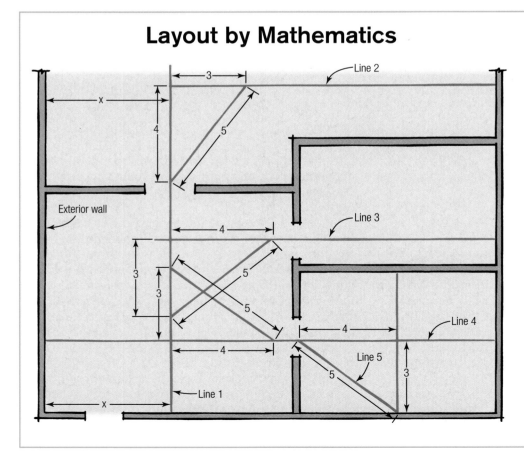

Layout by Mathematics

Figure 9-10. Before right-angle lasers were available, the author plotted reference lines using only math and the Pythagorean theorem to extend a layout from one room to another.

these. The layout lines, in turn, provide the information I need to estimate, stage, and install all tile and installation materials.

Checking Surfaces for Flatness

Nowadays, I check most horizontal surfaces for level and flat with a laser, as described above. However, for many years, I accomplished the same task using 5- and 10-foot straightedges. This method is equally accurate if done carefully, but it takes more time. I still often use it on jobs smaller than 100 square feet.

To check manually, I use a straightedge and spirit level to determine if the surface is level and flat enough for the size tile I am installing (see Table 6-1, "Recommended Setting Bed Flatness," page 155). For floors larger than 100 square feet, I use a 10-foot straightedge because it corresponds to the industry standard of flat to within $\frac{1}{4}$ inch in 10 feet. If there are any gaps greater than $\frac{1}{4}$ inch between the straightedge and the surface, I know instantly if it is off spec. For surfaces smaller than 10 feet, I use a 5-foot-long straightedge and look for gaps greater than $\frac{1}{8}$ inch.

I can use the same straightedges to check for the tighter tolerances that apply to larger tiles. For example, a 10-foot straightedge allows me to easily determine flatness to within $\frac{1}{8}$, $\frac{1}{16}$, or $\frac{1}{32}$ inch in 10 feet to suit tiles as large as 24 inches long or square.

The pattern I use to check for flatness is simple and

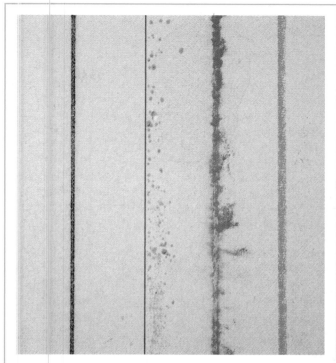

Figure 9-11. Fine lines provide more accuracy than thick or fuzzy ones. From left to right: new standard chalk line, fine chalk line, worn standard chalk line, lumber crayon.

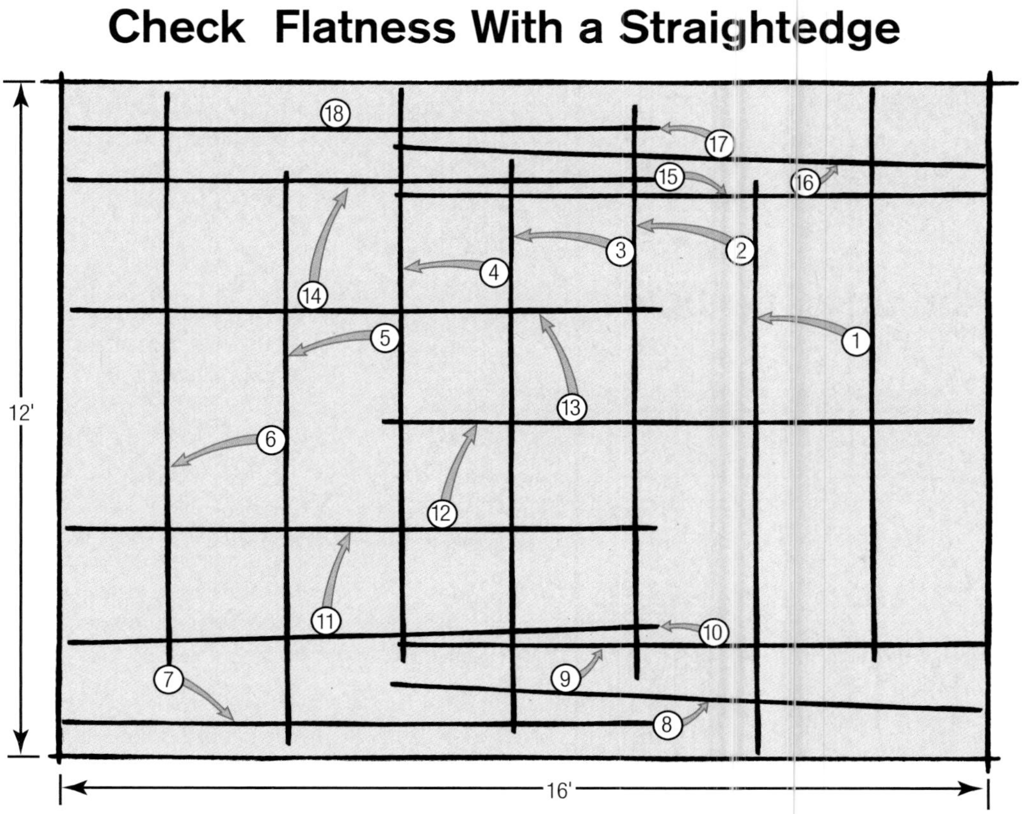

Check Flatness With a Straightedge

Figure 9-12. The author systematically determines flatness by stepping across the floor in each direction with a 5- or 10-foot straightedge.

12'

16'

straightforward. On floors, it starts with holding the straightedge against the floor, about one foot from the base of the wall, checking with the straightedge every foot across the length of the floor (Figure 9-12). After checking the floor in one direction, I rotate the straightedge 90 degrees and repeat the above steps to check the floor in the other direction.

While I have the straightedge in my hands, I also check the walls around the perimeter of the floor for straightness. If the wall has a bow or waviness, I will have to compensate for this in my layout.

If a surface is off spec, it is the responsibility of the installer to notify the architect or building owner before attempting to install tile or membrane. When the ANSI standards are invoked in a tile installation contract, it is easier to get such surfaces fixed or repaired. When the issue of surface flatness is not clearly defined, the building owner may not always want the problem fixed. If a building owner wants a good finish on the tile, it is unreasonable to expect that an installer can "fix" an out-of-level floor by

building up the thinset mortar under tiles. A patching compound or self-leveling underlayment should be used to correct an uneven floor—not thinset mortar.

Checking Horizontal Surfaces for Level and Vertical Surfaces for Plumb

Once I have determined that a floor, wall, or ceiling is flat enough, the next layout step is to determine if the surface is level or plumb. This can be done as a separate step or it can be done while checking a surface for flatness with a laser or straightedge (with a level placed on top). If done as a separate step, the same checking pattern used to determine flatness should be used. Placing a level on only one spot is not an accurate way to check for level. Floors and ceilings can also be checked for level with a laser and measuring tape or jury stick.

The industry minimum standard is level to within ¼ inch in 10 feet, but there can be exceptions either way. A fountain or pool spillway, for example, will require a higher tolerance of $\frac{1}{32}$ inch in 10 feet; the minimum standard for floors and ceilings would result in a lopsided cascade of water. On the other hand, I have installed floor tiles in older homes over setting beds that curved, sloped, dipped, and were anything but level; and yet the owners were happy with the results. Each floor has to be judged on its own.

A plumb bob, spirit level, or laser can be used to determine if a surface is plumb. For tiling, the two most critical plumb areas are inside and outside corners. If not corrected, out-of-plumb inside corners reveal themselves through unattractive, tapering cuts; and out-of-plumb outside corners make the smooth installation of factory-made trim pieces impossible.

Tile size is also a factor. Smaller tiles (less than 8 inches) exaggerate the appearance of tapered cuts at inside corners, while larger tiles tend to mask this problem. For example, with 12-inch wall tiles (laid out

---

Trade Tip:

Although I may be willing to tile an out-of-level floor under some dry-area conditions, I am very strict about eliminating negative slopes on wet-area floors, which can trap water or cause "birdbaths." The exceptions are floors that slope to drains. Wet-area ceilings may also require a slope. For example, a slope of 2 inches per foot is required on steam shower ceilings and recommended on regular showers by industry standards.

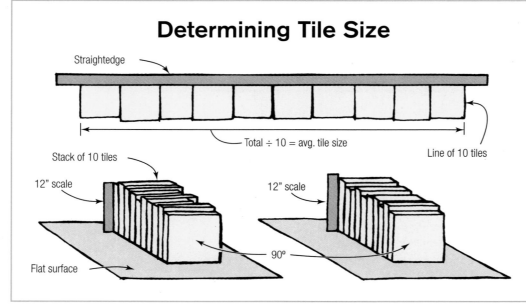

Determining Tile Size

Straightedge

Total ÷ 10 = avg. tile size

Line of 10 tiles

Stack of 10 tiles

12" scale

12" scale

90°

Flat surface

Figure 9-13. To find the average tile size, the author lines up 10 randomly selected tiles against a straightedge and divides their total length by 10 (shown along top). To find the longest dimension, he stacks the tiles sideways and measures the height, then rotates the stack 90-degrees and measures again.

properly, with no tiles less than half size), tapered side cuts on a wall that is out of plumb by a half inch, or even one inch, in 10 feet, may not be noticeable. Conversely, on walls that just meet the ¼-inch-in-10-foot standard, covered with ½-inch sheet mosaics (as an extreme example), a taper equal to ¼ inch would be difficult to ignore.

When tiling walls, as long as the inside and outside corners of a setting bed are plumb, I am not too concerned if the remaining parts of the wall don't meet the industry spec. This is especially true on remodeling projects where correcting existing out-of-plumb walls may not be feasible. A good example is a tub surround whose three walls are out of plumb. If the tile setting bed is corrected and made plumb, the inside corners of the tub surround will look good. However, the highly visible taper where the plumb tub surround meets the out-of-plumb bathroom walls would be totally unacceptable (see Figure 6-41, page 185). To create the appearance that the vertical edge of the tiled tub surround is plumb, the setting bed must be flush with the drywall. If corrections to an out-of-plumb inside corner cannot be made, the out-of condition can be neutralized by installing tiles larger than 10 inches. Selecting large tiles can give the illusion of plumb (or square) without the expense of rebuilding or correcting the structure.

Checking for Square

A floor that is level and flat can still be out of square. This will not affect the performance of the floor, but unless it is skillfully laid out, the finished installation may not be attractive. A carpenter's square can be used to determine if a floor is square, but it is only accurate to 2 feet, so I use a larger folding square or a laser square.

Lasers provide a much faster, more accurate method of checking for square over long distances. Under the right lighting conditions (twilight or darker), the laser square I use throws two perpendicular lines about 300 feet long. Under normal daytime lighting, the beams are visible up to about 100 feet.

If a floor is out of square, and no corrections can be made, I then have to determine if rotating the reference lines in one direction or another would help mask the problem. While this may work for single-floor applications, the method may cause more problems than it solves if it is used on a multi-floor job. Again, tile size plays a big role, with smaller tiles accentuating the problem and larger tiles masking it. At this point, though, I cannot make any determination about the final layout unless I know the size of the tiles being installed and the width of the grout joints. This is the second part of layout.

Measuring Tiles

Dealers and installers refer to tiles as 4 inch, 6 inch, 12 inch, and so on. In reality, though, very few tiles are manufactured in whole-number sizes. The numbers 4, 6, and 12 refer to a tile's nominal size, that is, its name for marketing purposes, not its actual size. To plot layout lines on a setting-bed surface, though, an installer needs to know the actual size of a tile plus the width of

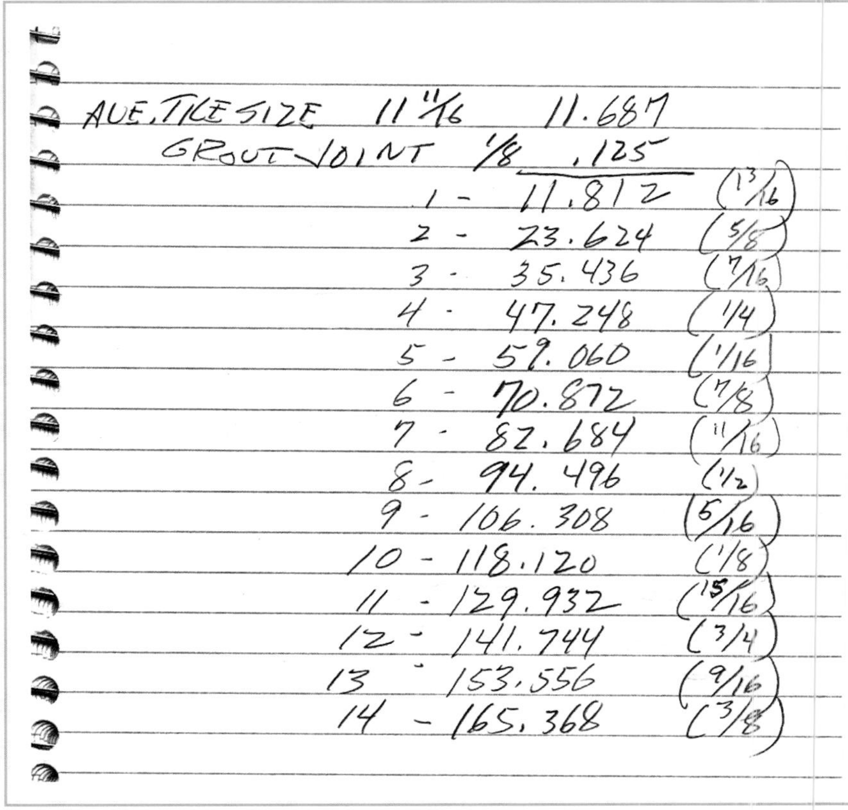

Figure 9-14. Using a calculator to tally progressive measurements, the author keeps track of single and multiple tile sizes, including grout joints, and jots the results in a notebook for future reference.

the grout joint. Actual size is something of a misnomer, however, because industry tolerances allow for around ⅛ inch of variance for a 12-inch tile. To help determine the true average size, I randomly select ten tiles from all the boxes of tile supplied for an installation, line them up against a straightedge (or chalk line) so there are no gaps between tiles, and divide the gross length by ten. This gives me an actual average tile size.

Next, I measure the ten tiles for the longest dimension. As shown in Figure 9-13, this is done by stacking ten tiles on edge and measuring the tallest height, then rotating the horizontal stack 90 degrees and measuring those heights. As a compromise, I find the midpoint between the tiles' average size and maximum size and use this as the average unit measurement for a single tile. (I make this adjustment so that large tiles in proximity will not appear too crowded, and small tiles will not have oversized grout joints.)

To this unit tile size, I add the desired grout joint width for a combined tile/grout-joint dimension that I use to plot a grid of layout lines. For 12-inch tiles, I like to plot a layout grid that produces approximately 3-foot squares. This is about the limit of my reach. To get the precise spacing, I multiply the unit average measurement by 2, 3, 4, 5, 6, 7, 8, 9, 10, or more, depending on floor size, and jot the results in my notebook for reference when I am plotting the lines (Figure 9-14). On large installations where it is impractical to dry-fit tiles to determine a layout, I transfer the unit measurements to a story pole.

Layouts for square or rectangular tiles are pretty straightforward, with layout lines visible through some of the grout joints for easy reference. When laying out tiles of other shapes, such as hexagon, octagon, or ogee, I still plot a grid of perpendicular layout lines, although the lines may be partially obscured by the tiles (Figure 9-15).

Determining a Layout

The final step in layout involves marking the setting bed with enough lines to guide the positioning of the tiles. Depending on the complexity and size of the

Layout of Non-Square Tiles

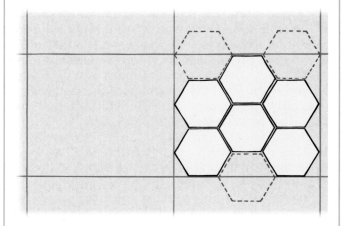

Figure 9-15. With non-square or non-rectangular tiles, a right-angle layout is the most accurate way to guide the placement of tiles.

Balanced Versus Unbalanced Layout

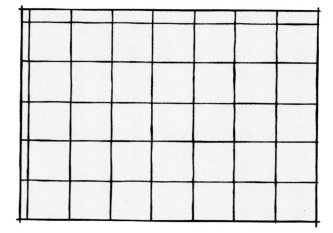 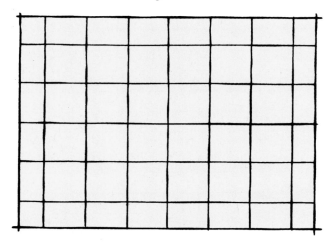

Figure 9-16. This unbalanced layout (left), marked by thirteen sliver cuts along two sides, looks uneven and amateurish. By centering and balancing the layout (right), the floor is symmetrical, with no tiles cut smaller than half size.

installation, I may need as few as one or two lines, or the job may call for dozens.

For example, when installing rectified 12-inch tiles that can be positioned with tile spacers on a floor less than 100 square feet, I rarely snap more than two perpendicular layout lines. When installing handcrafted tiles, whose variable sizing makes tile spacers unusable, I may snap 30 or 40 lines for a 1,000-square-foot floor.

The goal of a layout is to provide a balanced, attractive tiled surface, regardless of the quality or cost of the tile. I begin the layout process by using just two of the industry's workmanship standards:

- center and balance tiled areas (ANSI A108.02, 4.3.1)

- no cuts smaller than half-size (ANSI A108.02, 4.3.2)

For most installations, these are the only two standards an installer needs to produce a balanced layout. Some installers don't even bother with a balanced layout and, instead, begin with full tiles on two sides without regard to the size of the cuts needed on the other two sides. The result is an uneven layout, often with slivers on one or two sides—a very unprofessional appearance (Figure 9-16). Creating a balanced look requires more than just time spent on layout, it requires more tiles as well. The bottom layout in Figure 9-16 needs 48 tiles, while the top layout needs 42.

Using the same size as the examples above, Figure 9-17 shows another amateurish layout. This diagonal

installation requires 42 tiles and is marked by an unbalanced look and lots of different size pieces. Compare this to the layout in Figure 9-18. Thanks to the insert made from whole tiles and half and quarter diagonals only, and a border made from tiles greater than half size, it looks balanced and professional, although it needs more time to lay out and requires 48 tiles to complete. When a diagonal checkerboard is desired, quarter diagonals in the four corners of the insert create a balanced interface between the insert and border tiles (Figure 9-19).

The above examples are based on surfaces that meet the industry standards for straight and square. Layout orientation is even more important when the dimensions of a surface do not meet the minimum standards. The approach taken on the left of Figure 9-20 is an example of a worst-case layout, with no attempt to balance the cuts. The center layout eliminates the sliv-

Layout Tip

On most floors, I use a diagonal insert with a border made of tiles larger than half size, as shown in Figure 9-18. This layout has been used for thousands of years for two good reasons: The look is timeless, and this layout is very effective at masking "out-of" conditions because it draws the viewer's attention to the insert.

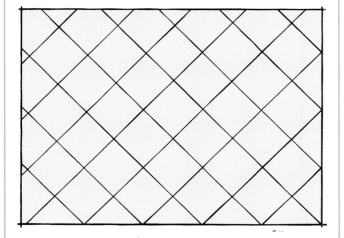

Unacceptable Diagonal Layout

Figure 9-17. With half diagonals and whole tiles along two sides, this floor looks unbalanced and uncentered, with several tiles far less than half size.

Classic Layout: Diagonal Inset With Border

Figure 9-18. With all the insert and border tiles balanced and with no tiles less than half size, this layout has a timeless, tailored look.

ers by shifting the layout so that all the perimeter cuts are greater than half size, but the resulting layout is rather plain. With its diagonal insert drawing a viewer's attention away from the perimeter, the layout on the right is the most elegant way to mask an out-of-square surface.

Plotting Reference Lines

I use a variety of mechanical and laser tools, but I prefer to use a laser square when checking a floor for square or when plotting reference lines for a layout because of its speed, simplicity, and accuracy. The laser square setup shown in Figure 9-21 helps explain the process I use to establish square:

1. mark the floor at equal distances (X) near each end of one wall

2. align one laser beam across the two marks

3. measure outward from the two perpendicular laser beams

Balancing reference lines. I make the first two measurements on the longest exterior wall or on the longest interior wall if no side of the floor runs parallel to an exterior wall. The reference lines are about one foot in from the wall for convenience—the exact distance doesn't matter. In a few minutes, and with measurements taken every foot or so, I can see how close the floor is to square (or not) and make adjustments to the reference lines as needed. The goal is to balance the reference lines in a way that helps mask problem areas when one or more sides of the floor are not straight or square. The adjustments involve shifting the reference lines one way or another and/or rotating them around the point where they cross. Keep in mind that if one reference line gets shifted slightly to compensate for an extreme out-of-square condition, the other line must be adjusted as well to maintain an exact right angle. This balancing process necessarily involves some compromise.

Once I am satisfied that the two perpendicular beams are balanced with the room, I use the 3-4-5 method to verify the accuracy of the beams and then convert the beams to chalk or pencil reference lines. Once the reference lines are plotted, they (instead of the inaccurate structural surfaces) become the foundation and point of reference for any layout lines that are added.

Plotting the Layout

Once I have determined the dimensions of the surfaces, tiles, and grout joint width, I use the reference

Consistent Border for Diagonal Checkerboard

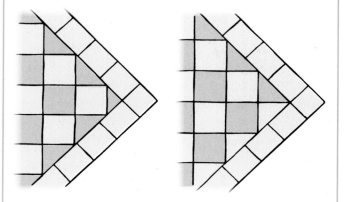

Figure 9-19. To avoid an inconsistent appearance where the insert tiles meet border tiles (right), a checkerboard layout requires quarter-diagonals in each corner of the insert (left).

Layout Tricks for Out-of-Square Surfaces

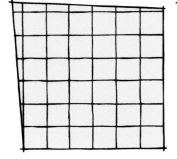
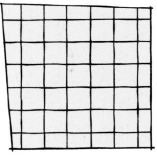
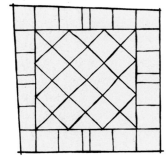

Figure 9-20. The example on the left shows how a poor layout exaggerates an out-of-square condition. The center example, adhering to the industry standard for workmanship, helps mask the problem. The example on the right, with its diagonal insert and border of tiles greater than half-size, effectively draws attention away from the out-of-square surface.

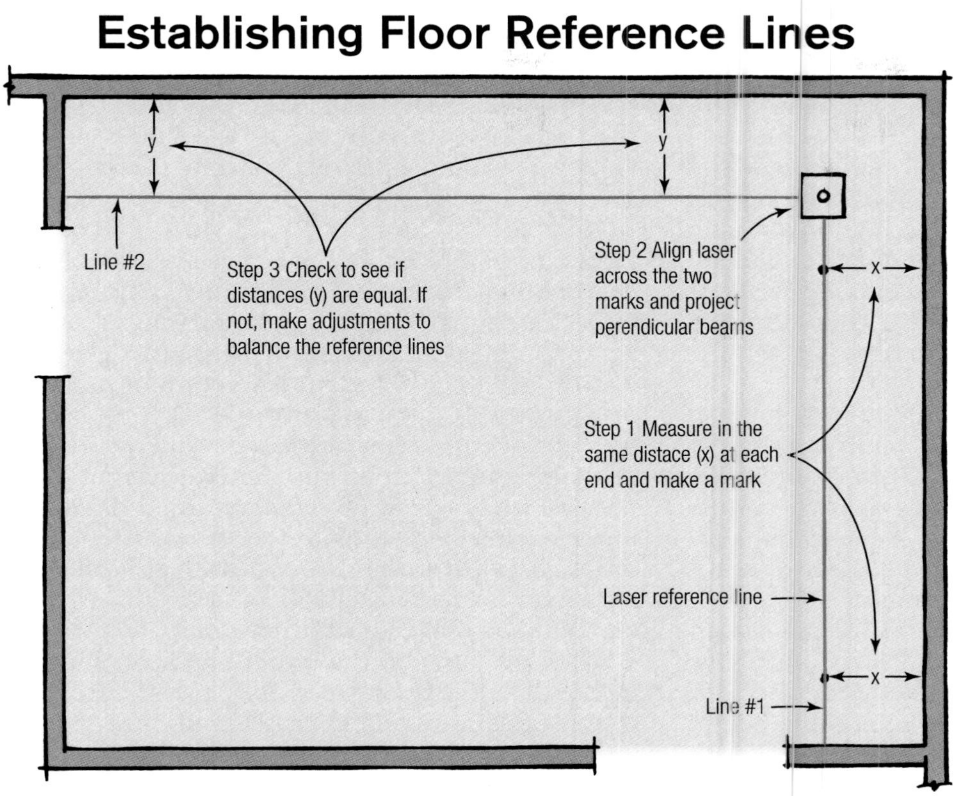

Establishing Floor Reference Lines

Line #2

y   y

Step 3 Check to see if distances (y) are equal. If not, make adjustments to balance the reference lines

Step 2 Align laser across the two marks and project perendicular beams

x

Step 1 Measure in the same distance (x) at each end and make a mark

Laser reference line

x

Line #1

Figure 9-21. The first step in floor layout is to measure the shape of the floor against two perpendicular laser (or chalk) lines. Snap chalk lines over the laser lines for a lasting reference. These reference lines can be made without a laser by first chalking the line that represents distance "x" from the wall and then using a square to establish the second reference line. With either method, some adjustment to "balance" the reference lines against the unevenness of the room may be required.

Plotting Floor Layout Lines

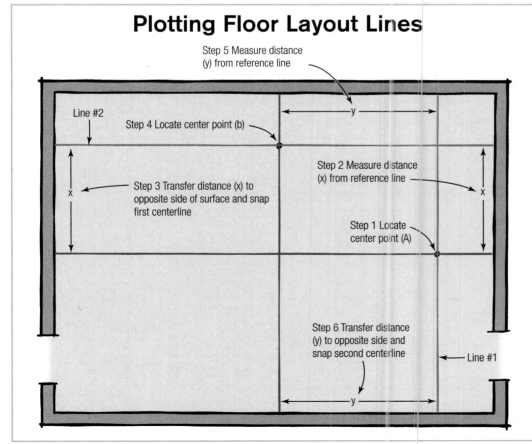

Step 5 Measure distance (y) from reference line

Line #2

Step 4 Locate center point (b)

y

Step 2 Measure distance (x) from reference line

x

Step 3 Transfer distance (x) to opposite side of surface and snap first centerline

x

Step 1 Locate center point (A)

Step 6 Transfer distance (y) to opposite side and snap second centerline

Line #1

y

Figure 9-22. Projecting center layout lines off the reference lines is the simplest approach to any size layout. Starting on one side of a surface, mark the center point and note its distance from the reference line. Transfer this distance to the other side of the surface, snap a line across the two points, and add another centerline, placed at 90 degrees to the first.

lines to plot layout lines. The layout lines determine the tile positions for most floor, wall, and countertop surfaces.

I use a centerline layout for most jobs, based on two perpendicular centerlines. I begin by marking the center point of Reference Line #1, in Figure 9-24, and then transfer the mark to Reference Line #2 and join the two marks with a chalk or pencil line to form a centerline. Next, I plot a second centerline at a right angle from the first. This is a basic two-line layout, and it is useful for small installations (less than 50 square feet) and for installations of machine-made tiles that can be installed with spacers. I sometimes forgo chalk or pencil lines and use a laser beam instead.

If a centerline layout produces cut tiles less than half size at the perimeter of the surface, I shift the lines to one side or another a distance equal to one half the size of the tiles. This produces a layout with no tiles smaller than half size (Figure 9-23). A tile layout with slivers along one or two edges of the tiled surface is very unprofessional, but all too common.

As the size of a surface increases, instead of centerlines, I tend to plot a grid of layout lines to suit the size of the tiles. For 12- or 18-inch tiles, I plot a 3x3-foot (nominal) grid; and for 16- or 24-inch tiles, I plot a 4x4-foot grid. To mark accurately, I begin at the longest reference line (#1) and plot a second parallel reference line (#3) at the opposite side of the room (Figure 9-24). Then working off the perpendicular ref-

erence line (#2), I plot another parallel line (#4) at the opposite side of the room. Next, to avoid sliver cuts, I use a list of tile/grout-joint-width dimensions (see Figure 9-14, page 239) to locate grid positions on the reference lines. The grid spacing should yield no cut tiles smaller than half size at the floor's perimeter. Finally, I snap the gridlines over the marks.

Estimating

Professional estimators have made a science out of determining amounts of tile and materials for a given project. For many installers, estimating is based on square or linear footage and is often just a guesstimate —with 10% or 15% added to account for broken tiles or mis-cuts. I don't use any special formula, and I don't have any estimating secrets to share, but when possible, I work out an installation's layout—tile for tile—on paper or on the actual setting bed. This is the most practical way to be certain there is enough tile on hand to cover the cuts and normal breakage that are a part of every installation and to ensure there are enough materials to finish the work.

When working out the layout on paper, a scale of 1 inch = 1 foot permits plenty of detail for an accurate count. When finished, I can determine the amount of whole tiles needed to cover the surface and provide stock for all the cut tiles that are required. When laying out a surface with 12-inch tiles, the resulting whole-tile count is useful for estimating installation materials.

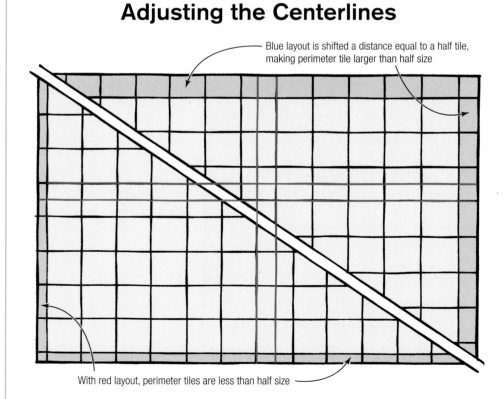

Adjusting the Centerlines

Blue layout is shifted a distance equal to a half tile, making perimeter tile larger than half size

With red layout, perimeter tiles are less than half size

Figure 9-23. No tile layout should have border tiles smaller than one-half tile. When a centerline layout produces tiles less than half size, the author shifts one or both centerlines a distance equal to one half the dimension of the tile to yield properly sized perimeter cuts.

When the installation calls for straight cuts with tiles 12 inches or less, I add 2 or 3 more tiles per 100 square feet to account for breakage. For a diagonal layout, I generally add 3 or 4 tiles per 100 square feet. When working with tiles larger than 12 inches, I add fewer tiles; with tiles smaller than 12 inches, I add more.

Staging

A grid of layout lines is helpful for more than just the positioning of tiles. A grid allows tiles to be staged for a more efficient, flexible, and productive installation. A comprehensive grid of lines allows helpers to make cuts ahead of the installer and minimizes the number of times an installer has to handle the tiles. Or stated another way, a grid of layout lines allows the installer to put his energy into production instead of lugging tiles around the site. Also, a layout grid gives an installer the opportunity to have all whole and cut

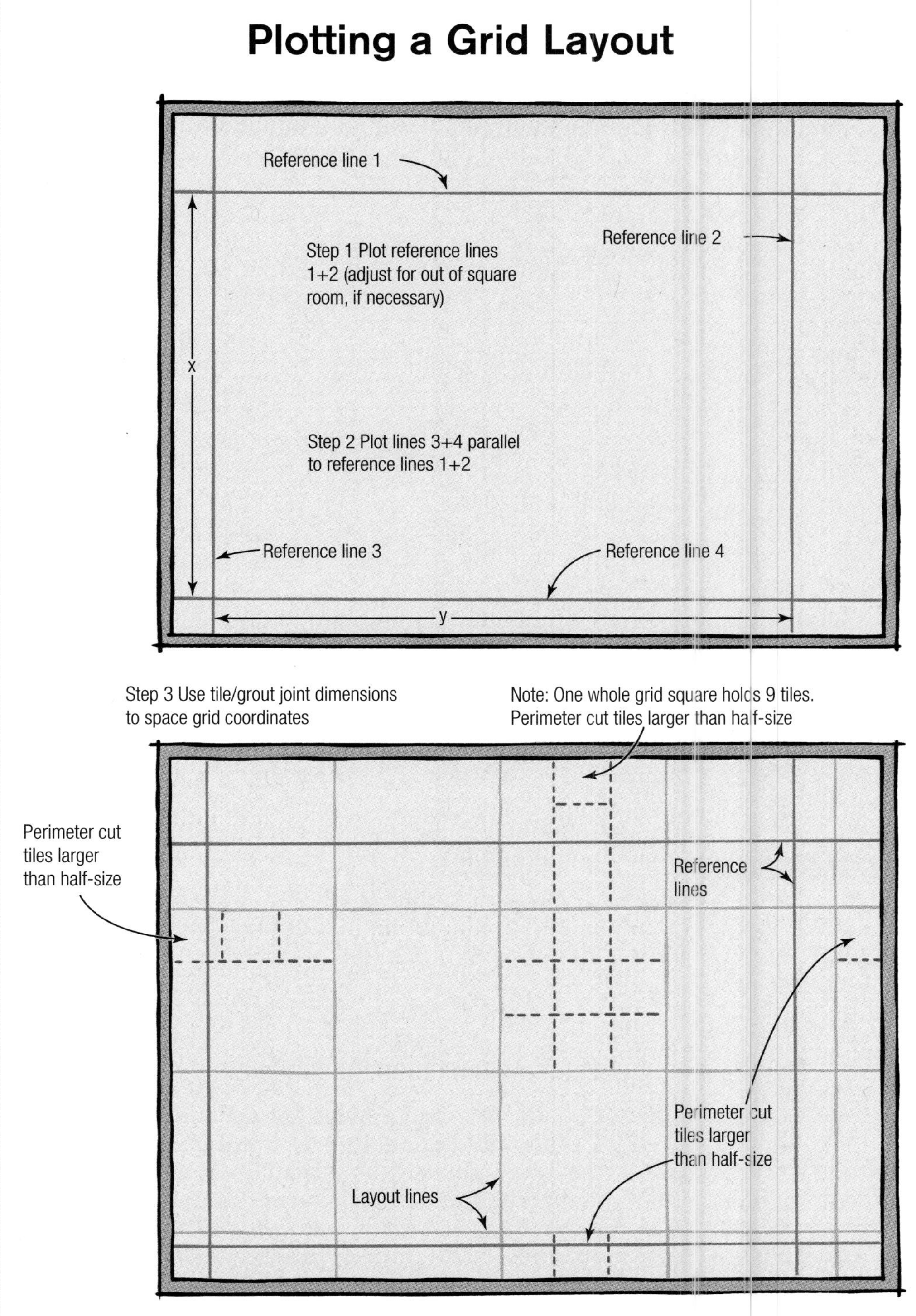

Plotting a Grid Layout

Reference line 1

Step 1 Plot reference lines 1+2 (adjust for out of square room, if necessary)

Reference line 2

x

Step 2 Plot lines 3+4 parallel to reference lines 1+2

Reference line 3

Reference line 4

y

Figure 9-24. To plot a grid of lines for larger surfaces, start with two sets of parallel reference lines, establishing a square layout (top).Then use tile/grout joint dimensions to plot a grid, making sure perimeter tiles are balanced and greater than a half tile wide (bottom). The size of the grid is related to how far the author can reach when installing tile. For example, he uses a 3x3-foot grid for 12-inch tiles.

Step 3 Use tile/grout joint dimensions to space grid coordinates

Note: One whole grid square holds 9 tiles. Perimeter cut tiles larger than half-size

Perimeter cut tiles larger than half-size

Reference lines

Perimeter cut tiles larger than half-size

Layout lines

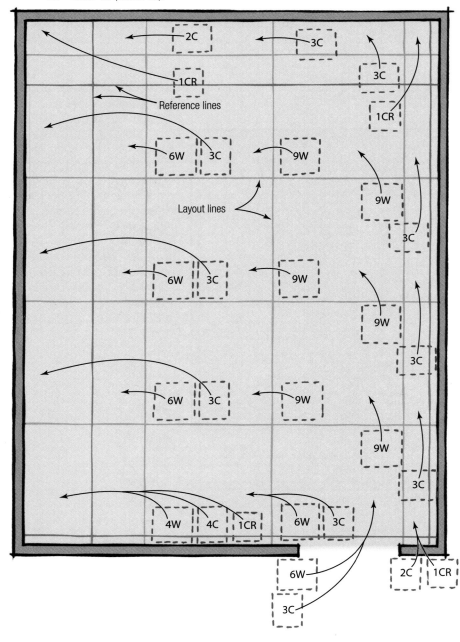

Staging Tiles for Increased Production

W = Whole Tile
C = Cut tile
CR = Corner tile (double cut)

Reference lines

Layout lines

2C
3C
1CR
3C
3C
1CR
6W 3C
9W
9W
3C
6W 3C
9W
9W
3C
6W 3C
9W
9W
3C
4W 4C 1CR
6W 3C
6W
3C
2C 1CR

Figure 9-25. Whether working alone or with a helper, the author prefers to stage all whole and cut tiles prior to the actual installation. When installing from left to right, tiles for each grid square should be stacked close by.

tiles staged within an arm's reach of the exact location each will be installed.

On larger floors, I typically stack tiles in such a way that as an installer uses a stack of tiles from one layout grid square he uncovers the next grid square on which tiles will be installed (Figure 9-25). Enough whole tiles are stacked to account for each square's whole and cut tiles. The cuts can be made at the time of the installa-tion, or they can be made beforehand.

When installing solo, I tend to make all cuts first, so they are immediately available while I am installing the whole tiles. If I have one or more helpers, I prefer to have the helpers cut as the whole-tile installation proceeds. If this is the case, only whole tiles are staged. Tiles needed for cuts are stacked close to the snap cut-ter or wet saw.

NOTES

NOTES

Chapter 10

MORTAR AND GROUT

ountless materials and mixtures have been used to secure and finish tiles. One of the earliest adhesives used for mosaics was an asphalt-like material gathered from naturally occurring pools and puddles over 4,500 years ago. Two thousand years ago mortars and colored grouts were made by mixing volcanic ash with powdered stone. First century Roman ruins at Bath reveal not just beautiful tile, but also all the underpinnings necessary for long tile life, such as waterproofing membranes, movement joints, mortar beds, and adhesives. For millennia, mortars of all types have been used to build and decorate structures that have endured and outlived their original owners by countless generations.

Today, with the exception of a few brands of genuine pozzolanic (fine volcanic ash) cement, tile installers use portland cement-based mortar beds, adhesives, and grouts. Portland-cement based materials are relatively inexpensive, easy to work with, and offer a level of performance and permanence that other materials cannot achieve. Perhaps most important for me, portland-cement grout has a look that has been inseparable from tile for thousands of years.

Epoxy grouts are another option widely available today. I reserve epoxy grouts for industrial, commercial, and other applications where appearance is secondary to performance. They are also required for certain chemical-resistant applications.

Mortar Selection

Like any other industry, tile installation has its own vocabulary, with regional dialects that may be completely meaningless in other regions. Even though I have tried to avoid jargon and use generic terminology, there still exists some confusion regarding concrete, mortar, and cement. Concrete is not considered a tile installation material, but it can be a solid base for setting-bed mortars. What is the difference between concrete and mortar? The primary difference is that concrete mixtures contain gravel and larger aggregates, while mortar mixtures contain no particles larger than sand grains, whose size and composition

change according to a particular mortar's application.

There are literally hundreds of different mortars available for construction, but for tiling, there are only two categories of mortar: filler and adhesive.

- Filler mortars include grout and mortars used to create or repair setting beds for floors, walls, and countertops.

- Adhesive mortars include all types of thinset mortars used to bond tile and membranes and to provide support for backerboards.

Most brands of portland cement-based thinset mortar are effective only when used in thin layers (with the exception of some brands of epoxy thinset that can be used as both tile adhesive and grout). Most regular thinset mortars should be applied from $3/32$ to $3/8$ inch thick. Medium-bed thinset mortars, which are specifically designed to be used in thicker cross sections, are effective up to $3/4$ inch thick.

Grouts are available either unsanded, for joints less than $1/8$ inch, or sanded, for joints $1/8$ inch or more. Sanded is something of a relative term since fine aggregates other than sand may be used for some lightweight grouts and thinset mortars. Generally, grouts used for wide joints contain coarser grades of sand or other aggregates in the recipe. In the past, packaged grouts were usually made according to a recipe of the Tile Council of North America (TCNA). Modern grouts, however, are highly proprietary, with each manufacturer carefully guarding its secret recipes.

Adhesive Mortar Types

Adhesive mortars (thinset mortars) are used to glue tiles and some types of membranes to a setting bed. They may also be used to bond filler mortars to concrete or existing mortar. Adhesive mortars achieve maximum strength when used in relatively thin layers, and most have thickness limits. For example, the industry standard minimum thickness for all types of adhesive mortars is $3/32$ inch, while the upper thickness limit is about $3/8$ inch for regular thinset mortar and around ¾ inch for medium-bed thinset mortar, depending on the brand (Figure 10-1).

Adhesive mortar should never be used as a filler, because it loses much of its structural properties once its thickness exceeds ⅜ inch (except medium-bed, which can be used up to ¾ inch thick.). However, adhesive mortar can be highly effective when used as a thin-film adhesive layer for bonding mortar to concrete to create a "bonded mortar bed" (the sloped shower bed floor in Project 3, Chapter 3, is an example of a bonded mortar bed). There are several distinct types of thinset mortar described below. Their performance levels tend to correspond with their cost. Expect to pay more for a high performance latex-thinset mortar, less for dry-set thinset mortar.

Of all the requirements for a low-maintenance, long-life tile installation, none is more critical than the adhesive bond between a tile and its setting bed. In practical terms, the adhesive layer is the glue that holds the setting bed and the tile together. The more a tile's back makes contact with the adhesive—increasing the contact area between the tile and setting bed—the stronger and more durable an installation becomes. One reason the industry has tile and installation standards for flatness is to get the back of the tile and the setting bed in plane to help improve adhesion. But more than flat surfaces are required. The thinset mortar selected must have the right properties to match the needs of the application, and the thinset mortar must also be applied carefully. Adhesive mortars include:

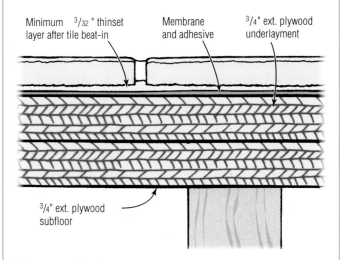

Thinset Mortar Application

Minimum ³⁄₃₂ " thinset layer after tile beat-in

Membrane and adhesive

¾" ext. plywood underlayment

¾" ext. plywood subfloor

Figure 10-1. Unlike filler mortars and concrete, regular thinset mortars (dry-set or latex/acrylic) achieve their highest strength in thin layers, from ³⁄₃₂ to ⅜ inch after the tiles are installed. Medium-bed thinset mortars can be installed up to ¾ inch in some applications.

Dry-set thinset mortar (ANSI A108.5, 118.1). It is composed of sand, portland cement, and trace ingredients that help retain water and is mixed without latex or acrylic additives. Its *dry-set* name comes from the fact that porous tiles can be set without first soaking them, as was required with older mortar bed installations.

Dry-set thinset mortar is the most basic, least expensive thinset. On the plus side, dry-set has high impact strength and compressive strength, and it can be used for both interior and exterior work. When cured, dry-set mortar is unaffected by exposure to water, but it is not a barrier to water. Dry-set mortar can be used to install many types of ceramic and stone tiles and as a bond coat between a concrete slab and leveling mortar.

On the downside, dry-set mortar must be damp-cured to achieve its anticipated strength. In practice, it usually dries out too quickly and never properly cures. This inconvenience is one reason I usually avoid dry-set thinset mortar (curing requirements are less stringent for latex-modified thinset). Although dryset has high compressive strength, it has little tensile strength or flexibility, making it unsuitable for use over wood floors. It is also not suitable for impervious materials such as porcelain, to which it does not bond well.

Latex portland cement thinset mortar (ANSI A108.5, 118.4). It is composed of sand, portland cement, and trace ingredients and is mixed with a liquid latex, acrylic, or other polymer instead of water. Generally speaking, latex-thinset mortars have greater adhesion, bond strength, compressive strength, and resistance to shock or impact than dry-set mortars. They are also more resistant to water absorption. Latex-thinset mortar is required for the installation of porcelain tiles.

Many latex-thinset mortars can achieve the 28-day cured strength of dryset thinset mortars in about a week. Nevertheless, latex and polymer-modified thinset mortars have special curing requirements if they are used on any installation whose tiles are partially or completely submerged in water (ponds, pools, etc.). Often, a full 28 days of curing is required before the installation can be submerged. (Note: 28 days of curing is the industry standard for measuring the strength of cement products, since they achieve most of their strength by that time.)

Polymer-modified portland cement thinset mortar (ANSI A108.5, 118.4). It is composed of sand, portland cement, trace ingredients, plus a latex or other polymer additive in powdered form. Polymer-modified thinset mortars require only the addition of water for mixing, and like latex-thinset mortars, they generally have greater strength and less absorption than dry-set thinset mortar. Polymer-modified thinset mortar is also recommended for installing porcelain tiles.

Some polymer-modified thinset mortars can be mixed with a specified liquid latex for higher strengths and lower absorption rates. However, this must be done in strict accordance with the manufacturer's recommendations. Polymer-modified mortars require special curing procedures for submerged installations, similar to the requirements for latex portland cement thinset mortars, described above.

Exterior glue plywood (EGP) latex portland cement mortar (ANSI A108.12, 118.11). This thinset mortar is specially formulated for directly bonding tiles to plywood underlayment. Depending on the brand, it is either mixed with a liquid latex additive, or it contains a dry polymer ingredient and is mixed with water. It is stored, mixed, applied, and cured like all other latex portland cement thinset mortars.

Epoxy resin mortar (ANSI A108.4, A108.6, A118.3). Sometimes referred to as "100% solids epoxy," it is available in two forms: chemical-resistant (ANSI A108.6, 118.3) and non-chemical resistant (ANSI A108.4, 118.3). Both are site mixed and comprise a liquid resin, a liquid hardener, and an inert gritty powder base. Compared with dry-set thinset mortar, epoxy mortars generally have more bond strength. Since their site-mixed resin and hardener components contain no water, they are recommended particularly for stone tiles, which are known to warp when installed with dry-set or latex portland cement mortars.

> *Trade Tip:* Epoxy resin thinset mortars are best mixed in small batches by hand. Power mixing generates heat, which can significantly reduce this thinset mortar's pot life. Epoxy resin thinset mortar is applied the same way other thinset mortars are spread and combed out, but its free-flowing nature demands that this work be done quickly. It is also sensitive to temperature.

Unlike portland-cement thinset mortars, which can be mixed in virtually any amount from a spoonful to a full sack, a batch of epoxy resin thinset mortar must be mixed in its entirety (most brands are available in multiple-size kits). The thicker the mass of the mixed epoxy, the more heat is generated by the catalyzation of its components. When working with this material, I maintain as low a room temperature as practical and schedule work in the evening or early morning, when the sun is not out and ambient temperatures are at their lowest. If possible, air conditioning before and during an installation can greatly prolong pot life.

On the other hand, cold epoxy resin and hardener are difficult to mix. For this reason, I tend to acclimate the epoxy ingredients to around 70°F for ease of mixing and spreading and usually empty the mixing bucket as soon as possible. For tiles 12 inches or larger, I keep the mix in the bucket because it will be used within 5 or 10 minutes—not long enough for heat to build up. But when working with smaller tiles that take more time and attention and fewer dips into the bucket, the chemical reaction can generate enough heat to turn a half bucket of mix into a hot, smoldering, bubbling eruption that quickly turns to stone—an extreme event, but I've seen it happen. (This problem can also be triggered by mixing a new batch in a bucket containing unhardened epoxy residue from a previous batch.)

To avoid problems when working with tiles that take a lot of time to install, I get the epoxy out of the bucket, where heat will build up. Once the epoxy resin is mixed, I dump it onto the floor, scrape the bucket clean, and let the mix spread out into a thin puddle, which will not concentrate heat. I dip into the thin layer with a trowel each time more epoxy thinset is needed.

Epoxy-emulsion thinset mortar (ANSI A108.9, 118.8). This is a mixture of resin and hardener with a powder base of sand and portland cement. This type of epoxy mortar is usually less expensive than the resin type. It has high bond strength, but it is not chemical resistant. Unlike the resin type, epoxy emulsion thinset mortar cannot be used over plywood underlayment, but only over concrete, mortar, and cement backerboards. When first introduced, its bond and cohesive strength were higher than existing portland cement thinsets, but with improvements in technology, many of today's latex thinsets have bond and cohesive strengths higher than this type of epoxy thinset mortar.

Furan resin mortar (ANSI A108.8, 118.8). This resin-and-hardener thinset has very high chemical resistance, making it ideal for many types of industrial and food-service applications. It is also one of the most difficult thinset mortars to mix and install. The material is highly caustic until it has cured hard. Installers need eye, nose, mouth, throat, lung, and skin protection during the mixing, application, and initial cleaning of furan thinset mortar.

I can think of no reason for this type of thinset to be used on any residential or light-commercial building. My own experience with the material, limited to dairy operations, convinced me to avoid it whenever possible. When furan is specified, I recommend you approach the manufacturer (or others) to see if there is a reasonable alternative. For me, it is only used as a last resort.

Specialty mortars. These are generally marketed as excelling at one thing. For example, Custom Building Product's MegaLite Crack Prevention Mortar is a combination adhesive and crack-isolation membrane.

Most specialty mortars are latex based and are specifically designed for use with hard-to-install tile materials, such as impervious stone, porcelain, metal, and glass. Depending on the brand, they can be a dry polymer that is activated by mixing with water, a dry-set powder base mixed with a latex, or a dry polymer thinset mortar mixed with a latex. Although their strength and performance properties are usually much higher than the minimum standard, specialty mortars should be marked that they comply with ANSI A108.5 and 118.4.

Medium-bed thinset mortar. This term refers to a thinset mortar that can be used in layers up to ¾ inch thick. At the time of this writing, it does not have either an installation or material specification, so the term *medium bed* is primarily a marketing term. Medium-bed thinset mortars are particularly useful when installing large tiles (larger than 12 inches), a batch of tiles whose thickness varies, or tiles whose backs are not flat (Project 2, Chapter 3 demonstrates the installation of 24x24-inch tiles with a medium-bed thinset). Some medium-bed thinset mortars are not recommended for installing porcelain or glass tiles. Medium-bed installations require more time than regular thinset mortars for drying and curing before grouting can begin. Since most medium-bed thinset mixes are dry polymer or latex added, they should meet ANSI A108.5 and 118.4 standards.

Organic adhesives. Forty years ago, I used carloads of solvent-based organic adhesives with few problems in wet or dry areas. With many solvents banned by law, most organic adhesives for tile installation now have a latex base. Unfortunately, many latex-based organic adhesives have one property that is not shared by their solvent-based cousins: They re-emulsify if they become wet. That means that after a certain amount of exposure to water or moisture (varies by brand), cured organic adhesive can soften or even dissolve. For this reason alone, organic adhesives should never be used to install tiles in wet areas.

Another problem with organic adhesive makes it unsuitable for many dry installations as well, i.e., those with large tiles. As the size of a tile increases, so should the amount of glue beneath it. According to industry recommendations, adhesive for a 12-inch tile should be spread with a ¼x½x¼-inch U-notch trowel, producing an adhesive layer about ¼ inch thick. This amount of organic adhesive under a 12-inch tile takes a long time to evaporate the solvent and harden. During inspections, I have found organic adhesive that is still soft 12 months after it was applied and covered with tile (Figure 10-2). For this reason, many tile manufacturers specify latex-thinset mortar or epoxy adhesive for installing large tiles, not organic mastic adhesive.

The problems and limitations of organic mastic, combined with its relatively low compressive and shear strength, make it a suitable choice for decorative, dry-area, interior installations located away from any heat sources or the direct rays of the sun. However, for functional tilework, I avoid organic adhesives and recommend latex-thinset mortar, instead.

Using Adhesive Mortars

Assuming that a particular structure is sound, flat, plumb, and level enough to meet installation requirements, the first job is to select the right thinset mortar. For me, that begins with a look at the blueprints or a visit to the installation site. Then, once I establish the needs of a particular installation, it is not too difficult to select the most appropriate materials.

I start by looking at the inventories of my local suppliers and check vendor websites with full product lines (if I need to order a material not stocked locally). For most residential or light-commercial applications, rather than order special materials, I am more likely to choose the best latex or polymer thinset available, with cost a secondary consideration. If I was buying for a multi-installation tract project, I would be more cost conscious, but for smaller scale work, the difference in cost between the best and good enough is minimal. When buying less common materials—medium-bed thinset mortar, for example—there may not be a choice unless you are fortunate enough to be near a large distributor carrying several competing brands.

Storage and Mixing

All the suppliers I buy from have indoor storage so materials are never exposed to the elements. Exposure to sunlight and extreme cycles of heating and cooling can ruin a thinset or grout sitting on a pallet outdoors.

Storage on site. Upon pickup, tile and installation materials should be stored close to the site in a covered location, ideally at room temperature. For best results, room temperature conditions should be main-

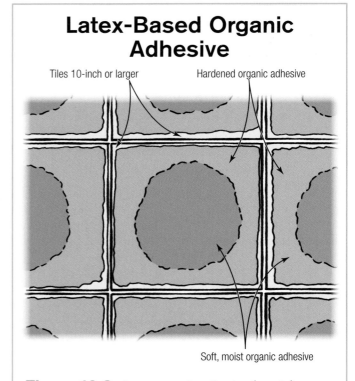

Latex-Based Organic Adhesive

Tiles 10-inch or larger

Hardened organic adhesive

Soft, moist organic adhesive

Figure 10-2. As an organic adhesive (mastic) cures under a large-format tile, the resulting tough hide around the exterior prevents the interior adhesive from curing, resulting in a soft area that cannot properly support the tile.

tained at the installation site until all materials have cured. If you must mix thinset powder that is hotter than room temperature, you can reduce its temperature—and extend its pot life—by mixing with ice water. However, do not use hot water to raise the temperature of thinset powder that is colder than room temperature! Hot water triggers and accelerates the hydration process that turns powder into stone.

Mixing. There are several keys to good mixing: clean mixing container, consistent wet/dry ratios, and low-speed mixing. Mixing at higher than 300 RPM whips air into the mortar and weakens it. A clean mixing container for each batch is essential. Thinset residue left over from a previous batch can accelerate hardening and reduce pot life. If more than one batch is needed, maintaining consistent wet/dry ratios is simplified when whole sacks and a smart bucket are used. The smart bucket (page 280) I have now is good for all the materials I can obtain locally, including thinset mortars, grouts, and self-leveling underlayment. For small batches (less than a gallon of thinset), I use a margin trowel for mixing. For larger amounts, I use a power mixer with a two-handed grip that is made specifically for tile installation materials (Figure 10-3).

The process begins by reading and complying with package instructions. Next, I pour the required amount of water (or latex) into the mixing container and, with the mixer powered on, gradually add from one-half to three-quarters of the amount of powder until there are few or no lumps (never pour in the powder first, or you risk leaving the bottom of the bucket filled with unmixed material). When the mix is smooth, I add the remaining powder, continue mixing until the entire batch is finished, allow it to slake for 10 minutes or as required by the brand, and then give it another 30 to 60 seconds of mixing. Slaking allows moisture to penetrate any dry lumps or particles and is an essential part of mixing thinset mortar. Some brands may have a specific time limit for power mixing.

If I cannot use a 5-gallon bucket of mix within 10 or 15 minutes, I scrape down the bucket and re-mix to prolong pot life (mortar that just sits motionless in the bucket begins to set up early). As mentioned above, when another batch is needed, the new batch should be mixed in a clean bucket. Either use a new bucket or completely remove all traces of the old batch.

Testing for Proper Notch Size

A ¼-inch square notch trowel was all an installer needed when only 4- and 6-inch tiles were available. But for 12-, 24-, and 36-inch tiles, a much wider selection of trowels is required, all of them larger than the ¼-inch square notch. Charts have long been available to help pick the right trowel to use (see Table 10-1,

What About Mastic?

Called mastic in the trade, organic adhesives are premixed materials (under ANSI A108.4) for bonding ceramic tiles. Despite the ready availability of quality thinset mortars, mastic is still widely used today by many installers. Mastics are ready to use and require no further mixing other than to stir in the moisture that may have separated out of the adhesive during storage.

Mastic is convenient and easy to use. However, in my opinion, it is only good for interior applications and only with ceramic tile—not stone, glass, or porcelain. I rarely use or recommend it for anything other than purely decorative applications located away from sources of heat, dampness, and direct sunlight. Organic adhesives should not be used on any surfaces and in any environment that exceeds 140°F, and most should never be used to install porcelain or glass tile, because mastic doesn't bond well to impervious surfaces.

Figure 10-3. Using a specialty mortar mixer is the safest, most economical way to mix thinset mortar, grout, and other tiling materials. Here, the author mixes a batch of self-leveling compound.

below), but charts are merely a rough guide. Testing a trowel on site using the project adhesive, tiles, and setting bed is the only way to determine which trowel gives the desired coverage. The industry standard for minimum adhesive coverage on the back of each tile is:

- 80% coverage for dry-area installations

- 95% coverage for wet-area or exterior installations

- adhesive to be uniformly distributed across tile surface

I generally do the test while the bucket of thinset mortar is slaking after being mixed. To test, I spread thinset mortar with my best-guess trowel on the surface to be tiled. I use the trowel's smooth edge to force the mortar into the setting bed surface and build up a thick layer, then comb with the trowel's notched edge. Next, I press a tile into the adhesive ridges and remove

it to see if the trowel delivers the coverage I want (Figure 10-4). The goal is to find the smallest notch-size trowel that will provide at least 95% thinset coverage, the industry standard for wet-area installations (and the standard I use for all my installations). If I don't achieve 95% coverage, I make another guess and test it, spreading and combing thinset on an unused section of the setting bed. It may take a few tests to determine the right trowel to use.

If the setting bed is uneven, I may need to go up a trowel notch size or two to account for the degree of unevenness.

Once the right-size notch trowel has been selected, I use it to spread and comb thinset mortar on the setting bed. To maximize adhesion, on most jobs I supplement the thinset I spread on the setting bed by back buttering each tile (Figure 10-5). Back buttering techniques are described in more detail below.

Spreading Thinset Mortar

The first step in spreading thinset mortar is to use the smooth edge of the notched trowel to fully coat the surface with thinset mortar (Figure 10-6). This first step of "keying" the mortar to the setting bed is done whether the installation is horizontal, vertical, or upside down on a ceiling. The harder you can press against the surface, the greater the adhesion of the thinset to the setting bed. The next step is to add more thinset to the skim coat—at least half the depth of the notch. Then use the notched side of the trowel, held at a consistent angle, to comb out uniform ridges of adhesive and remove excess thinset mortar.

For best results, comb the ridges in one direction only. It may take several passes to remove the excess. Also, you may need to add more thinset to ensure all ridges are fully formed. The purpose of combing the

Table 10-1. Notched Trowel Selection	
Trowel Size	**Tile Size**
$1/4$x$1/4$x$1/4$-inch square notch	Up to 6 inches
$1/4$x$3/8$x$1/4$-inch square notch	4 to 10 inches
$1/4$x$1/2$x$1/4$-inch U-notch	8 to 14 inches
$3/8$x$3/4$x$3/4$-inch U-notch trowel	12 to 18 inches

Note: Use as a rough guide only. Test trowel size on site to make final selection.

Figure 10-4. The tile on the far left exceeds the industry standard of 95% adhesive coverage. The tile on the right falls short with about 50% coverage, which could lead to cracking and moisture penetration.

Figure 10-5. To maximize the adhesive bond, the author back butters a thin layer of thinset mortar on this 6-inch tile with a flat trowel.

Figure 10-6. When spreading thinset mortar, the author first scoops thinset onto the floor with a notched trowel (A). Next, he uses the smooth edge of the trowel to "key" the mortar into the setting bed (B) and then uses the notched side to comb out uniform ridges of mortar (C).

thinset with a notch trowel is to produce a uniform layer. Far from being a one-step process, it requires multiple passes of the trowel to ensure that the adhesive layer really is uniform and the desired thickness (Figure 10-7).

For an installer, the most important part of handling a notched trowel is maintaining a consistent trowel-to-setting-bed angle. A slow, consistent speed is important, too; spreading too quickly results in ridges that are slender rather than full. When doing floor work, I use a notch trowel to scoop thinset mortar from a bucket, dump it on the floor, and begin spreading and combing. On wall work, I generally scoop thinset mortar out of its mixing bucket with a margin trowel, transfer this to the notch trowel, and then onto the wall. Gravity helps for floor work, but it works against an installer doing wall work. For best results when applying thinset mortar to a wall surface, don't load the notch trowel with too much thinset mortar.

Controlling squeeze-out. The notch trowel, and the ridges it produces, are essential for applying a uniform layer of thinset mortar. However, if the tiles are very thin, the ridges of thinset are likely to be squeezed out into the grout joints, requiring extra time spent on cleaning. (This type of cleaning can become your worst nightmare if the tiles are thin mounted mosaic tiles.) A thinner layer of mortar will solve that, but switching to a smaller notch size causes an even greater problem: not enough adhesive coverage. The solution is to spread and comb the thinset mortar as

Figure 10-7. To ensure a uniformly thick layer, the author re-combs the mortar in multiple passes.

usual to produce uniform layer. Then, to solve the ooze problem, use the smooth edge of the trowel to gently flatten the adhesive ridges (Figure 10-8). The ridges are not essential for good bonding, but rather for gauging the desired amount of adhesive.

Lippage

Lippage is a term used to describe differences in height between neighboring tiles. Traditionally, when most tiles were installed over a soft, fresh mortar bed, lippage was kept to a minimum by using a beating block and gentle taps of a hammer to coax the surface of the tiles into a smooth, even plane. Tiles were adhered with a very thin (approximately $1/16$-inch) layer of adhesive made from a mixture of portland cement and water mixed to the consistency of a runny paste. Regardless of the size or flatness of a tile, the thickness of the adhesive layer remained more or less the same.

Today, using thinbed techniques and hard setting beds, this method can easily result in broken tiles. Instead of using a beating block and hammer to reduce lippage, a thinbed installer needs to adjust the thickness of the adhesive layer (Figure 10-9) to account for a setting bed surface that is not perfectly flat. Varying the adhesive thickness may also be required because tile manufacturing standards allow a certain amount of warpage—a deviation from flatness. Table 10-2 shows industry standard allowances for lippage and warpage for common types of tile. Adding the two, the "Combined" column shows the total allowable tolerance for unevenness between tiles.

I prefer to limit lippage to the thickness of a dime—about $1/32$ inch—for tiles of any size and often have to

Table 10-2. Lippage and Warpage Allowances

Tile Type	Tile Size	Joint Width	Lippage	Warpage	Combined
Glazed Wall	1" to 6"	< $1/8$"	$1/32$"	$1/32$"	$1/16$"
Quarry	6" to 8"	> $1/4$"	$1/16$"	$1/16$"	$1/8$"
Paver	All	$1/8$" to $1/4$"	$1/32$"	$1/8$"	$5/32$"
Paver	All	> $1/4$"	$1/16$"	$1/8$"	$3/16$"

Note: Industry standards include tolerances for both lippage and warpage.

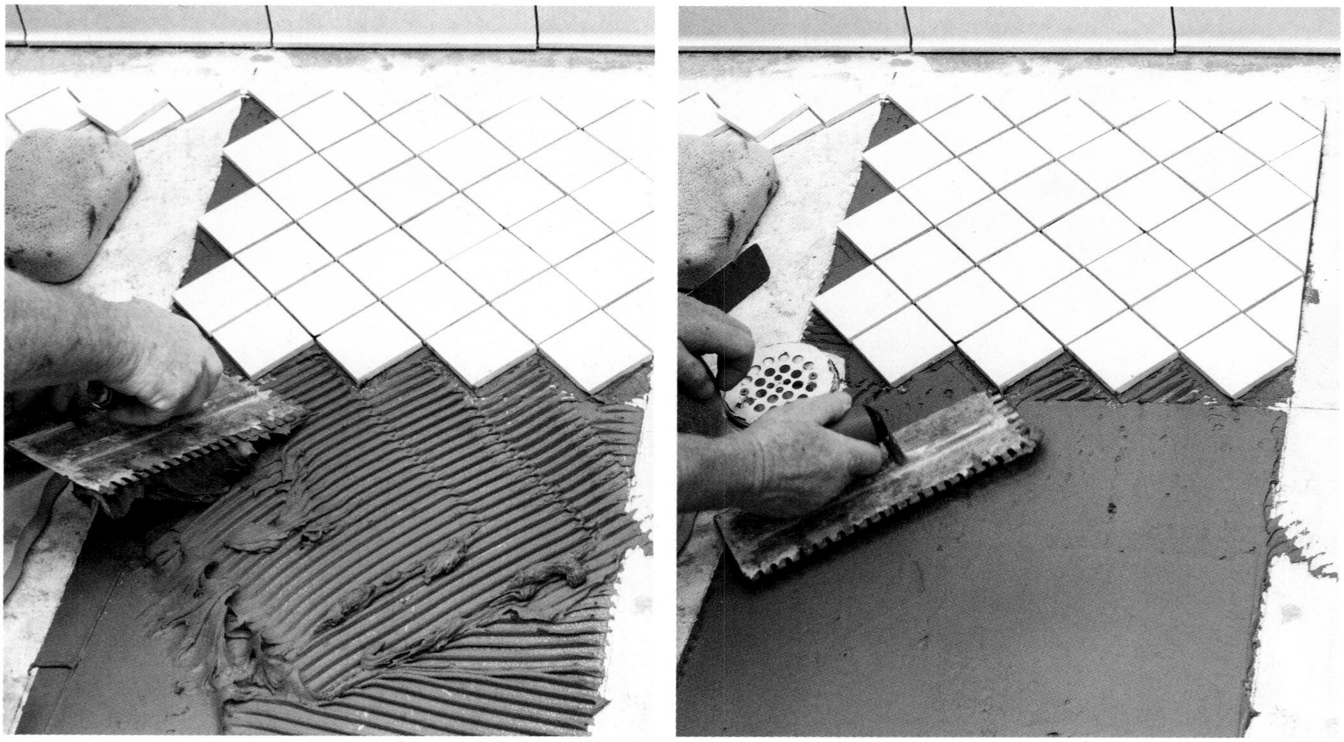

Figure 10-8. To prevent the adhesive ridges from clogging the grout joints of thin tiles, the author first keys the mortar into the setting bed with the smooth edge of the trowel, combs out uniform ridges with the notched edge (left), then uses the smooth edge to gently flatten the ridges (right).

cull out a few extremely warped tiles to maintain the smooth surface I want. By careful selection, and with enough tiles to be picky, it is possible to produce a smooth installation as long as the adhesive layer is thick enough to allow for some tile adjustment. As the combined allowance increases, so too must the adhesive layer be proportionately increased (Figure 10-9).

Installing Tiles

After layout lines are plotted, the time for installing tiles has arrived. What to do first? When tiling floors, I usually begin tiling as far from the exit as possible and tile my way out of the room. Gravity makes spreading adhesive and positioning tiles easier than wall installations, and it helps press the tiles against the adhesive. When tiling walls, I generally begin by setting up a ledge (Figure 10-10) on which I can install tiles in the second row and all rows above. The next day, or as soon as the thinset mortar has set up, I remove the ledge and install the first row of wall tiles.

Checking for Coverage

Most industries maintain quality by inspecting a statistical sample of the parts or products they make. For quality assurance in tile setting, the industry recommends that installers remove every tenth tile to see if there is 80% to 95% uniform adhesive coverage. Industry specs call for 80% coverage in dry areas, but I apply the wet-area standard of 95% coverage to all my installations for maximum performance. Removing and replacing an installed tile can be messy, but I use a quick-release suction cup (Figure 10-11), plus a little help with a margin trowel, to keep the tile and my hands clean and to avoid disturbing neighboring tiles.

Caution: Spot-bonding (sometimes referred to as "4 spot" or "5 spot") has long been used by some installers to set tile. However, this method has proved to be very problematic when used to install tiles on floors in wet-area applications and on exterior tilework (Figure 10-12). So I do not recommend the practice, even though the TCA Handbook contains a spot-bonding method (TCA Method W215-09) that calls for large-format tiles to be installed over dry-area walls (only) using a special spot-bonding epoxy. Tiles may certainly stick to a wall with this method, but condensation patterns on the surface of the tiles may reveal the locations of the spots of epoxy. Additionally, 4 or 5 spotting does not provide enough support for floor tiles, and when used in wet areas, voids below the tile can harbor moisture and mold. When used on exterior tile installations, this method harbors moisture and mold in warm climates and causes freeze/thaw damage in cold climates.

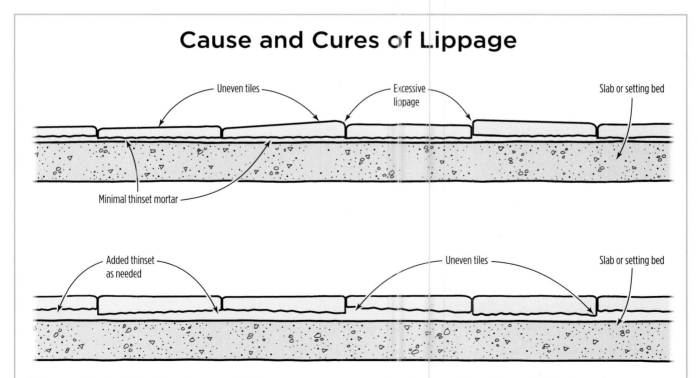

Cause and Cures of Lippage

Uneven tiles — Excessive lippage — Slab or setting bed

Minimal thinset mortar —

Added thinset as needed — Uneven tiles — Slab or setting bed

Figure 10-9. With tiles of uneven thickness or an uneven setting bed, a minimal layer of thinset mortar always results in a heavily lipped installation (top). Applying additional thinset allows for some adjustment when tiling over a less-than-perfect surface or with irregular tiles (bottom).

Back Buttering

Back buttering is the simplest way to improve adhesion with most tiles over 4x4 inches. It is generally not practical for sheet-mounted or face-mounted tiles under 3x3 inches (which should be installed according to ANSI A108.14, A108.15, or A108.16 standards). Back buttering serves two main functions:

- to key the adhesive to the back surface of the tile, ensuring a good bond

- to vary the thickness of the adhesive layer to make up for unevenness in the setting bed or tile.

With some types of tile, back buttering may be the only way to achieve 95% minimum adhesive coverage. For example, some hollow-backed tiles require back buttering to fill manufacturing voids or hollow patterns on the backs of the tiles. Filling the hollows is necessary to maintain adhesive coverage as well as eliminate voids in the adhesive layer.

Back buttering is not a slap-dash troweling of some adhesive onto a tile's back, but rather it is carefully applying a uniform layer of adhesive. When back buttering is used to improve the adhesive bond (with flat tiles and a flat setting bed), only a thin layer is needed—less than $\frac{1}{16}$ inch is fine—applied with the smooth edge of the trowel. The back-buttered layer should be wet and tacky when it is set onto the setting bed adhesive.

When back buttering is used to help compensate for unevenness in the tile or setting bed, I apply the thinset at varying thicknesses with a notched trowel to account for variations in the tile or setting bed. For most floor tiles, I use a small wooden work platform that moves around the floor as the work proceeds. But for very large tiles, I tend to use a portable folding work table that remains in one place (Figure 10-13). With smaller tiles, I simply hold the tile in one hand and a trowel in the other (Figure 10-14).

When installing floor tiles in heavy-traffic areas, I am always concerned about tile-corner cracking. To ensure this does not happen, I supplement back buttering by adding a small amount of thinset to the corner of each tile just before installing (Figure 10-15).

When installing cement backerboards in a hybrid shower (backerboard walls, sloped mortar bed floor), I back butter the lower edges of boards in a process described in Chapter 2, page 46.

Tile Types

Different tile types require different installation techniques. The main types of tile I generally work with are described below.

Tiles with spacing lugs. A level ledge, as shown in Figure 10-10, provides necessary support for wall tiles and allows me to work quickly. Installing self-spacing tiles requires skill, patience, and consistency to keep the spacing lugs clean. Before making contact with the adhesive, the first step is to ensure that opposing lugs are in contact (Figure 10-16), then push the tile into

Figure 10-10. By clamping straightedges together to bridge over the curb (top), the author creates a straight, level ledge to support the wall tiles until their adhesive sets up. Tile and wood shims help level the ledge and support it after the straightedge is removed (bottom).

Figure 10-11. To avoid a mess or displacing neighboring tiles, the author uses a quick-release suction cup to remove tiles for inspection.

Spot Bonding Tile

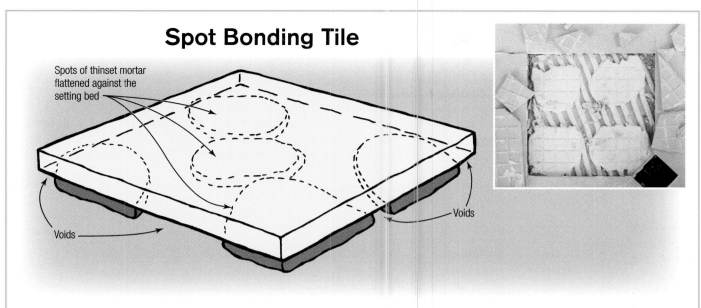

Spots of thinset mortar flattened against the setting bed

Voids

Voids

Figure 10-12. Because of the voids it causes, spot bonding (above) should never be used to install tiles on floors, wet areas, or exteriors. This floor tile (right) cracked and came loose because the 4-spot method did not meet the industry's 80% adhesive coverage standard and could not adequately support the tile.

Figure 10-13. When back buttering floor tiles, the author uses a small wood bench that moves with the work (top). For larger tiles, he uses an auxiliary table (above).

Figure 10-14. Small tiles can be hand-held for back buttering.

Figure 10-15. To bolster corners in heavy-traffic areas, the author applies a small amount of extra thinset to tile corners.

the adhesive. If spacing lugs are soiled with thinset mortar, the tile's length increases, and the regularity of the tile spacing is ruined.

Non-lugged tiles. Being ultra-careful about proper positioning is not an issue with hand-molded tiles or tiles made without spacing lugs. However, wall tiles need to be supported. To save time and effort when working with non-lugged tiles, I usually set two rows of wall tile before stopping to align the tiles with a straightedge (Figure 10-17). Since each tile is a differ-

ent size, small tile shims are used instead of plastic spacers. Once all the tiles are shimmed, I put a level over the straightedge to check for level and make any needed adjustments. Then I spread enough thinset mortar for another two or three rows of tile and continue upward until the entire wall is tiled.

Normally, when using machine-made tiles with crisp, defined edges and uniform sizing, I tend to install an entire wall plane—never just a portion of the wall. For some reason, perhaps holding the trowel

Spacing Lugs Must Be Clean

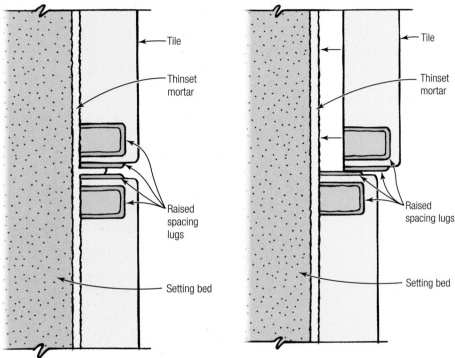

Tile

Thinset mortar

Raised spacing lugs

Setting bed

Tile

Thinset mortar

Raised spacing lugs

Setting bed

Figure 10-16. Pressing a wall tile against the adhesive first, and then making contact with the spacing lugs, can cause tiles to misalign (left). By making contact with the spacing lugs first, then pushing the tile into the adhesive, the lugs remain clean (right).

Figure 10-17. After installing two rows, the author uses small tile shims to space the tiles and align them to a straightedge (above). Installing two or three rows at a time, he periodically checks alignment as he completes the wall (right).

at a slightly different angle, whenever I go back the next day to complete a wall, it is always difficult to get day two's tiles to lie in plane with day one's. When installing hand-molded tiles, however, being precisely in plane is less of an issue (Figure 10-18).

Large-format tiles. When installing tiles less than 8x8 inches, the direction of the adhesive ridges is not critical. However, when large-format tiles are installed, adhesive swirls can result in air pockets trapped below a tile (Figure 10-19). The air pockets can actually reduce adhesive contact. When the tile is pressed deeper into the adhesive layer, air pressure can build in the pockets and force thinset mortar out from under the tile. To guard against this, spread thinset mortar in one direction only, and align the ridges with the direction of the grout joints. To install a tile, "hinge" it into the thinset mortar, slide it approximately ½ to ¾ inch perpendicular to the direction of the adhesive ridges, then slide it back into position (Figure 10-20).

Figure 10-18. These tiles have set up overnight, and the author has spread enough fresh thinset for the next two or three rows. The new adhesive layer must match the thickness of the original layer for the two tiled sections to be in plane.

Adhesive Contact Problems

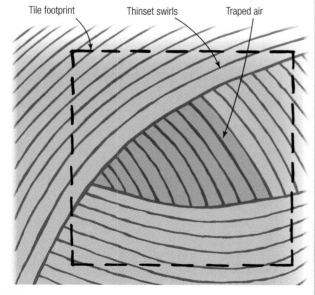

Figure 10-19. When a large-format tile (10 inch or larger) is installed over a trapped air pocket caused by adhesive swirls, contact can be reduced, and pressurized air can force thinset out the edges of the tile.

Large Tile Adhesive Coverage

Tile 10-inches or larger

Thinset ridges

Slide tile back and forth at 90° to thinset ridges

Figure 10-20. After the adhesive is spread in one direction only, large-format tiles are "hinged" onto the adhesive bed in line with the adhesive ridges (top). After the tile is positioned, it should be slid sideways about ½ to ¾ inch, then back into position (bottom).

Alternate Application Methods

A graduated set of notched trowels with fresh teeth is a must for any serious installer. However, there are situations where a notched, flat, or margin trowel won't get the job done. Examples include supplying a narrow band of extra thinset mortar to help install small rocks on a bathroom floor (described in Chapter 1, Project 3, pages 30-32) and applying thinset to narrow areas. (I use a grout bag made on site from a scrap of plastic film rolled into a cone with its tip cut for a ½-inch diameter opening, described in "Using a Grout Bag," page 264)

Hollow-backed tiles. With hollow-backed tiles, reinforcement is required or they will have low impact resistance and be vulnerable to cracking. To strengthen the tiles, I fill their hollow backs with bonded mortar just before installation (Figure 10-21). To apply the thin layer of thinset to the uneven cavity shape, I use a sponge. Then I fill the cavity with mortar (I generally use left-over sanded grout for this), cut off excess mortar with a trowel, and set the tile.

Curves and coves. The curved edge of a radius-type tile trim is also subject to impact damage unless it is filled with bonded mortar. Cove tiles are the most

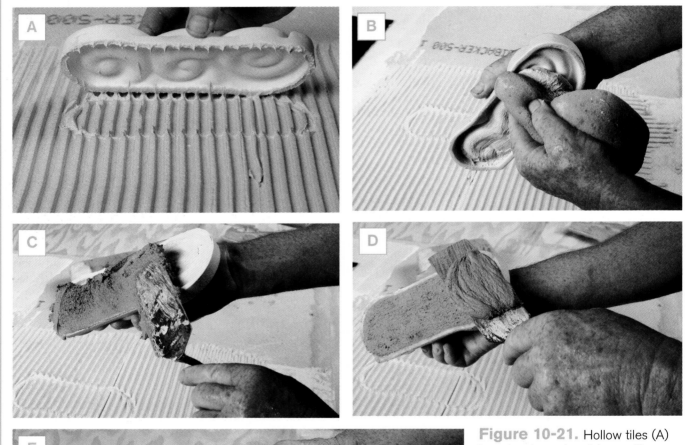

Figure 10-21. Hollow tiles (A) have low impact resistance. To overcome this problem, the author coats the back cavity with thinset mortar (B), fills the tile with sanded grout (C), removes the excess with a margin trowel (D), then sets the tile (E).

vulnerable to impact damage unless the void behind the curved edge is similarly filled (Figure 10-22).

Beating Block and Hammer

I am frequently asked how I use a beating block and hammer. The beating block (whether a simple 18-inch-long 2x4 or a manufactured block with a resilient, no-mar side to protect the tiles) was an essential tool when tiles were installed over thick beds of soft mortar. It was used to create a flat, level plane and to improve adhesion. This was at a time when tiles were soaked over-

Figure 10-22.
To prevent impact damage to unsupported radius-type trim (A), the author fills the cavity with bonded mortar (B). Cove tiles with a void at the curve are the most vulnerable to impact damage and must be filled. The void behind this cove tile (C) makes a great place for water to collect and for mold to hide.

night in water tubs, the tile bond coat was a runny layer of pure portland cement mixed with water, and the beating block was used delicately to nudge tiles into the cement paste and into a smooth, flat plane.

Unfortunately, some installers today take the term *beating* literally and whale away in an attempt to get the tiles to sit level. In the process, they break tiles because most tile setting beds today are hard, not soft like wet mortar. (I am always a proponent of mortar setting beds, but I only tile them when they have hardened.)

The tile surfaces of some installations are not smooth because the tiles have actually bottomed out on the setting bed and cannot be adjusted for height. For this reason, a beating block may do more harm than good. Since there is no longer the soft setting bed, the best way to achieve surface alignment is to ensure the adhesive layer is thick enough to allow for some adjustment. That is why I don't use a beating block. If adhesive coverage is less than 95%, I reach for a larger notch size, not the hammer.

Cleanup

Maintaining a clean work site is important at all stages of an installation, but it is essential during the tiling phase. I don't wait long before using a sponge. On a floor, I don't move to another area until all the tiles and joints within reach are clean. Saving a few minutes today by not cleaning the tiles as soon as they are installed will cost you an hour's worth of scraping tomorrow (Figure 10-24).

As thinset mortar is spread for successive courses, excess is bound to accumulate on the edges of the tiles. I use a margin trowel to cut away unwanted material (Figure 10-25). Otherwise, the excess can ooze up into the grout joints and cause another tedious cleaning chore. According to industry standards, one-third of the thickness of the tile (or the depth of the grout joint) should be submerged in thinset mortar. This helps block moisture from penetrating under the tiles. If the thinset rises to a uniform one-third thickness between the tiles, it is good for the installation. It also means that there should be no grout shadows caused by varying mortar depths in the grout joints. I use a ¼-inch tuck pointer to remove excess thinset mortar from grout or movement joints (Figure 10-26) and follow up with a clean sponge to remove all traces of mortar.

Curing

Like all other portland cement mortars, thinset mortar has three phases:

- The plastic state: The mortar can be spread on a setting bed or back of a tile and movement will cause no loss of bond (a tile can be repositioned without harming the adhesive bond).

- The setup state: The mortar has lost its plasticity but is still moist. Movement causes a reduction

Using A Grout Bag

Grout bags are often used to pipe grout into the joints of tiles that have a very rough surface, which prevents grout from clogging the tile surface. The method is simple: mix the grout, load it into the bag, close the back end with a twist, and continue squeezing to force grout out the tip. As the grout is beginning to set up in the joints, a striking tool is used to displace excess material and shape the joint. Afterward, when the grout has set up firm, grout crumbs can be removed with a vacuum. A grout bag can be site made with a scrap of plastic film rolled into a cone and held together with duct tape. With this type of bag, there is no tip, but instead, the pointed end is cut off with a knife or scissors to produce an opening about as wide as the grout joint. A site-made grout bag, used to pipe thinset mortar instead of grout, can be seen in Chapter 1, page 31.

Manufactured grout bags, fitted with a metal tip, are available through masonry supply stores. With the exception of the heavy duty bags, they are similar to what a baker would use to decorate a cake. A problem with grout bags, though, is the tendency for grout to jam at the tip. When this happens, the bag must be opened so a long wire can poke out whatever is clogging the tip— this can be frustrating and time consuming. Many installers who use grout bags get around the clogging problem by using more liquid than is recommended for mixing. While this produces a thinner mix that goes through the tip more smoothly and without clogging, it also deposits grout that cures much softer than normal because of the excess mixing liquid.

To solve the problem of clogging and avoid having to weaken the grout mix, I modify the tip of a manufactured grout bag. First I remove the cone-shaped metal tip and grind the end until the opening is considerably larger than the width of the joint. After removing the grinding burrs with a small, fine-cut, rounded file, I carefully squeeze the round opening into an oblong shape whose narrow width is equal to the grout joint and whose long width allows grout to flow more freely and without clogging.

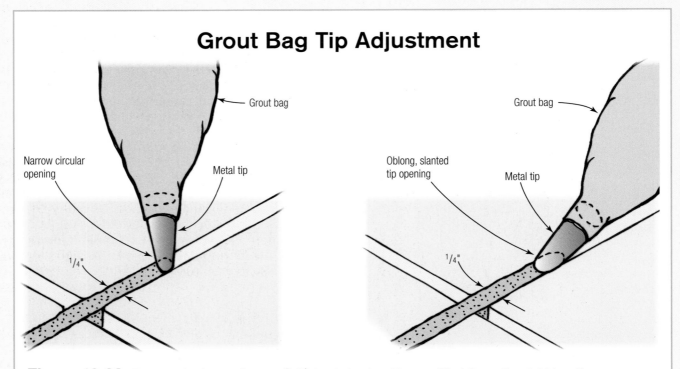

Grout Bag Tip Adjustment

Narrow circular opening

Grout bag

Metal tip

1/4"

Oblong, slanted tip opening

Grout bag

Metal tip

1/4"

Figure 10-23. The standard grout bag tip (left) tends to clog. The modified tip on the right has the same width opening, but its oblong shape allows grout to flow more freely.

Figure 10-24. Before installing the next course, the author prefers to sponge clean each tile after a full course is installed.

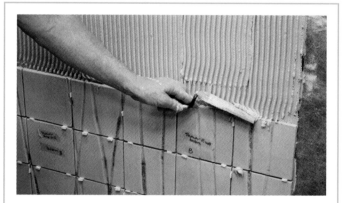

Figure 10-25. When spreading thinset mortar, it is bound to build up on the top edges of the installed tiles. Scraping it away before installing the next row of tiles avoids the problem of excess thinset squeezing up into the grout joint.

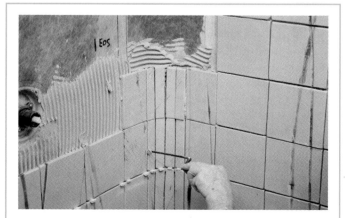

Figure 10-26. The author uses a tuck pointer to remove excess thinset mortar from grout joints and movement joints. Excess thinset in the grout joints can cause uneven shading of the grout.

or loss of bond (repositioning is not possible without the use of fresh adhesive).

- The hardening state: The mortar is increasing its hardness and strength until it reaches its maximum. During this period, all movement, flexing, and vibration should be avoided.

When can I walk on the floor? It is the first question most home or building owners, general contractors, and other subcontractors ask once a floor tile installation is finished. The answer can be found in the package instructions for the thinset mortar or other adhesive used on the job. General guidelines are:

- Dry-set thinset mortar sets up quickly (1 to 4 hours), has the lowest bond and shear strengths, and requires 28 days to cure, with light foot traffic allowed after 72 hours.

- Latex thinset mortars generally take longer to begin setting up and reach the 28-day strength of dryset thinset mortar in hours or days, but foot traffic should be restricted for 72 hours (or as required by the mortar manufacturer).

Any shocks or movement that occur in the adhesive layer before it is fully cured are likely to reduce the thinset mortar's cohesive, bond, shear, and compressive strengths. Drilling (especially hammer drilling), grinding, and nailing close to a fresh dry-set thinset mortar installation should be postponed until all the cementitious materials, including grouts and thinset mortars, have cured for 28 days—the standard for portland cement products—or as instructed by the mortar manufacturer.

When properly cured, many latex thinset mortars have considerably higher strengths than dry-set mortars. Some achieve 28-day dry-set strength in hours or a few days and can be drilled or worked on much sooner without fear of damaging the adhesive layer. Whether a mix uses latex or not, however, all precautions regarding length of cure must be followed. If an installation must be put into immediate service, special fast-curing thinset mortar should be used.

Grout Selection

Not all tile installations have identical materials lists, but all require grout. Yet grout is one of the least understood aspects of tiling. Before you can begin to grout, you should understand the properties of "good" grout and the consequences of "bad" grout.

- Good grout protects the edges of tiles from chipping, slows the penetration of water, and resists staining and the effects of regular cleaning.

- Bad grout cracks, chips, and powders. It abrades easily, allows water and stains to penetrate easily, and can be eroded by regular cleaning.

Good grout is the result of being specified, stored, mixed, spread, cleaned, and cured properly. Bad grout can initially look beautiful but its performance is always substandard. Eventually the beauty fades and problems begin. Some of the main reasons grouts fail are:

- careless storage

- bad proportions (too much liquid)

- inadequate mixing (too many lumps)

- poor spreading

- tempering with water (adding water to soften grout that is already mixed and beginning to set up)

- cleaned with too much water (dilutes the cement in grout)

- thoughtless curing (driving moisture out of the mix by excess heat, exposure to sunlight, air-conditioning, etc.)

There are several different types of grout that are used for tiling.

Site-Mixed Sand and Portland Cement Grout

This natural cement-colored gray grout is made on site by combining portland cement and fine sand in varying proportions, depending on the width of the grout joint: one-to-one (cement to sand) for joints up to $\frac{1}{8}$ inch wide, one-to-two for joints up to $\frac{1}{2}$ inch wide, and one-to-three for joints over $\frac{1}{2}$ inch.

Often used for grouting irregular stone, quarry tile, or on applications where performance is more important than color, this grout can be mixed with up to one-fifth part lime to improve workability. When mixed with water, this grout needs to be damp-cured for 28 days. When liquid latex is used instead of water to improve performance, it is important to follow the latex manufacturer's instructions regarding proportions, application, and curing. Sand can range from 100-mesh to 30-mesh (or coarser), depending on the width of the joint: fine sand for slender joints, with aggregate size increasing as grout joint width increases. When this type of grout is specified for very wide joints, I generally use clean, bagged utility sand that contains fine grains as well as gravel up to $\frac{1}{8}$ inch.

Standard Portland Cement Grout (ANSI A118.6)

This grout is a manufactured product that can be used indoors or outdoors and is available sanded and unsanded. Some brands are available in a wide range of colors. While it is not affected by exposure to water or moisture, it has only a moderate resistance to water penetration and stains. If allowed by the manufacturer, it can be used in submerged installations, such as ponds and swimming pools where freezing does not occur. When properly mixed, spread, and compacted, this type of grout will give reasonable service, but it requires 28 days to cure.

Polymer-Modified Portland Cement Grout (ANSI A118.7)

Grout with latex additives is commonly referred to as polymer-modified grout (latex is a type of polymer additive). There are two ways to produce a bucketful of polymer-modified grout. The first is to mix standard portland cement grout powder with latex instead of water. For about 40 years, this was the only way. The second way is to use a grout formulated with a dry latex powder. This type of grout requires only the addition of water to produce a spreadable mix. Generally, depending on the latex content, polymer-modified grouts have greater bond strength, stain resistance, color retention, and resistance to water penetration than standard grouts.

For the installer, mixing polymer-modified grouts to the right consistency is more demanding, and this type of grout is a bit more difficult to spread and clean than standard grouts. Also, if not cleaned thoroughly, a film of latex residue that hardens like paint can remain on the tile and be difficult to remove.

Advantages of polymer additives. The advantages of polymer-modified grout, when properly installed, can far outweigh its initial cost increase over standard grout. When mixed to the proper consistency, packed fully into each joint, and allowed to cure properly, polymer grout resists deep penetration of moisture and stains (below the surface) better than regular grout. Adding a sealer or impregnator to protect the surface of the polymer grout (and tiles) should ensure many years of low maintenance service for the user.

In addition to the enhanced performance compared with industry-standard cement grout, tile installations with polymer-modified grout provide low life-cycle costs and many green benefits. They include less frequent cleaning due to low absorption rates and a longer replacement cycle than any other finishing material due to better abrasion resistance. As with the setting-bed mortars and thinset mortars I use for all my tile installations, latex is an essential component of the grouts I install.

Epoxy Grout (ANSI A108.6, A118.3)

Epoxy grout is a mixture of epoxy resin and hardener, plus sand and other ingredients, that produces a non-portland cement grout often specified for applications that require chemical resistance. I am frequently asked about using epoxy grout on residential tile applications, and my response, with few exceptions, is that the use of epoxy grout should be confined to those installations where aesthetics are not the primary consideration: a food-processing operation, for example. Epoxy grout has properties that make it ideal for many commercial and industrial tile installations, but it also has some properties that, in my opinion, render it unsatisfactory for residential work.

First, not all epoxy grouts are UV-resistant. When exposed to direct sunlight, they may yellow, discolor, or "sweat" (the surface of the grout becomes sticky). Second, the surface of most epoxy grouts looks shiny and plastic rather than matte and grainy, like traditional cement grout. Since some hardened epoxy materials soften when heated, high-temperature mixes are available from some manufacturers for steam rooms, stove backs, fireplace surrounds, and hot-climate exterior decks.

Ready-Mixed Grout

Some ready-to-use (premixed) grouts are nothing more than organic mastic, a color dye, and some fine sand. Some are made for use in dry-area applications only. These ready-to-use grouts are not worth the extra expense, are difficult to clean, are known to shrink or dry out, and are difficult to maintain. Next-generation, ready-to-use grouts made from urethane offer more performance, but they also carry several cautions regarding their use in wet-area applications. Also, cleanup of this type of grout is less convenient as only about 10 square feet can be installed before initial cleaning begins. Some brands advise users to employ a two-man crew approach: For increased production, one man installs the grout while another follows closely behind to clean excess grout off the tiles. There is no current industry standard for ready-to-use grouts.

Making the Final Selection

For a given job, the specific brand of grout I use is largely a matter of availability: What can I get close by and what is the best grade of latex grout in that inventory? To avoid material incompatibility, I prefer to source both the grout and thinset mortar from the same manufacturer. Are all brands identical or do they offer the same level of performance or selection? No, but in general, grouts of the same product class from different manufacturers perform at about the same level. In general, I use dry polymer grout mixtures as these are the most convenient for me to purchase and apply, given the added bulk and weight involved in transporting liquid additives.

Sanded versus unsanded. In addition to the grout types described above, there is one other important consideration when selecting grout: the joint width. Generally speaking, unsanded grout should be used to fill joints less than $1/8$ inch wide, sanded grout should be used on joints from $1/8$ to $3/8$ inch, and specialty grout (containing larger aggregates than in regular sanded grout) should be used on joints wider than $3/8$ inch. Most manufacturers offer sanded and unsanded grouts, but not all offer grout for extra-wide joints.

Lot numbers. Once a selection has been made, there is one more selection detail. For best appearance and performance, always check the manufacturer's lot numbers to make sure the sacks of grout you purchase all carry the same lot or production number. If a production date is included with the lot number, and more than one lot number is noted, always select the youngest material (old grout tends to absorb moisture, contains lumps of hardened material, and is generally less chemically active than newer batches).

Mixing and Installing Grout

Storage of grout is the same as for any cementitious material. Sacks should be kept in a cool, dry place, away from sunlight or exposure to high levels of humidity. About 72 hours prior to mixing, sacks of grout should be brought to the installation site to acclimate to ambient temperatures. In a pinch, if the grout powder exceeds 90°F and there is not enough time to lower its temperature prior to installation, I substitute ice cubes for as much of the mixing water as needed to lower the temperature of the mixed grout.

When the grout powder temperature is below 50°F, however, hot water should never be used to raise the temperature of the grout mix. Hot water tends to turn regular grout into a very rapid-setting mix that does not perform well after the installed grout dries.

Mixing Grout

Consistency is one of the key elements of a durable grout installation. This begins by acclimating the grout materials to the job-site temperature, and it extends through mixing and initial cleaning. When mixing more than one sack of grout, each sack should be mixed with the same amount of liquid so both batches will dry to the same color. To simplify this task, I use a smart bucket to measure all dry and liquid components. For less than full-sack batches, I estimate. Small batches of grout are best mixed by hand; for full-sack batches, I use a specialty mortar mixer designed for low-speed mixing with little strain on the operator (see Figure 10-3, page 253). Never use a mixer rotating faster than 300 rpm or you will entrain air into the mix, thereby reducing the grout's compressive strength.

Either way, at least 75% of the liquid component should be placed in the mixing bucket or container first, followed by a gradual addition of approximately 75% of the powder. When the mix appears free of lumps, I add the remaining liquid, the remaining powder, and mix until lump-free. Most regular or latex grout instructions call for a 10-minute slaking period, which allows moisture to penetrate any lingering lumps, followed by a thorough remixing. Now the grout is ready to install.

Prepping Tile for Grouting

In preparation for grouting, all grout and movement joints must be clean and free of excess thinset. Industry standards call for the top two-thirds of each joint to be clean and free of all adhesive. One of the best ways to prevent thinset mortar from clogging movement joints is to scrape off unnecessary thinset before installing tiles (Figure 10-27). Then as tile installation proceeds, remove excess soft thinset mortar from all grout and movement joints.

In spite of such preventive measures, however, there are always some joints that need to be cleaned after a group of tiles is installed. The best time to clean the joints is when the thinset is still soft (Figure 10-28). I do this with a margin trowel, making sure I don't slice into the membrane (if there is one below the tiles). As a final step, I remove all tile spacers or shims and any traces of thinset with a knife and give the surface a thorough cleaning with a vacuum (Figure 10-29). When tile spacers are left between tiles, a ghost of the spacer often appears on the surface of the cured grout.

Grouting Wall Tiles

There is no right or wrong place to start grouting, but I tend to begin where trim tiles meet drywall and then pack the field tile joints, working from bottom to the top (Figure 10-30). When grouting smaller tiles, I work the grout trowel over the whole field, but with large-format tiles, I concentrate my efforts on the joints only. Regardless of the size of the tile or the width or depth of the grout joints, the most important part of installing grout is to hold the grout trowel at a low angle and exert as much pressure as possible with the grout trowel so each joint is completely filled with hard-packed grout.

Grouting is hard work, and it requires considerably more energy than any other part of the thinbed installation process. Grout that is just swished on rarely fills the joints completely, and it lacks the density of grout that is forced into the joints. Some installers use too much liquid when mixing grout to make the process easier. Yes, it is a lot easier filling joints with "loose" grout, but once it dries and cures, this type of grout is somewhat soft, very porous, and incapable of slowing the penetration of moisture. These problems cause mold to grow within the grout cross section, increase the need for cleaning, and shorten an installation's useful life. If you don't sweat during the grout process, either the grout is poorly mixed or you are not putting enough pressure on the grout trowel.

Once a section of tiles has been grouted (about 10 square feet), I use the edge of the grout trowel to scrape excess grout off the tile faces before moving to another section. If the tiles have a smooth surface, this process can remove most of the excess. If the tiles are honed or textured, more grout will remain on the surface, and there is a danger that the grout trowel will plow material out of the joints. To avoid this problem, I only grout a small area at one time unless I'm working with a helper.

The area of tile that can be grouted before initial cleanup begins is determined by a number of factors:

- the width of the joint (wide joints need more time to set up)

- the number of joints, as determined by the size of the tiles

- the absorbency of the tiles (porous, non-vitreous tiles set up faster than impervious porcelain tiles)

- the texture of the surface of the tiles (as mentioned above)

Figure 10-27. To prevent thinset from squeezing up into the movement joints, the author uses a $1/2$-inch margin trowel to scrape off excess thinset mortar.

Figure 10-28. The best time to clean excess thinset mortar out of the grout joints is when the mortar is still soft.

- the job-site environment (more time is required for initial setup when temperatures are low; less time is needed when the weather is hot)

According to most grout manufacturers, the job-site temperature should be between 50°F and 90°F. Also, tiles being grouted must be protected from air conditioning or breezes, which can draw moisture from the grout, and from the direct rays of the sun, which can evaporate moisture from the grout (or cause epoxy grout to set up prematurely).

Movement joints must be free of grout and other hard materials, but trying to keep fresh grout out of these joints is difficult. Also, by trying to keep grout out of the movement joints, the adjacent grout joints will not be as dense. To ensure that the density of the grouted joints is consistent, I pay no attention to any grout that might fill a movement joint. I can easily remove the grout later, once it has set up firm, with the tip of a margin trowel.

Because there were so few joints on the 24-inch tile installation featured in this section, I was able to grout both shower walls before starting initial cleanup. Before cleaning, though, I took a few minutes to cut away excess grout, pack any voids, and smooth the grout with a margin trowel where the trim tiles meet drywall (Figure 10-31).

Figure 10-30. Where trim tiles meet drywall, the author uses a grout trowel to pack the grout so it is square to the wall (A). Along the top, he packs the grout and gives it a slope so it will not trap water (B). After grouting the trim tiles, he packs the lower field grout joints and works his way to the top of the wall (C).

Figure 10-29. All tile spacers and shims need to be removed prior to grouting (top). Next, the author uses a sharp knife to cut away hardened thinset and a vacuum to remove the crumbs and dust (bottom).

Cleaning Wall Grout

An installer has to balance the need for the fresh grout to partially set up against the problem of excess grout crusting or hardening on the surface of the tiles. There is no time chart for this because every installation is different. However, all cement grouts need time to begin setting up; otherwise, it may be so loose that the process of cleaning removes too much material from the joint. Patience and testing the firmness of the grout should be your guide.

I begin initial cleaning with a grout sponge in good condition and wrung out tightly so the sponge does not drip any water. First, working from top to bottom, I use a light, circular motion to loosen grout remaining on the tile surface. The pores of a grout sponge are designed to trap grout particles. However, if the pores are filled, the sponge acts more like a snowplow and ends up removing too much grout from the joints. To avoid problems, the sponge should be thoroughly rinsed and wrung out frequently before the sponge pores are filled. Once again, patience is required, along with a light touch. Grouting is not a rough process, but rather a finishing process. Careless grouting habits can ruin an otherwise perfect tile installation, and careful, attentive grouting can sometimes elevate a poor installation.

The method I use to clean grout is a four-part process:

1. move the sponge in a circular motion with light pressure until most of the sand particles (if sanded grout is used) are off the surface (Figure 10-32A)

2. use a circular motion to dilute and reduce the visible dye that colors the grout and to uniformly shape the surface of the grout

3. use parallel wipes to remove the remaining residue (10-32B, C)

4. use a soft, clean cloth to buff the haze that appears on the surface of the tiles once they have dried. If voids appear as the surfaces of the tiles and grout are revealed, I fill them promptly (Figure 10-33) and continue wiping.

The parallel wiping must be done in a specific way. Rinse and wring out the sponge until it is barely damp, hold one face of the sponge lightly against the surface of the tile and make a single 2- to 3-foot wipe in one direction only. Then turn the sponge over and make another single, light pass parallel to the first and in one direction only, repeating the process until one area is finished. Backing up the sponge or moving it in a circular motion merely redistributes the residue.

My tile students always comment that the parallel wiping is gruesomely boring and would tax the patience of a saint. "Why wipe what you cannot see?" they ask. But without this step, the invisible residue on the surface of the tiles turns into a hard-to-remove haze after the grout

has dried. Because the final parallel wipes remove and dilute any lingering grout or latex residues, only a light dusting with a soft cloth is needed about 15 to 30 minutes after the sponge work is done. This removes any dried surface haze that remains on the tiles. When students return to the field, they often call or email that with this method, they no longer are plagued with a haze removal chore that usually involves the use of a grout or latex residue remover. Yes, it takes time to do the parallel wiping, but every minute spent doing this saves five minutes of intense cleaning later on.

Usually, after the final sponge wipe down, I pack up tools, clean the site, and take care of any last-minute chores while the surface of the tiles dries. After about 15 to 30 minutes, I use cheesecloth or a clean, white cotton rag (colored cloths or rags can sometimes stain the grout) to remove any remaining haze that appears on the tiles. Then I use a margin trowel to slice through unwanted grout that has found its way into any of the movement joints. By this time, the grout is still a bit moist, but it has set up firm and is actually quite crumbly (Figure 10-34). To avoid marring the grout remaining in the joints, I make no attempt to remove these crumbs, but instead wait until I return to fill the movement joints with sealant or caulk, then the crumbs are safely removed with a vacuum.

Grouting Floors

Grouting floors is more or less the same as grouting any other surface, but because floor tiles must endure foot traffic and other loads, the wet-to-dry mixing ratios and packing the grout into each joint are more important to the longevity of the installation.

Because gravity works with you, grouting floors is actually a bit easier than grouting walls. The only drawback for me is that grouting floors requires knee pads. Since I hate having straps around my knees, I prefer a kneeling pad or a folded tarp (at the end of the day, my

Figure 10-31. After packing the joints, the author uses a margin trowel to slice off excess grout where trim tiles meet drywall.

toes hurt—not my knees). Grouting floors or countertops requires the same equipment and approach needed for wall work. If you have limited experience grouting any surface, go back to the beginning of the "Grouting Wall Tiles" section (page 268), since the process of grouting floors is almost identical.

Striking Grout Joints

It may seem strange that a war would affect tile installation, but WWII put an end to many tile apprenticeship programs. In the process, it broke the chain of skills transfer from one generation to the next, and many skills and methods were lost. One of the most important lost skills is striking grout joints—a simple process that does wonders for grout.

Striking the grout joints after the fresh grout has set up, but before it hardens, is the key to low-maintenance, easy-to-clean joints. Striking the joints presses grout sand grains into the grout cross section and produces a smooth grout surface in much the same way as a mason strikes brick joints to smooth them.

Why strike? What does finished, cured, sanded grout feel like? It resembles narrow strips of sandpaper. (Please put that thought on hold.) Consumers are

Figure 10-32. The author moves the sponge in a circular motion to remove the bulk of the grout from the surface of the tiles and to shape the surface of the grout joint (A). Then he uses parallel wipes of the sponge, all in the same direction, to remove the remaining visible particles and grout dyes (B and C).

Figure 10-33. The author keeps a small amount of fresh grout close by in case any voids need to be backfilled during cleaning.

Figure 10-34. After buffing the grout haze with a soft cloth, the author uses a margin trowel to slice through excess grout in the movement joints.

always asking about tile and grout sealers and whether they are useful at reducing maintenance. Sealers and impregnators range from the very inexpensive (a waste of time and money, and almost useless) to the surprisingly expensive (and sometimes just as useless).

Now let's bring back the narrow strips of sandpaper. Try this experiment: Take a piece of 125-grit sandpaper, spread a little peanut butter over its surface, and then try to clean it with a sponge. It's almost impossible to remove all the peanut butter. Now take a top-tier sealer or impregnator (Miracle 511, for example—the only impregnator I use), apply it to another piece of sandpaper, and allow it to cure and dry. Now spread another layer of peanut butter over the paper and try to remove the mess. You will notice instantly that the addition of a quality impregnator makes little difference—a lot of the peanut butter still remains because it is mechanically stuck to the exposed sand grains. This is the main reason why some applications of sealer or impregnator may appear not to offer any protection. The solution? Striking the joints.

Striking techniques. I strike kitchen countertop grout joints as part of the installation and produce a finished grout joint that does not trap food bits. With a well-struck joint, it is worth spending the extra money on impregnators or sealers, which are designed primarily to resist stains.

Striking can be done with a mason's striking tool, but any hard, slick, rounded object can be used for this purpose. I use the shanks of old drill bits because I can get the precise striking profile for a grout joint of any width, but I also use found objects like metal tubing or—my favorite for wide joints—the neck of a beer bottle cut off with a tile wet saw (Figure 10-35). To strike a joint, wait until the grout has been cleaned and the grout has set up, but not dried. For most applications, this can take place 20 to 30 minutes after initial grout cleaning. The process is simple: press the striking tool against the grout and move it like a sled runner. Only one or two passes will create a smooth grout profile. Once the grout has dried, a sealer or impregnator can be applied. Striking can be used on floors, walls, and countertop grout joints.

Mixing and Installing Epoxy Grout

To eliminate airborne dust, the makers of some epoxy grout have combined the resin with the dry ingredients, making it a two-part system. Other mixes include jars or cans of resin and hardener portions plus bags of dry filler powder. Packets or bags of anti-sag ingredients (microballoons) may also be available for wall grouting.

Mixing Epoxy Grout

Because of its chemistry, the contents of all the bags and containers in each epoxy grout kit must be combined in their entirety. There is no such thing as mixing a partial batch of epoxy grout. Mixing should be done only by hand since power mixing can create

enough heat to prematurely trigger the grout, significantly reducing its pot life. All the ingredients should be acclimated to normal room temperatures, and the temperature of all surfaces to be grouted should be room temperature or less; hot tiles can trigger epoxy grout to prematurely catalyze.

To further prevent reduction of pot life once the grout is mixed, it is important to dump all the grout on the floor (or a mortar board, if grouting a wall) and spread it around into a thin pancake. Thin epoxy cross sections do not generate heat. If left in the bucket, some brands of epoxy grout have the potential to generate enough internal heat to cause the mix to churn and bubble within a few minutes, rendering the mix useless.

Applying Epoxy Grout

Installing epoxy grout is similar to cement grout only in that a rubber grout trowel should be used to spread and compact the material—all else is different. Some epoxy grout mixes have an ingredient that prevents sagging or slumping (particularly useful for wall grouting). But since many epoxy grouts readily slump and flow, the movement joints on floor installations need to be filled before grouting with epoxy. If this is the case, epoxy grout must not be installed until the sealant or caulk in the movement joints has cured. Epoxy grout should only be installed over tiles and a setting bed that are dry —never dampened (something routinely done to absorbent tiles when regular grouts are used). Epoxy has the consistency of taffy. It is thick, viscous, and tough to spread, but like cement grouts, best results are achieved when each grout joint is packed full.

I use a stiff rubber grout trowel, being particularly careful to pack each joint and remove excess from the surface. Depending on the brand, epoxy needs to relax and begin to catalyze for a period of time (as short as 10 minutes to as long as an hour or more) before cleaning begins. When cleaning cement grouts, very little water should be used, but with epoxy grout, just the opposite is true. Cleaning begins with a white scrubbing pad and a bucket of lukewarm water mixed with a small handful of dishwashing detergent.

Cleaning Epoxy Grout

To start, I tip some of the water onto the floor, so the scrubbing pad is well lubricated, and remove excess material by lightly moving the pad in a circular motion. The pad's pores fill up quickly. When they do, I rinse the pad in the warm water, otherwise the loaded pad would force grout out of the joints. I replace the pad with a new one as soon as it fails to rinse easily. It is not essential to fuss with the joints because small dings or grooves are capable of healing themselves. Once an area of floor has been thoroughly scrubbed, I use a barely damp sponge to lightly remove the liquid remains from the tiles, using parallel sweeps as I would normally finish cement grout.

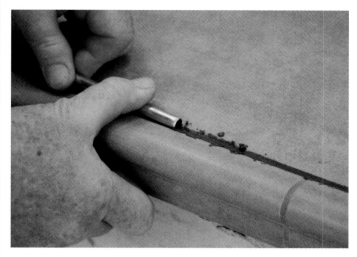
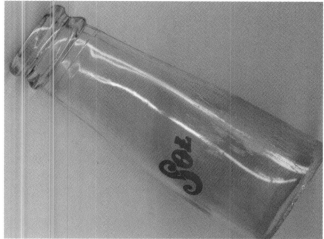

Figure 10-35. The author uses a short length of brass tubing to strike the grout joints on this countertop (left). The neck of a beer bottle cut on a tile wet saw (right) makes a dandy strike for wide joints.

At this point, the floor is finished. No further work is required, and in about 24 hours the grout will be completely cured and hard enough for light traffic. Since some epoxy grout mixtures sag, the sagging continues until the epoxy is hard. If there are voids under any of the tiles, the grout will flow downward, displacing any air bubbles, which rise to the surface leaving small voids, like ant holes, at the surface of the grout joint. Unfortunately, the excess grout that was scraped into a box or bag is rock hard and useless as a filler. Holes that appear on the surface of epoxy grout joints are to be expected. And while using up an entire small kit of epoxy grout to finish a large commercial application may be economically justifiable, using a small batch to fill a handful of holes on a residential-scale installation is not. This is another reason I prefer not to use this type of grout.

Impregnators and Sealers

Sealers and impregnators (marketing terms for the same basic materials) are liquids made specifically for application over ceramic tiles, stone tiles, and grout to reduce staining and simplify maintenance. Generally, neither sealers nor impregnators can be considered waterproofing, and neither will stop moisture penetration through grout that has not been mixed, applied, cleaned, and cured properly.

There are numerous sealers and impregnators available from tile dealers and home supply stores, and each brand has its own level of effectiveness. Inexpensive silicone sealers, whether water-based or solvent-based, are generally the least effective at preventing stains. At a few dollars a bottle, silicone sealers do not provide the same level of protection as impregnators. Impregnators were designed to make it easier to remove spray paint and graffiti from stone tiles and

blocks. Each brand of sealer or impregnator has its own specific installation instructions, but usually a liberal amount of liquid is applied to the surface of the tiles and grout. The liquid is given some time to soak in (5 to 15 minutes depending on the brand), the excess is removed with clean rags or towels, and the material is allowed to dry and cure.

After several negative experiences with sealers and impregnators, one lesson I have learned is that both materials should be applied to both the grout and 100% of the tile surface. Otherwise a partially treated tile may show a pattern of discoloration when the tile gets wet. In my opinion, sealers and impregnators should never be used to "waterproof" a porous stone tile installed in a wet area; instead, select a stone tile with the same absorption rate as vitreous or impervious ceramic tiles and apply sealer or impregnator to reduce staining. Re-application is required since no sealer or impregnator can be considered permanent. The length of time before re-application depends on many factors, including frequency of use and intensity of use. For most tiles under normal conditions, re-application once a year will do, but there are no hard and fast rules.

I don't rely on a single impregnator or sealer, but use several products for different tiles and conditions. I prefer Miracle 511 impregnator (www.miraclesealants.com) because it does more than protect tile—grout treated with this product seems to become harder. When a low-VOC sealer is specified, I use Aqua Mix Sealer's Choice Gold (www.custombuildingproducts.com). For saltillo pavers finished with wax, I use clear, exterior-grade Watco Penetrating Oil (www.rustoleum.com) to seal tiles and grout. Miracle 511 and Aqua Mix are available at many tile supply stores. Watco Oil is available through hardware and paint stores.

NOTES

Chapter 11
TOOLS AND SAFETY

Most general contractors should already have a large percentage of the tools required for tile installation. Power saws and drills, hand tools, and layout tools are all required for tiling, along with a number of specialty tools, such as wet saws, snap cutters, biters, and notch trowels. My tool kit has other power tools, including bench sanders, angle grinders, wet grinders, and mortar mixers. Some tile installations require the barest minimum of tools, such as a snap cutter, pair of biters, and a notched trowel; while others may require a truckload of tools.

It has taken me over 40 years to put together my complete tiling tool kit, which also includes a box full of tile spacers and shims, and dozens of hand-made trowels and screeding forms for extruding shapes with mortar. Installing stone tiles requires additional tools for profiling, cutting, and polishing. And, of course, for good housekeeping on the job, all ceramic and stone tile installations require a set of cleaning and masking tools that include tarps, plastic film or protective papers, masking tape, painter's tape, and duct tape.

This chapter is not going to tell you how to use and operate a circular or reciprocal saw, how to get the best use out of a framing hammer, or how to put on a bandage. But it will cover the specialty tools I use for tiling and the methods I use to maintain a clean, safe work environment.

Personal Safety

I was fortunate at the beginning of my work career to be put through a lengthy and extensive safety and first-aid course. A very large repair machine shop, set in the middle of a huge steel-making complex, was the site of my first real job. It was a dangerous place to work, but the machine shop's 4,000-man workforce operated without lost time for over three years while I was there because of the safety course and management's insistence that every employee have up-to-date personal safety gear. I have tried to put what I learned in the machine shop to good use as a tile installer. I still have all ten fingers, both eyes, decent knees, and reasonable hearing as a result. To me, tools and safety are inseparable, and that is why I have lumped together both topics in this chapter.

Awareness and Attitude

Safety with tile starts with the installer, but it also involves people in the immediate vicinity of the installation site and in the community. Installers handle a variety of alkaline materials that are potentially harmful to the skin and lungs. When fully cured, cement materials are benign, but in the powder or paste states, portland cement grouts and mortars can be a problem to people who are exposed to the dust and to people whose skin is exposed to thinset mortars and grouts. Proper disposal of waste tile-installation materials is part of the responsibility of maintaining a safe working environment and limiting exposure to both the installer and others. A safe tile workplace should be free not only of the waste tiling materials and usual job-site trash that can be carted away, but also of the dust generated by the numerous prepping, cutting, and mixing tasks required on every installation. To maintain safe conditions, an installer has to have a specialized safety tool kit that includes not only safety glasses, ear plugs, and filter masks, but also a robust vacuum fitted with a high efficiency particulate air (HEPA) filter, plastic film for containing dust and storing mortar and grout sludge, and plenty of buckets, with lids, for settling the solids in cleaning water.

Every installer owes it to him or herself to maintain safe working conditions. A few clouds of backerboard dust or a few cuts on a wet saw are not going to rot your lungs or cause hearing loss. But over the span of a career, exposure to caustic materials and to the sound generated by wet saws and other cutting, abrading, mixing, and vacuuming machines can take a toll on your body. Even in a clean environment, using the best personal safety equipment, tiling can be hard on the knees (unless you only do countertops and walls). Some individuals may be extremely sensitive to alkaline materials, but even those not bothered by continued exposure may develop long-term skin problems on their hands and forearms.

In addition to the usual safety glasses, ear buds, and

dust masks (available at most hardware and building supply stores), I bring snug-fitting rubber gloves (www. dubarryari.com), kneeling pads, a well-stocked first-aid kit, and a jug of vinegar to every job site. I like to keep a separate bucket of clean water just for rinsing my hands, and to keep my skin flexible and prevent cracking, I add vinegar to counteract the alkaline cements I handle. A safety tool I never could have conceived of when I first started tiling is an app on my GPS cell phone that directs me to the closest hospital or emergency room. Tiling takes me into unfamiliar surroundings, and this feature might prove invaluable, when seconds count, if a serious accident occurs.

Some tiling tasks generate piercing sounds, flying chips, and clouds of dust that can affect the health and safety of others at the job site. When possible, I try to locate the tile-cutting station away from pathways and other workers. When bush hammering a concrete slab, I line walls with tarps to prevent impact damage from flying bits of concrete and stone and use a HEPA-filtered vac to remove and help control dust. The HEPA vac is also used, most effectively, to contain dust generated by the cutting of cement backerboards with a dry-cutting diamond blade. A new tool called the WaleTale (www. waletale.net), which clips to the side of a bucket and attaches to a HEPA vac, helps control the dust generated by mixing grout, thinset, and other mortars (Figure 11-1). By stopping dust at the source, safety for everybody in the work zone is assured.

Dry dust is easy to see, but wet dust is also a problem. One of the wet saws I use (a DeWalt D2400) is designed to reduce the amount of spray coming off the saw. Wet saw spray is not water, it's water mixed with very small particles of porcelain, stoneware, natural stone, glass, or whatever is being cut on the saw. Breathing this wet dust is just as potentially harmful as breathing dry dust. When working on a particularly intricate installation, I sometimes spend the entire day

cutting tile. When this is the case, I wear a vapor-resistant filter mask.

Safety is more than just wearing protection, however. It's an attitude that should be with you even when you are not using a potentially hazardous tool or material, and it involves thinking clearly and acting decisively.

In the remainder of this chapter, I will review the tools I use for tiling, and each review will address the potential hazards for each tool.

Demolition Tools

Surface prep can be a complicated affair requiring dozens of tools and steps, or it can be as simple as vacuuming dust off a floor. When the installation includes removing old tilework, the range of tools increases and so does the potential for personal injury.

Hammers, Scalers, and Scabblers.

Bush hammers (see Chapter 1, Project 3, page 26), scalers, and scabblers are used to remove bits of con-

Figure 11-2. When used for tile demolition, pry bars (1) and cold chisels (2) can cause tile shards to fly up with tremendous force and, when beaten with a hammer, can create their own metal shards, as well. Eye protection is a must.. Carbide scoring tools (3) can be used to remove grout as well as to cut cement backerboards. When removing grout, be careful that the tool does not jump out of the grout line; it can scratch the tile.

Figure 11-1. When clipped to the rim of a bucket and connected to a HEPA vac, the WaleTale significantly reduces mixing dust.

crete from the surface of a slab. Gloves, boots, and heavy clothing are advised when operating these tools, along with goggles or full-face shield, ear buds, and a filter mask. A vacuum or dust collection system can eliminate the need for a filter mask and make the renovation work more comfortable. Excess vibration, caused by these types of power tools and sustained over several hours, can cause nerve and other damage. I try not to man one of these machines (especially the bush hammer) for more than an hour at a time, alternating with a helper to keep the work moving.

When using hammers to remove old tilework, be aware that small, incredibly sharp flakes of ceramic material can rocket off tiles when struck. Make sure no innocent bystanders are in the line of fire when hammering tile surfaces! Safety glasses with side shields or a full-face shield are recommended.

Pry Bars, Chisels, and Carbide Scoring Tools

Used primarily for demolition work, chisels and pry bars (shown in Figure 11-2) share one trait with ham-mers: They can exert tremendous force and cause razor-sharp ceramic shards to fly off the surface of the tiles and travel considerable distances (I have seen tile shards stuck in ceiling drywall), so wear safety glasses, at a minimum, and keep bystanders or other workers away from the demolition area.

For structural demolition, thick crow bars are fine, but for removing tiles and tilework, I prefer flat bars. Power tools are essential for removing large areas of tile, mortar, or concrete, but for small repairs and detail work, I use a set of cold chisels (Figure 11-2), from ¼ to 2 inches wide, with extra ¼- and ½-inch chisels, well sharpened, in reserve.

Removing grout from the perimeter of a tile is essential if one tile needs removal and replacement, but it is not required if the entire installation must be removed. For this task, a plain utility knife can sometimes be used to remove soft, cured grout that was improperly mixed, cleaned, or cured; but for removing hard grout, the most efficient tool is usually a power angle grinder fitted with a diamond blade. For small jobs, however, the most efficient way to remove grout

Figure 11-3. Saws of every stripe are required for tile work. Clockwise from left: (1) reciprocating saw for demolition work; (2) circular saw with carbide-toothed blade (mounted on saw) for cutting wood and a segmented diamond blade for cutting tile, mortar, and concrete; (3) wet-cutting angle grinder with hose coupling and polishing pads; (4) regular and compact hacksaws, each with a metal-cutting blade and a third saw fitted with a tile-cutting carbide blade; (5) two pull-action wood saws; (6) a reversible blade flush-cutting wood saw; (7) an angle grinder and an assortment of dry-cutting diamond blades; and (8) a jig saw fitted with a carbide blade for cutting holes or openings in cement backerboards.

may be a carbide scoring tool (Figure 11-2) normally used to score cement backerboards for snap-cutting. Be advised that while a carbide scoring tool is relatively safe to use, its super-hard tip can permanently mark tiles if the tool jumps out of a grout joint.

Tin Snips, Bolt Cutters, and Nippers

A variety of metal cutting tools are necessary for cutting reinforcing wire, rebar, pipes, and other materials encountered on the job site. Aside from the fact that any of these tools can cut deeply, an installer also has to be aware of the sharp or jagged edges on the materials cut with these tools.

Demolition Saws and Grinders

This category includes reciprocal saws, grinders, segmented dry-cutting diamond blades, carborundum blades, wood saws, and hacksaws (Figure 11-3).

To prevent damage and limit the shock that pounding and vibrating tools can transfer to parts of the building, I use a dry-cutting blade, mounted in either an angle grinder or a circular saw, to make a series of parallel cuts (12 inches or so apart, with the blade set to the depth of the tile and its setting bed) into the field of tiles to be removed. I prefer to use a dry-cutting, segmented diamond blade because of its aggressiveness and speed through materials that do not require a finished edge. To extend blade life, I cut through grout joints, which are usually much softer and easier to cut than hard tiles. With this done, most tile floors or walls can be removed in small, easy-to-manage chunks. I use this method primarily when removing tile/mortar bed installations.

When dry grinding or cutting metal in a bathroom or kitchen environment, make sure all porcelain enamel finishes (sinks, bathtubs, toilets, etc.) are covered: White-hot steel sparks can melt and embed themselves in porcelain enamel and become impossible to remove.

Power saws cannot differentiate between wood, tile, flesh, or bone; they will cut through them all quickly. Even hand saws can be dangerous. Non-segmented diamond wet-saw blades, however, are relatively harmless because their "teeth" protrude only a few thousandths of an inch, and they are only efficient when cutting hard tiles—not soft materials such as wood or flesh.

Dry-cutting diamond blades, on the other hand—especially segmented blades—can be very dangerous, and they most definitely will cut through skin and bone if used carelessly. Unfortunately, after visiting hundreds of installation sites, I am no longer surprised when I see an installer using a high-speed angle grinder fitted with a segmented dry-cutting blade, with no safety guard around the blade. It only takes a split second for a dry-cutting blade to do irreparable damage to a user's hands or fingers: Safety guards should never be removed or defeated!

Installation Tools

Surface prep also includes the work of installing substrates, requiring screw guns for securing substrates and power shears for cutting cement backerboard (Figure 11-4). Then comes the work of mixing and installing thinset mortar, grout, and self-leveling underlayments, which requires another passel of tools, including power mixers and a selection of trowels.

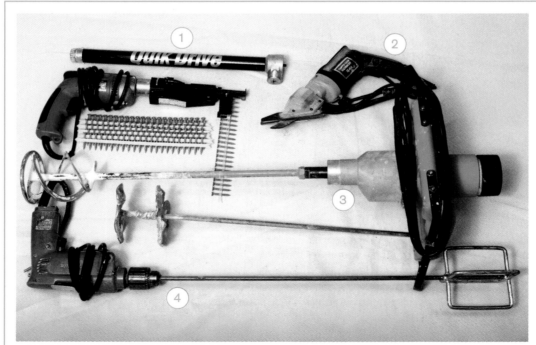

Figure 11-4. Power tools help speed the work of installing substrates, leaving installers with more energy to install tiles. From the top: (1) magazine-load screw gun with extension (above drill body) for floor work, and collated backerboard screws (below drill body); (2) shears for cutting fiber-cement backerboards; (3) specialty mixer for thinset mortar, grout, and self-leveling underlayments; and (4) mixers for use in a 1/2-inch chuck, slow-speed drill.

Screw Guns

Driving screws individually can be hazardous to an installer's forefinger. Even if it is not impaled by the driver tip, by the end of an installation my forefinger has been worn down from handling so many screws. It was a real problem until I began using an auto-feed screw gun that is loaded with cement backerboard screws.

I use a short, one-handed wall gun, which can convert with an extension to a two-handed, stand-up floor gun that is easy on the back. Other than when loading screw clips into the unit's slide magazine, the operator's fingers are never in contact with screws: The gun's feeding mechanism starts and drives the screws smoothly, and its controls enable me to adjust screw-head depth and create a smooth finished surface. In addition, an auto-feed screw gun can pay for itself in one day. Compared with the laborious method of kneeling for every screw, I can drive a clip of 21 screws in under a minute, if I want to go fast, and do it standing up. The screw clips are no more expensive than the loose backerboard screws available from the local supplier. I would consider buying one for a single bathroom or moderate-size floor project just for its efficiency, but for any installer who has ever had his forefinger penetrated by a driver tip, the best reason to have one is for safety.

Power Shears

This is a power tool adapted from a power sheet-metal cutter that is used to cut fiber-cement backerboards. Although many different brands are available, I like the Snapper Shear SS-424 shears, made by PacTool International (www.pactool.us) because it makes both straight and curved cuts on $5/16$- and $1/2$-inch fiber-cement boards. The blades are reversible for longer life, and replacement blades are available. For the cleanest edges, make a cutting guideline on the back side of the board with a sharp knife, then cut with the shears. This tool makes cutting fiber-cement board easy and fast, but its most important feature is that it does not generate anywhere near the amount of dust thrown off by a dry-cutting diamond blade.

Power Mixers

A paddle chucked into a $1/2$-inch drill was how I used to mix thinset and grout, but I switched to a specialized mixer the first time I worked with self-leveling materials, which had special mixing requirements. With a paddle mixer, I was always bent over when mixing, the grip was awkward, and once, when I was working in a pair of ragged jeans, the paddle's shaft grabbed the worn denim and twisted it into a tourniquet around my leg that had to be cut off with a knife. The two-handed mixer I now use allows me to stand

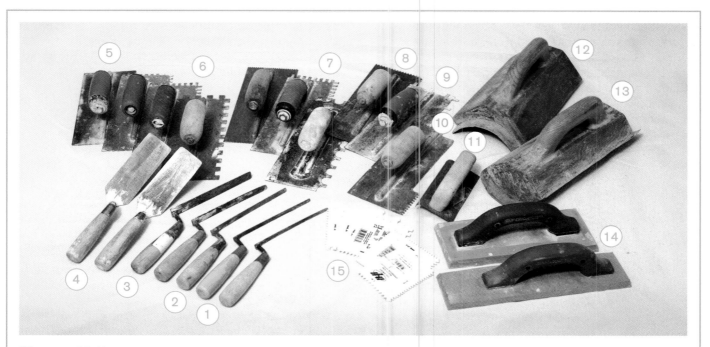

Figure 11-5. Essential for tiling, trowels are highly personal tools and the author's tool kit includes numerous flat, notched, margin, and specialty trowels. Clockwise from lower left: (1) two $1/4$-inch tuck pointers; (2) two $1/2$-inch tuck pointers; (3) $3/4$-inch margin trowel; (4) two 2x6-inch margin trowels; (5) flat trowel; (6) square notch trowels—$1/4$ x $1/4$, $1/4$ x $3/8$, $3/4$ x $3/4$; (7) U-notch trowels—$3/32$ x $3/32$, $1/4$ x $1/2$, $3/4$ x $3/4$; (8) $1/8$-inch V-notch trowel; (9) field-ground $1/4$ x $1/2$ x $1/4$-inch trowel (used in Chapter 1, Project 3); (10) field-ground trowel for one-row baseboard tiles; (11) $1/2$-inch radius edge trowel; (12 and 13) custom-made $3 1/2$-inch inside and outside radius trowels; (14) rubber grout trowels; and (15) small plastic notch trowels (for tight areas).

erect while mixing, is easy to clean (self-cleaning after rotating in a bucket of water for a few seconds), and most importantly, I don't have to hug the mixer's shaft like I did with the chuck-in paddle. The unit's widespread grip allows me to stand a safe distance

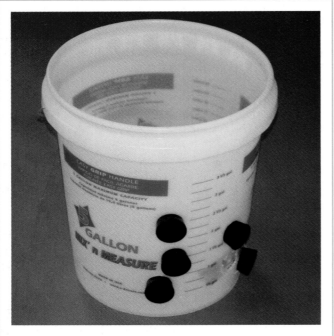

Figure 11-6. Used for mixing full batches of grout, thinset, and self-leveling underlayment, the author has made a "smart bucket" to quickly measure the correct amount of fluid for each brand. The location of each 1-inch hole was determined by pouring a correct amount of liquid for one sack of dry mix, then plugged with a stopper. When the author needs to mix a batch, he locates the appropriate hole and pulls out the stopper. The hole assures that each batch will have the same wet/dry ratio.

away from the rotating shaft and farther from the cloud of dust that hovers over every mixing bucket.

Smart bucket. An important part of the mixing process is measuring the liquids, which can be done far more accurately and efficiently with a "smart bucket." Made from an old 5-gallon bucket, it's filled with a measured amount of water needed for mixing one sack of each type of dry mix I need, be it grout, thinset, or self-leveling underlayment. For each liquid level, I mark the height, then drill a 1-inch hole so the bucket will drain to this exact level. A few stoppers in all the other holes ensure that I have a quick way to measure an exact amount of liquid for a given sack (Figure 11-6).

Sponges. Equally important is the cleanup process. For general cleanup chores and grouting, sponges are indispensable. Practically any sponge will do for general cleanup, but for grouting, I use Hydra tile sponges exclusively (www.hydra-sponge.com). The rounded edges of this sponge won't gouge grout out of the joints, and the fine pore structure removes excess grout material quickly.

Trowels

Trowels are the extensions of an installer's hands that mix mortars, gauge thicknesses, scrape surfaces clean, and perform countless other tasks. Trowels are highly personal tools because they do what my fingers cannot and must fit comfortably in my hand, because on some installations I will be holding them all day long. Mortar residues can easily build up on the handles, putting the installer at risk of blood poisoning and can cause serious, chronic skin problems. The person using a dirty trowel is literally squeezing mortar into his skin, forcing cement deep into the pores of his hands. To prevent this, I keep a bucket of fresh water for rinsing my hands and cleaning trowel handles.

Figure 11-7. For cutting, grinding, and polishing work, the author uses a variety of hand and power tools. Clockwise from left: (1) snap cutter; (2) angle grinder with continuous-rim dry-cutting diamond blade and an assortment of diamond blades (left) and grinding discs (right); (3) wet grinder with water feed hose and several wet polishing discs; (4) tile biters; (5) grinding stone; (6) sanding block with 80-,120-, and 240-grit inserts.

Gone are the days when an installer could head for the job site with only one or two notched trowels. With mosaic and tile sizes ranging from less than $\frac{1}{4}$ inch square to 1x3 meters, the installer has to be prepared to apply the right amount of thinset mortar to suit the tile size and job-site conditions. My trowel tool kit includes margin trowels for hand mixing, scraping, back buttering, and cleanup chores; flat trowels for spreading and shaping mortar; a set of V-, square-, and U-notched trowels; custom trowels I have made from scratch or modified; and a handful of specialty trowels I use for tight spaces (Figure 11-5). I prefer wood to plastic handles. Most of the trowels I use are Marshalltown; a few are SuperiorBilt stainless-steel notch trowels.

Tile Cutting Tools

Tile cutting tools roughly divide into two groups: simple hand-held tools and table-mounted wet saws.

Hand-Held Tile Cutters

For cutting, grinding, and polishing work, I use a variety of hand-held tools, including biters, snap cutters,

wet grinders, and dry grinders (Figure 11-7).

Biters. In the beginning of my tile career, I wore out three or four pairs of tile biters a year working mostly with soft, non-vitreous 4¼- or 6-inch wall tiles. All kinds of trimming can be done with biters on soft material, but since I now work mostly with vitreous tiles and very hard stone tiles, I use a dry-diamond blade mounted in an angle grinder for more accurate cutting and far less shock on the tiles. I rarely use biters any more, but consider them an essential tile tool for an installer. A daily drop of oil in the hinge extends its life considerably. The narrow jaws of this tool can exert tremendous crushing pressure and inflict severe pinching damage. That's the most obvious safety hazard; not so obvious are the hundreds of tiny ceramic shards that flake off tiles being worked by the biters. Eye protection is required for all tile cutting—even with this simple tool.

Snap cutters. Available in a variety of shapes, sizes, and capacities, snap cutters are the workhorses of ceramic tile cutting, producing quick cutting without a lot of setup or water. Snap cutters work easiest with soft, non-vitreous tiles, but they can also be used to make straight cuts with porcelain tiles. The basic

Figure 11-8. On large or complicated installations, the author may bring four tile saws and a bench grinder to the job site. From left, an MK wet saw for continuous production cutting; a DeWalt wet saw with a tilting arbor for cutting bevels and a plunge-cutting feature for inside cutting; a 50+ year-old Rizzo wet saw for freehand cutting; a Rockwell benchtop belt sander; and a small MK circular saw fitted with a dry-cutting diamond blade.

design of most snap cutters is the same: a sturdy, yet resilient frame to hold and position the tile being cut, a carbide wheel mounted on a sliding track for scoring the tile, and a levered bar for splitting the tile apart. Think of a snap cutter as a compact, heavy-duty glass cutter. Some snap cutters are capable of cutting a 24-inch tile diagonally.

The trick to getting consistent scores is to align your shoulder, elbow, wrist, grip, and scoring wheel in a single plane. It takes getting used to, but for me, it is the key to a straight score. Whether or not the tile snaps apart after scoring depends on how smoothly the carbide wheel rolls across the top of the tile and on a wheel score that extends from one extreme edge of the tile to another—not just part-way down the face of the tile. Keeping the wheel lubricated with a light oil helps prevent skipping, and the process works best when cutting glazed wall tiles. The reason is that these tiles have a very thin vitreous coating applied over a rather porous and weak bisque—easy to score and easy to break. Only light pressure is required for soft tiles, with more pressure required for increasingly harder grades of tile.

As the wheel pressure increases (the pressure between the wheel and the surface of the tile being scored), so, too, does the possibility that razor-sharp shards of glaze or ceramic materials can fly away from the tile as it is being scored by the ultra-hard carbide scoring wheel. Unfortunately, even with the most consistent score running fully from one edge of the tile to the other, attempts to snap cut porcelain tiles often result in cuts that go straight for about two-thirds of the way across the tile and then suddenly swerve off course.

To overcome this problem, I set the snap-cutter's fence for the repeat straight cuts I need and, after positioning a tile in the cutter's frame, paint the surface of the scoring path with a light oil or kerosene. I then snap the tile apart (Figure 5-4, page 136). The oil prevents porcelain (opaque glass, actually) from holding its surface tension across a score and allows the tile to split along the straight scoring line. Using this technique, I can score and snap a dozen 12-inch tiles in less than a minute. As a side benefit, the film of oil seems to prevent shards of ceramic material from leaving the surface of the tile. Before they are installed, any tiles cut this way should be cleaned to remove any traces of oil that could interfere with the adhesive bond or discolor the grout.

On residential or commercial floors, to get through the most square footage as possible, I concentrate first on installing full tiles and partial tiles that can be trimmed to size on a snap-cutter. I leave those tiles that must be cut on a wet saw (L-shaped or inside cuts) for the very end of the installation, unless I have a helper who can process and install all the cuts while I focus on full tiles.

Wet cutting requires a setup of the wet saw, plus a usually overlooked step: drying the cut before bedding it in thinset mortar. Whether done naturally by stacking wet tiles in the sunlight for a few minutes or by drying them with an absorbent towel, this is an essential step because a thin film of water is a bond breaker for porcelain tiles.

Stone workers. When working with stone slabs or tiles, I will often process the cuts in my shop with a set of pneumatic, water-feed tools for cutting and polishing. On site, however, I use an electric angle grinder with through-spindle water feed. When polishing stone in an occupied space, I use dry blades, polishing discs, and a HEPA vac to control dust.

Wet Saws

A wet saw can be one of the most versatile cutting tools available to the installer (Figure 11-8). It takes considerable strength to score and snap some robust porcelain tiles, but even the hardest ceramic or stone tile can be cut with comparative ease on a wet saw. The main components of a wet saw are a table to position tile for cutting, a wet-cutting diamond blade, and a means of cooling the blade with water. The most

---

Tile-Cutting Station

If space allows, I set up a complete cutting station at the job site that includes at least two wet saws (one for straight cutting and another for handwork); a benchtop belt sander and a supply of carbide belts (50 to 100 grit); a 1/2-inch slow-speed drill and a set of diamond hole saws; an angle grinder fitted with a dry-cutting diamond blade for roughing work on tiles; and a small circular saw, also fitted with a dry diamond blade, for cutting cement backerboards or, when paired with a straightedge, for cutting very large tiles (that will not fit the wet saw) on the diagonal. If there is a lot of cutting to do, and I have a helper, I will setup another wet saw for straight cutting, provided there is room at the site. If I am working with stone tiles, I set up another table for a wet grinder. Each saw, as well as the benchtop sander, has its own folding stand or table. I also may use additional folding tables for stacking tiles and cuts, holding saw accessories and tools, and other cutting-related tasks.

The benchtop belt sander is used for smoothing exposed cut tile edges. Handheld grinding stones can be used for this purpose, but this tool is faster and uses less of my energy. In a pinch, when only a few pieces of stone tile bullnose are required, I use this tool for rough-edge profiling (and finish with the wet polishing grinder).

---

accurate and durable saws have a sliding table to mount the tile for cutting and a water pump that delivers water right to the saw blade. Less durable entry-level saws designed for occasional cutting are often nothing more complicated than a box holding a blade that sits in a water bath. Both can cut most types of ceramic or stone tiles, but a particular saw may be limited by the maximum size that can fit into the framework of the saw. Some portable wet saws are available with a capacity to cut up to a 24-inch tile on the diagonal. No two wet saws are alike, and they are priced from under $200 to $10,000 or more for feature-laden, large-capacity saws.

Apart from a truck, a wet saw represents an installer's biggest financial investment. As with other tools, a cheap wet saw is a poor investment and possibly a complete waste of money if it cannot keep up with your production and quality expectations. There are hundreds (maybe thousands) of wet saws available on line, but unless a seller offers a reasonable warranty, it may be better to purchase from a tile distributor or tool dealer who can back up the sale. If you cannot afford to buy a saw, rent or borrow one. Some tile distributors may give you access to a wet saw for a limited number of cuts if you are a regular customer.

Because my installations feature a lot of inlay work, and because I demand a lot from my saws, the most important saw feature for me is whether the saw can be field adjusted if it starts making errant cuts. Many saws have no adjustment and, consequently, are not very useful to me if their frames get tweaked out of alignment during use or in the back of the truck.

Wet-Saw Maintenance

For the most accurate cutting and longest life, every wet saw requires pre- and post-cutting maintenance, as well as other maintenance that is required once the saw goes into production. For starters, every installer's saw kit should include a small oiler filled with 20/30/40/50-weight oil for lubing bearings and rollers and for protecting saw surfaces. A spray can of a light lubricant, such as WD-40, is also useful for cleaning surfaces, purging bearings of moisture, and keeping the blades rustfree. Prior to use, the saw should be clean, bearing surfaces lubed, saw surfaces wiped down with an oily rag, and the saw's reservoir filled with clean water. After use, if only a few cuts are made, the reservoir and pump can be drained, saw wiped dry, bearings blasted with WD-40 and re-oiled with the heavier weight oil, and the entire saw given a good wiping with an oily rag.

If the saw has to make many cuts or is used almost continuously, additional maintenance is required. It is the lack of production maintenance that causes many saws and coolant pumps to burn out prematurely. For longest blade and pump life, since particles made by the diamond blade turn clean water into abrasive fluid, the pump water should be replaced with fresh water as

Wet-Saw Power Safety

The first accessory an installer needs to obtain for the saw kit (unless the saw is already equipped) is a GFCI adapter plug. For safety, I locate the GFCI plug at the male end of the extension cord I use for the saws, drill, wet grinder, and belt sander. A GFCI plug reduces the potential for electric shock when using water with electric tools.

needed. If I am cutting more or less continuously, making dozens of cuts per hour, I may change water two or three times a day, or more frequently if needed. Adding fresh water to the reservoir when it is low without replacing all the contaminated coolant water sludge is extremely hard on both blade and pump.

Even harder on the pump is when an installer fails to drain, clean, and rinse the reservoir and pump after each day's use. Overnight, or over the weekend, the sludge settles and hardens around the pump impeller. A lot of sludge and a three-day weekend has been known to shear the impeller upon re-start. In addition to draining and cleaning the reservoir after use, I dunk the pump in a small container of clean water to flush it out and position it so it will drain completely.

Tile Cutting Blades

As part of a complete saw kit, an installer needs to have an array of blades for soft and hard materials, specialty blades for porcelain or glass, and perhaps a cleaning block (I reverse the blade—if allowed—or cut through an old wire-cut brick for this). Using a single blade for all materials can severely reduce the life of the blade, cause errant cuts, and cause unsightly spalled edges. For this reason, I typically have a half-dozen wet blades in my tool kit, including hard, soft, porcelain, glass, one or more spare blades, and one or more blades reserved strictly for handheld cutting. This is in addition to three or four small-diameter dry-cutting blades.

The rim that performs the actual cutting is composed of diamond bits embedded in copper beryllium (or other soft metal) bonded to a steel core. Since their "teeth" protrude only a few thousandths of an inch, continuous-rim, wet-cutting diamond blades are relatively safe. To demonstrate their somewhat benign nature to workers or students, I turn on the saw, wait for the water to hit the blade, and lightly run my fingers over the rim of the rotating blade. My fingers routinely brush up against the rotating blade without causing any damage, but I take great care to ensure my hands or fingers do not get caught between the spinning blade and the saw's table. That can cause severe injury!

Another real hazard to an installer using a wet saw

can occur when bits, chunks, or sections of this rim become disbonded from the core, strike the saw table, and careen into his chest, throat, eyes, face, or head. This fact has affected the way I cut tiles even though I have neither experienced or witnessed the hazard: After lining up a cut mark on the tile with the wet-saw blade, I move my head to the side of the blade and then make contact with and cut the tile. This practice keeps my head away from the "throw zone" should parts of the rim dislodge while the blade is stressed and cutting. For greater safety, I line up the mark on a tile with the edge of the blade's rim while the blade is not spinning, move my head out of the way, turn the saw's motor on, and cut the tile. When using a fence to gauge the cut, keeping your head away from the plane of the blade—and the potential orbit of its disbonded parts—is a matter or training yourself to be aware of the danger and adjusting your stance while cutting.

Blade life. Brand new diamond blades should be broken in slowly, rather than immediately subjecting them to production pressures. In my opinion, only after a blade's sharp rim edge is rounded over slightly does a saw cut smoothly and without vibration. Some blades are meant to be used in one direction only, while others can be run in any direction. If a blade starts to cut slower or more push is required, the blade may be clogged. If a blade becomes sluggish, the first thing I do is cut a slice off a wire-cut brick (manufactured diamond-wheel cleaning blocks are also available). If dressing the wheel does not work, I turn the blade around and cut another slice of hard brick (and return the blade to its original orientation if it is one direction only). Bi-directional blades seem to cut cleaner and smoother if their direction of rotation is reversed periodically.

As a diamond blade is used up, its cutting efficiency begins to fade until, at the very end of its life, it has so few diamonds that the blade can stall in the kerf or, even worse, throw the tile being cut out the back of the saw. To prevent this, I start by measuring the diameter of the blade and the width of the cutting rim with a micrometer and record the measurements in my files. When approximately 60% of the cutting rim has been used up, I stop using the blade for straight cutting and, instead, use it solely for freehand cutting. When less than 5% of the cutting rim remains, I stop cutting tiles with the blade, but I don't throw it away because old, worn-out blades are still very useful for re-pointing carbide drill bits.

Safe Cutting Practices

Largely as a result of my earliest safety and mechanical training, I have always had the greatest respect for hefty tools, whether they were cutting, mechanical, hand, or power tools. When a blade, drill, or chisel is attached to a power tool, I become even more attentive and observant, asking myself: Is there anything I am about to do or use or cut or drill or mix or modify or otherwise handle that could hurt me or anyone around me?

When operating any tile saw or cutter, first consideration must always be given to the safety of the operator. After that, the safety of the tile being cut can be evaluated. As explained previously, most straight cuts larger than 1 inch wide, whether they are non-vitreous or porcelain, are most efficiently processed on a snap cutter. Slivers less than 1 inch, though, are best processed with a wet saw.

When using a properly aligned wet saw, there is a

Figure 11-9. There are snap cutters and wet saws large enough for cutting 2- and 3-foot tiles, but a reasonable alternative is to combine a circular saw fitted with a diamond blade, several clamps, and a straightedge. Plan to make several light passes, increasing the depth of cut with each one.

Figure 11-10. When cutting glass tiles, the author bolts a section of ¾-inch plywood to the wet saw's table to reduce chatter and shattering. The narrow kerf, providing support for the glass tile's cut edge, is made by the saw's blade.

basic method for straight cutting any type of tile, whether hard- or soft-bodied: hold the tile firmly against the table, introduce the blade very slowly into the edge of the tile, increase the feed rate through the body of the tile, and very slowly cut through the remaining 15% of the tile. Forcing the edge of the tile into the blade sometimes causes the blade to wander off cut, and maintaining production speed at the end of a cut may produce a pressure-induced, wandering break instead of a clean cut. The rate of feed will change according to the density and hardness of the tiles being cut, but the same slow-start/slow-finish cutting method applies to tiles of any density or hardness.

When more than one cut of the same size is needed, I use a fence to ensure that each cut is identical. Since the size of each tile in a given batch varies, placement of the fence is important: The desired cut should be between the blade and the fence. If the off cut is located between the blade and the fence, the size of each cut will vary.

Freehand cutting is not recommended by saw manufacturers. By freehand cutting I mean holding the tile to be cut in your hands rather than placing the tile on the saw's table. When freehand cutting, I hold the tile with both hands and rest them on the saw table to stabilize the tile. As long as you take your time and make sure the kerf does not pinch the blade, it can be done, but proceed at your own risk. Because I do a lot of inlay work, I use my old tile saw for this cutting method and begin by scribing the cut line on the tile with an indelible marker. To start, I make a series of roughing cuts to quickly remove unwanted material, then I use the side of the blade to gradually work close to the cut line. I make light cuts, sawing no more than $\frac{1}{16}$ inch with each pass. The final pass is done very

slowly so I can cut as close to the mark as possible. To improve the look of the irregular cut, I use a hand stone to soften the edge.

Cutting large tiles can be a problem if the saw is too small. This is a particular problem when cutting diagonals. If you are cutting large-format tiles frequently, a larger saw is a convenience, but if you are cutting large tiles infrequently, the cost of a large saw plus the chore of lugging a heavy piece of equipment may not suit your budget or work style. A reasonable option is to use a straightedge with a circular saw (Figure 11-9). For cutting diagonals, I use a small circular saw fitted with a dry-cutting diamond blade and pair it with a straightedge (held on with two spring clamps). With this setup, the shoe of the saw rides against the straightedge for a straight cut. To put less pressure and stress on the blade, I adjust its depth so the cut is made with several light passes. Hogging through a porcelain tile with one pass is a good way to reduce the life of the blade or generate enough heat to damage the tile being cut. When cutting glass tiles, I use a purpose-manufactured glass-cutting blade for a smoother cut edge, and to reduce chatter, vibration, spalling, and shattering, I bolt a section of $\frac{3}{4}$-inch exterior plywood to the wet saw's table (Figure 11-10). To ensure maximum support for the glass tile's cut edge, I create a very narrow kerf slot—about $\frac{1}{4}$ inch deep—cutting the plywood with the wet-saw blade.

Cutting Holes in Tile

To drill holes through tiles with conventional power drills, I use carbide bits for softer tiles and diamond bits for hard tiles. Whenever possible, I use water to cool the bit and the tile, even if I am using dry-cutting bits. One problem with diamond core bits is the inef-

Figure 11-11. For drilling holes, the author uses both wet- and dry-cutting core bits. Clockwise from upper left: (1) Tile Dock (for securing tiles to be cut); (2) RotoZip tool fitted with right-angle attachment; (3) assorted RotoZip dry-cutting wood, metal, and tile blades; (4) Tile Dock cutting templates; (5) conventional wet-cutting diamond core bits; (6) carbide core bit; (7) standard carbide drill bit; (8) RotoZip dry-cutting core bits; (9) RotoZip tool fitted with 1$\frac{3}{8}$-inch core bit.

fective carbide pilot bit (found on most core bits) that will usually break a tile before the hole gets drilled. To get around this, I use a guide made from a scrap piece of ¾-inch plywood with three holes to match the three sizes of core bits I use. To keep the bit and tile cool and wet during the cutting process, I place another scrap of ¾ ply on the bottom of the wet saw's reservoir (to keep the drill from puncturing it), place the tile over that, and center the guide over the tile. The tile should be submerged in water, and the guide must be held motionless for the first part of the cut, which is nothing more than creating a groove on the face of the tile. Once the tile is grooved, I remove the

guide to allow water to flow freely over the tile and bit, and I continue drilling through the tile. The bit, whether its diameter is small or large, should never be forced into the tile. Light pressure only is required, with less pressure as the bit exits the tile.

To drill through tiles that have been installed, I use the same bits but a slightly different drilling method. For floor tiles, I begin by marking the hole location, adjusting the plywood cutting guide, and cutting a shallow groove in the tile. Then I remove the guide, surround the hole area with a fat ring made of plumber's putty (suction-type, non-staining silicone rings for drilling stone tiles that could be permanently stained by the plumbers' putty are also available), fill the ring with water, and complete the hole. On walls, small holes are needed for attaching doors and enclosures. To do this, I use a diamond drill made for drilling holes in glass and cool the bit and tile with a spray bottle. When many deep holes need to be drilled through installed floor tiles, I rent a heavy-duty drill with a vacuum mount and a feed lever to get through the work quickly.

Two of the most recent additions to my cutting and drilling tool kit are two companion tools that can be used in place of biters or freehand cutting—the RotoZip (www.rotozip.com), a hand-held, router-type tool for drilling and tile cutting, and RotoZip's Tile Dock, a portable clamping table for cutting or drilling tiles (Figure 11-11). For years, I have relied on wet-cutting diamond core bits for larger holes and carbide-tipped bits for drilling (I pair these bits with a slow-turning ½-inch drill). I still use wet bits, but RotoZip's dry-cutting core bits can drill a 1⅜-inch hole through a hard porcelain tile in about 10 sec-

Figure 11-12. When the author needs to cut a small number of bullnose-profile tiles from stone or porcelain stock, he uses an MK profiling wheel in the wet saw.

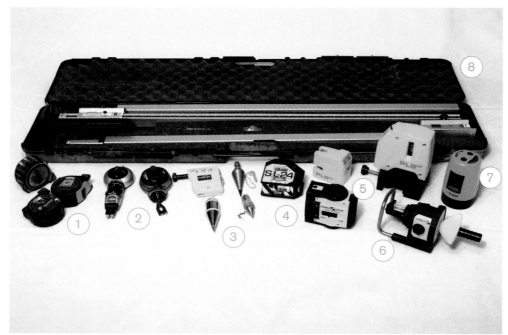

Figure 11-13. Accurate measuring is essential for tiling, and the author relies on an assortment of both traditional and modern measuring tools. From left to right: (1) measuring tapes; (2) wet and dry chalk boxes; (3) plumb bobs; (4) an SL-24 laser square; (5) three cross-hair lasers; (6) a specialty laser for cutting holes through studs for pipe or conduit (lower right foreground); (7) CST Gizmo cross-hair laser; and (8) at the top, an adjustable Laserjamb for vertical positioning of a cross-hair laser.

onds. Tiles that are dry cut can be installed immediately and do not require toweling or sunning to remove all traces of moisture—a problem with tiles that are wet cut. To drill small holes on wall tile work, for mounting shower doors, enclosures, or other fixtures, for example, I use a companion $5/32$-inch bit designed for hard porcelain tiles.

Small bits are also available for removing old grout, but for this task, I prefer to use a very thin (just under $1/16$ inch thick), dry-cutting diamond blade (made for the RotoZip system). A right-angle drive attachment turns the 30,000 rpm RotoZip tool into a 15,000 rpm grinder with a dust port and an adjustable depth-of-cut gauge. With other blades available for cutting wood, laminates, and metal, this tool is highly useful for flush-cutting door trim and cutting metal studs, reinforcing mesh or wire, rebar, angle iron, etc. An optional jigsaw handle has a soft, non-marring base that is ideal for making countertop cuts in wood and stone slabs.

The Tile Dock uses several types of bench dogs and a levered clamp for securing the tile, making cutting and drilling safer and more efficient. This tool also has an adjustable clamp for a vac hose, plus a set of templates for marking the most common openings (electrical outlet box, closet flanges, and pipe openings).

Profiling and Polishing

When the installation calls for bullnose or other edge finishes on stone and porcelain tiles, I use a carbide, wet-cutting profile saw blade (Figure 11-12). Depending on the manufacturer, these are available from several blade manufacturers. Combination cut-off/profile wheels are also available, but I prefer to use a regular diamond blade to cut to size, then use the profile wheel. Like other diamond or carbide cutting tools, profile blades give the best service and have the longest life if profiling is done gradually. Quality can be an issue: Cheap profile saw blades cut poorly and don't last very long. I once watched an installer mount a new profile wheel on his wet saw and ruin the blade and the tile after only one pass. Profile blades also need plenty of coolant water, which is why I fitted the saw I use for profiling with two coolant pumps.

To profile, begin by cutting all the tiles to size with a regular blade. When all the pieces required for the installation are cut, switch out the regular blade for the profile, set the blade for a light cut, adjust the cutting fence, and make the first pass on all the tiles. With that done, I reset the blade depth about $1/16$ inch lower (more or less, depending on the hardness of the tile), and make a second pass on all the tiles. This is repeated until all the required tiles are rough profiled. The profiled edge now needs to be smoothed and polished, and for that, I use an angle grinder and a set of three or four polishing discs (three for a honed finish, four for a high polish). Dry and wet disc sets are available, depending on the manufacturer, in grits up to 3000. For new work where cutting is done outside or in the shop, I use wet discs. For polishing, touch-up, or renovation of existing porcelain or stone tiles, I use dry discs and a vacuum to collect the dust.

Polishing must be done in stages, starting with the coarsest disc and working up to honing or polishing discs. Whether you use wet or dry discs, set up an assembly line and process all the profiled tiles one grit stage at a time. Subsequent discs should be used until all the scratches left by the previous discs are removed.

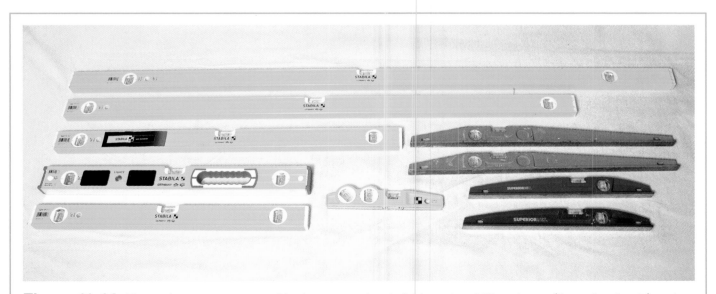

Figure 11-14. The author uses a variety of high-accuracy levels for layout and tiling chores (the yellow levels) and sometimes pairs the small master level (center near bottom) with a straightedge instead of using a long level. The red and blue levels are used for mortar and concrete work.

Skipping a grit will leave scratches, so don't try to rush the process.

With patience, it is possible to do a reasonable job of making bullnose or other edge styles without a profile wheel. To ensure that the profile of one tile matches that of its neighbors, I clamp two or more tiles at a time to my workbench and use a wet or dry grinding wheel mounted in an angle grinder to ensure that the profile is consistent. I work on two tiles at a time, in the order they will be installed, until all the required tiles are profiled. I usually use manufactured disc sets for polishing, but in a pinch, when a honed finish is required, I have also used wet/dry sandpaper, with graduated grits up to 1500 grit.

Layout Tools

Layout tools are needed at three stages of tiling: checking the structure for square, plumb, flat, etc.; plotting layout lines on setting bed surfaces and membrane sheets; and marking tiles for cutting. I obtain most of my layout tools from the local hardware store, some from tile tool dealers, and a few from machinist supply stores (Figure 11-13).

Tape Measures and Rulers

The most obvious layout tool is an accurate measuring tape with a sliding hooked end for both inside and outside measurements. Another tool I use to check the accuracy of the hooked end is a 12-inch scale (ruler). This is not the type of scale you might find attached to a combination square, but rather it is a precision scale used by machinists for accurate work and com-

parisons. I use this scale to "prove" all the measuring tapes I use. This is particularly important when I use one tape to measure a space on the setting bed for a cut tile, and my helper uses another tape to make the cut on a snap cutter or wet saw: I want all tapes in my tool kit to read the same. All that is generally required to make small corrections is to bend the tape's sliding hook one way or another. The sliding feature of the hook allows for both inside and outside measuring, but when the slots that allow the hook to move back and forth (the movement is equal to the thickness of the hook) begin to elongate and affect the measurement, no more adjustments can be made: time to replace the tape.

Chalk-Line Boxes

I stay away from the cheap hardware store variety "chalk box" because most of them leak chalk, jam up, and have thick chalk lines. Instead, I use a chalk-line box made by Tajima Tools (www.tajimatool.com) that leaks minimal chalk; has a positive line lock; and is fitted with what looks like thin, braided fishing line for laying down a very slender line. A chalk line has a number of uses on tiling jobs: Snapping lines is one, but I also use the chalk line to determine if a wall is straight and flat. Yes, this can be done with a straightedge, but the Tajima chalk box weighs only a few ounces and can check walls that are much longer than my longest straightedge. I have three boxes—one with black chalk, one with red chalk, and another with blue —and use the three colors on complicated layouts so I can tell at a glance if a line is a reference line, a layout line, or a correction line. I use chalk lines primarily on

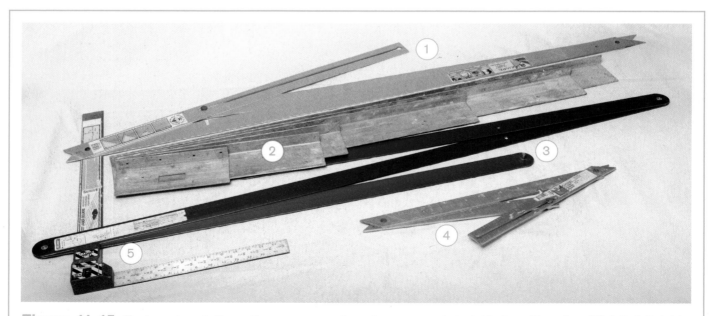

Figure 11-15. For layout work, the author uses a number of squares and straightedges. From top: (1) A 3-4-5 right-angle folding square; (2) six aluminum straightedges are part of the author's set of 14 that range from 8 to 72 inches; (3) a large 45-degree-angle folding square (blue); (4) a small folding 45-degree-angle square (gold); and (5) the FR-16 laser carpenter's square.

setting beds, but it is also useful to mark cut lines on backerboards or plywood sheets.

Plumb Bobs, Levels, and Lasers

Levels are important, but long before spirit levels were invented, builders used plumb bobs to check or mark vertical lines and plumb bobs fitted to framing squares to mark horizontal or angled lines. Plumb bobs owe their accuracy to gravity. Some claim to "settle down" faster than others, and some are beautiful and rather expensive. I have several regular brass plumb bobs and a fancy Tajima model that comes equipped with several mounting features, but practically any object can be suspended by a string to act as a plumb bob, and even the crudest, cheapest handmade bob will give readings as accurate as the most expensive (gravity does not discriminate). And while a plumb bob can accurately be paired with a framing square to establish level layout lines, spirit levels and lasers are more convenient.

Levels. While lasers have, to some extent, replaced the spirit level, I still use spirit levels to assess structures, plot lines, and check tile alignment. At one time, I strived to have a spirit level in every conceivable size: There were 8-, 10-, 12-, 18-, 24-, 30-, 32-, 36-, 42-, 48-, 60-, and 72-inch levels in my tool kit, and practically all of them were inscribed with marks indicating where and how much they were off. They also took up a lot of rack space on my truck.

Today, I have a collection of about 10 spirit levels (Figure 11-14). Most of these are used solely for layout work, plus I have three "sacrificial" levels I use during tile installation (thinset mortar is hell on levels). To check the accuracy of any level in my kit, I keep the 10-inch torpedo level stored in a cabinet in my shop. This practice has its roots in the machine shop where I once worked. There, sequestered in the tool room under lock and key, was our shop's single master level —the one that was used to check the levels that were used to install the heavy lathes and milling machines. All the employees treated our shop's Starrett Master Level with the same respect the pope might give the Holy Grail. Before starting any project involving a level, it was checked against the Master and certified for use. I rely on the same concept today, using a superb master level to check all other levels. I also use this master level with a good set of straightedges to accurately extend level lines (Figure 11-15).

One of the exercises I give students is to scribe a line around the perimeter walls of a room with a spirit level. After making a "begin" mark on the wall, I direct students to use a 3-foot-long spirit level to plot a line around the four walls. In spite of how accurate the level is, no student has ever been able to end the line at the beginning mark on the first try. One reason for the inaccuracy is that many people think level is achieved as long as the bubble rests anywhere between the vial marks (the bubble must be centered between the vial marks). Another reason is that reading the bubble from the side gives a false reading (the bubble should be read with your eyes in front of the bubble). Once students master how to check a level for accuracy and read the bubble properly, we move on to lasers.

Lasers. Using an accurate construction laser is the fastest way to check the accuracy of a structure or pro-

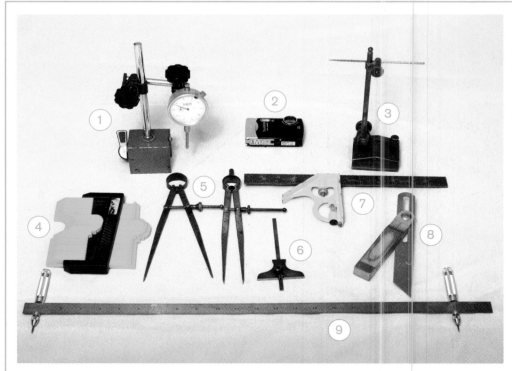

Figure 11-16. The author's measuring tool kit includes, top row from left: (1) a dial indicator with 1-inch travel and .001-inch increments; (2) a digital camera for recording structural problems and finished work; (3) a surface gauge for checking heights. Middle row from left: (4) a shaping template for transferring profiled and irregular shapes; (5); dividers; (6) depth gauge; (7) combination square; (8) bevel gauge; and (9) along the bottom, trammel points connected to a 24-inch scale (this combination is sometimes called a beam compass).

vide a layout for membrane or tile. I use several lasers for different tasks. The simplest is a framing square (FR-16 shown in Figure 11-15) with a built-in laser that extends two beams (90 degrees apart) up to 100 feet. Another is an adjustable laser square (SL-24 shown in Figure 11-13) whose beam extends even farther (both lasers are made by Laser Products Industries; www.laserproductsus.com). I use both primarily for floor work.

For wall work, I have used the original, self-leveling Gizmo (from CST/berger, www.cst/berger.com) cross-hair laser for over 10 years with excellent results. I have since retired the Gizmo for everyday layout chores and, instead, use it primarily to verify the beams of another laser I now use for wall work: the PLS 180. Made by Pacific Laser Systems (www.plslaser.com), this laser projects cross-hair beams to indicate plumb and level, but it has much wider beam fan angles than the Gizmo, so the beams cover more ground and require fewer setups than the Gizmo. In addition, the PLS 180 has a separate receiving unit for outdoor use in sunlight.

On many installations, I don't plot layout lines, but use the laser beams instead, which saves a lot of time. To make the wall lasers even more productive, I mount them on a device called the Laserjamb (www.laser-jamb.com), which allows for fast, unlimited vertical adjustment. When used with either the Gizmo or the PLS 180, I can set the horizontal beam as close as 6 inches to the floor or, with the extensions included with this accessory, as high as 148 inches.

Another productivity booster, made possible by the laser beams, is that I no longer have to be concerned about obscuring a chalk line with thinset mortar. Now,

instead of meticulously troweling mortar up to the lay-out lines (which often results in adhesive voids in the four corners of a layout square), I simply spread thinset an inch or two past the lines. Not only does this save time and energy, but it also results in a more uniform layer of thinset mortar and better support for the tiles. In my opinion, a properly functioning laser may be the most productive tool an installer can own.

Squares. When a laser is not practical for measuring a surface or plotting a layout, I have three folding squares made by the C. H. Hanson Company (www.chhanson.com). The first is a 3x4x5-foot square I use for general checking and layout; the second is a 54-inch, 45-degree angle square for diagonal layout work; and the third is a 16-inch, 45-degree angle square for checking and layout tasks where the larger square won't fit. I also have the usual assortment of small and large 90-degree-angle framing squares.

Establishing Angles and Straight Lines

For determining angles and marking tiles for cutting, I use a carpenter's bevel gauge. For transferring irregular shapes to a tile for cutting, I use a shaping template made by Plasplugs (www.plasplugs.com). For scribing arcs and marking off divisions, I use a pair of 10-inch dividers; for larger arcs and divisions, I mount a set of trammel points on a small wood beam (both tools available from General Tools; www.generaltools.com) (Figure 11-16).

Straightedges. Straightedges are essential for all types of mortar bed and thinset work. There are several professionally made straightedges, but I prefer a nesting set of aluminum straightedges available from Gundlach (www.benojgundlachco.com). A starter set consists of

Figure 11-17. For spacing and shimming, the author keeps tile spacers, shims, and construction spacers in a box for easy transport and selection.

five angled straightedges in varying lengths: 6 feet, 4 feet10 inches, 4 feet, 3 feet, and 2 feet (Figure 11-15). I still have the first set I bought, and I have also added more sets and sawed them to various lengths to produce a set that is from 8 inches to 6 feet long in roughly 4-inch increments. I use the set for screeding mortar beds, layout, and as ledges for wall tiling and other tile support tasks. I also keep a dozen 1-inch C-clamps so I can join two or more straightedges together when I need an edge longer than 6 feet.

One of my favorite straightedges—used primarily to determine the flatness of a surface—is a beefy, 10-foot-long aluminum sliding door track that I once removed from a dumpster filled with demolition trash. Its 10-foot length is ideal for seeing if a surface conforms to the industry's $\frac{1}{4}$-inch-in-10-feet standard. If more than $\frac{1}{4}$ inch of daylight shows when I hold this edge against a floor or wall, I know instantly that the surface has to be renovated. Any straight aluminum extrusion that is stiff enough to keep from bending can be put to use as a straightedge.

In a pinch, if no straightedge is available, a reasonable substitute for an aluminum edge is one made from the factory edge of a sheet of $\frac{1}{2}$-, $\frac{5}{8}$-, or $\frac{3}{4}$-inch plywood cut about 6 to 8 inches wide and as long as needed. I have even used the factory edge of a piece of $\frac{1}{2}$-inch gypsum drywall cut 6 inches wide. If there is no scrap pile to raid for a length of plywood or drywall, a ball of string can be put to use when a straightedge is needed.

Spacers and shims. When I first started out in the trade, most tiles I installed were non-vitreous with integral spacing lugs that produced a joint about $\frac{1}{16}$ inch wide. Once I moved away from absorbent, non-vitreous tiles to stoneware or porcelain tiles, I began to use spacers. Now, with a few exceptions for interior work, I prefer to install tiles with a $\frac{1}{8}$-inch grout joint and use spacers to keep the joints uniformly wide.

"Leave-in" spacers are available, but they create a weakness in the grout at joint intersections, and with colored grouts, it is not uncommon to see the faint outline of any spacer that has not been removed. I like $\frac{1}{8}$-inch joints because they are easier to pack with grout, are much easier to clean and maintain than wider joints, and look more stylish and tailored than wide joints. I prefer to use regular cross-type spacers because they allow me to install tiles with a much smoother surface than is obtainable with spacers that do not allow me to use my sense of touch to check tile-to-tile transitions. The reason? Regular spacers do not cover the corners of four intersecting tiles and allow my fingers to feel for differences in tile height. When using spacers that cover these four corners, I cannot check tile alignment without removing the spacers. Corner-covering spacers and spacers with a bent and extended leg were designed primarily for easy removal rather than tile installation accuracy. When it is time to remove spacers (just before grout-

ing or after the tile adhesive has hardened), I use a dental pick (available free from my dentist) or an awl. Yes, it takes a bit more time to remove regular tile spacers, but what is the purpose of a spacer—to make a better looking installation for the customer or to make it easier for the installer to remove the spacers? I'll choose the better looking installation.

A curious thing about the use of spacers: Only one spacer is required at the intersection of four tiles, but many installers defeat one of the functions of spacers by placing four spacers near the intersection, a practice I think is ridiculously wasteful and unproductive. First, it takes four times as long to slip in four spacers rather than one. Second, since the purpose of a spacer is to keep tiles in alignment, using four spacers—that do not lock all neighboring tiles together—causes more work when a row or column of tiles is pushed one way or another.

Spacers are great for floor work and for some wall applications where smaller (lighter) tiles are installed, but when installing 12-inch tiles or larger, the weight of the tiles tends to slightly compress the spacers: more at the bottom of a wall, less on the upper rows, resulting in non-uniform grout joint width. To counter this, I use a variety of shims to keep tiles spaced uniformly and sometimes add a regular spacer to protect tile-to-tile alignment. Small tile shims are available through QEP (www.qep.com) and other tile installation material manufacturers. When installing heavy tiles (thick stone, 24-inch tiles, etc.), I prefer shims normally used by carpenters: Handi-shims (www.handi-shim.com), available $\frac{1}{32}$, $\frac{1}{16}$, $\frac{1}{8}$, and $\frac{1}{4}$ inch thick (Figure 11-17). Thinset mortar is easily cleaned off these shims, so they can be removed once the adhesive sets up and re-used.

Other Essential Tools

As far as I am concerned, an installer can never have enough tools, and with my machinist's background, I am more fanatical than most about having the right tool. A tile installer working on residential or light commercial tile installations needs several tool kits: a full-blown kit full of tiling tools, of course, but smaller kits for carpentry, plumbing, and the other side work that accompanies a tile installation. As well, I bring a variety of power extension cords and splitters to the job site, including a 100-foot-long, OSHA-approved extension cord with two splitters for plugging into a power pole. I also have a number of pneumatic tools for nailing and chipping chores. Another tool that is invaluable for communicating problem situations to GCs, architects, and building owners; documenting the completion of work; and archiving is a small digital camera. For me, the ideal camera is the Olympus Stylus 850 SW (shown in Figure 11-16), which is shock and waterproof and has a protective lens cap that automatically slides into place when the camera is powered down. With it, I can upload photos via its removable chip or a USB cable.

NOTES

Properties of Ceramic Tile

Selecting a ceramic tile to match a specific application begins with understanding its material properties. A good place to start is with the industry standards. Because tile installation and tile manufacturing have so many variables, there are two distinct sets of standards: ANSI A108 for ceramic tile installation and ANSI A137.1 for ceramic tile manufacturing. Strictly speaking, an installer does not need to be fluent in the manufacturing standard to be able to install ceramic tiles, but full- or part-time career installers (and ultimately their customers) can benefit from the knowl-edge and with it, produce better installations. Also, since it is an installer's duty to alert the general contractor, architect, or building owner to any potential problems that may exist that could negatively affect the finished installation, understanding the various properties of ceramic tile is a valuable asset. The complete standards are too lengthy to include in this book, but if you need specific information about the properties of ceramic tile, I highly recommend consulting ANSI A137.1 (available from TCNA at www. tileusa.com).

Water Absorption

1. Water absorption. The ability of a tile's body (bisque) to absorb water or moisture. ASTM test method C373 measures the rate of absorption as a percent of the volume of the body of the tile, with different designations for dust pressed, extruded, and other body forms (see ANSI A137 Table 1). This test also can be used to determine the absorption rate of stone, cast cement, and any other hard tile.

	Impervious	Vitreous	Semi-Vitreous	Non-Vitreous
Rate of Absorption	≤0.5%	3-0.5%	3-7%	7-20%
Forming Method				
Pressed	P1	P2	P3	P4
Extruded	E1	E2	E3	E4
Other	O1	O2	O3	O4

Water absorption is one of the most important properties of tile because it is a measure of the voids within the bisque, or body, of a tile. This property is directly related to a tile's ability to support weight and absorb moisture: Fewer voids result in a stronger, more impermeable tile body. Because they absorb the least amount of moisture, impervious tiles are the obvious first choice for wet, exterior, or food-service applications; and their generally higher strength makes them ideal for floor applications. According to the chart, porcelain tiles fall into the "impervious" designation, while soft, white, talc-bodied glazed wall tiles are ranked as "non-vitreous."

Visual Abrasion Resistance

2. Visual abrasion resistance. A measure of the resistance of tile surfaces to visible surface abrasion (surface scratches). The ASTM C1027 test applies only to glazed floor, quarry, mosaic, and porcelain tiles. Note that the PEI scale is not valid for ceramic tiles (see ANSI A137 Table 12).

Rating	Application
O	Not recommended for floors
I	Light Residential
II	Residential
III	Heavy Residential/Light Commercial
IV	Commercial
V	Heavy Commercial

Since all standards are based on minimum performance, I usually reject any tiles rated O or I on this scale, regardless of the application (floor, wall, countertop, ceiling, exterior, interior, residential, light commercial, functional).

Abrasion resistance is an important consideration for floor tiles and is determined for glazed tiles by ASTM C1027. The test was designed to determine the resistance of a floor tile's glaze to visibly discernable surface wear and uses the 6-point rating system shown directly above to categorize test results. Non-vitreous glazed wall tile, for example, would be rated O. The other designations, I through V, are loosely based on the floor rating system found in the TCNA Handbook's Floor Tiling Installation Guide. The ASTM C1027 test measures the resistance of a glaze to abrasion and should not be confused with another test of abrasion resistance applied to unglazed floor tiles and described below in No.6: Deep Abrasion Resistance.

Aesthetic Class

3. Aesthetic class. A determination of a tile's uniformity of color, with a five-point rating system that ranges from very uniform (as tested by ASTM C609) to random color and texture differences (see ANSI A137 Table 3).

Rating	Description
V0	Very Uniform: Pieces of same shade value are very uniform
V1	Uniform: Difference among pieces of same production are minimal
V2	Slight Variation: Distinguishing differences in texture/pattern within similar colors
V3	Moderate Variations: Significant variations in color/texture
V4	Substantial Variation: Random color/texture differences from tile to tile

This is a classification that has long been needed by the tile industry—especially tile showrooms—to help educate tile consumers regarding color, blending, and shade variations. At one end of the spectrum, the class of very uniform tiles (VO) is determined by precise testing (ASTM C609); at the other extreme, tiles that vary considerably (V4) require no testing, but rather a subjective call by the manufacturer. Consequently, manufacturers, showrooms, installers, and consumers now have a positive standard and a simple classification for both commodity tiles (usually V0 or V1) and artisan tiles (which can range from VO to V4). This class and the designations VO through V4 are for appearances only, not performance.

Chemical Resistance

4. Chemical resistance. A measure of a tile's resistance to common cleaning chemicals, with a five-point rating system determined by ASTM C650 testing (see ANSI A137 Table 13).

Rating	Maximum number of affected samples
A	0
B	1
C	2
D	3
E	4 or more

The chemicals evaluated in this class include the most popular solutions and materials used to clean and maintain residential and light-commercial tile installations. The classes—A to E—are determined by ASTM test C650 and are based on resistance to staining. Samples unaffected by any of the chemicals are rated A, while samples affected by 4 or more chemicals are given an E rating. The test makes no note of which staining agents affected the test samples, only how many samples were affected. Although not critical for most residential applications, chemical resistance is an important issue for commercial work, especially in food-service areas, where three or four cleanings per day may be required. For this type of application, an A rating is recommended.

Stain Resistance

5. Stain resistance. Measured by ASTM C1378, which rates a tile's resistance to the most common household stains, with a rating similar to ASTM C650, above (see ANSI A137 Table 14).

Rating	Maximum Number of Samples that Retain a Stain
A	0
B	1
C	2
D	3
E	4 or more

Even though highly effective sealers and impregnators are available, stain resistance is an important property for tiles installed in residential and commercial food-service areas. Stain resistance may be less of a factor in dry, non-food service areas, but it is still an important consideration with most consumers. For residential or light commercial applications, look for a rating of A; for heavy commercial or industrial installations where performance is more important than appearance, B-, C-, D-, or E-rated tiles are preferred.

Deep Abrasion Resistance

6. Deep abrasion resistance. Measured by ASTM C1243 and refers to the resistance to wear of an unglazed tile intended for floor covering. Values depend upon the type of tile tested (see ANSI A137 Table 11).

Class	Maximum Value
P1, E1, O1	175
P2	225
E2, O2	275
P3	345
E3, O3	393
E4, O4	2365
P4	N/A

Intended solely for unglazed floor tiles, ASTM C1243 measures the amount of material worn from the face of a test tile during a prescribed number of cycles. Since only unglazed, color-through porcelain tiles and some unglazed vitreous tiles are suitable for floor use, I don't consider deep abrasion an aesthetic issue since the color of the tile remains the same whether it is new or worn. The real issue is how long the tile will last before it completely wears out and must be replaced. Examples of 100 hundred year old porcelain mosaic exterior commercial entry floors, worn but still attractive and providing great service, can be found all over the world. The patina of wear is attractive to me, as well as a good indication of a secure installation.

Freeze/thaw resistance

7. Freeze/thaw resistance. ASTM C1026 measures a tile's resistance to damage induced by cycles of freezing and thawing. This test lists the number of defects observed in 10 sample tiles after 5, 10, and 15 testing cycles.

For a given tile, a chart such as this would be provided, with the number of defects observed filled in for the left-hand column:

Number of Observed Defects	Number of Cycles
	5
	10
	15

Any tiles tested under ASTM C1026 and registering zero defects after 5, 10, and 15 cycles could be used to tile any interior or exterior surface in any climate. This test method has no chart indicating locations where tiles having one or more defects can be used safely in exterior applications, so beyond zero, it is a judgment call. The way I interpret the numbers is to pair the number of cycles with a range of temperatures and to balance the number of defects against the type of installation. For example, in hard-freeze areas, I tolerate no defects in the test tile after a full 15 test cycles (alternately freezing and thawing the test samples).

The 10-cycle test corresponds, in my view, to areas where the temperatures may dip slightly below freezing during a normal winter and where 1 or 2 defects may be acceptable if the exterior installation is protected against rain, snow, or moisture. The 5-cycle test corresponds to locations where it may freeze lightly once or twice a year, and again, where I may accept 1 or 2 defects for an exterior installation that will be shielded from inclement weather. Note that wherever tiles are used in exterior floor applications, the setting bed surface must be sloped to provide quick and complete surface drainage.

Coefficient of Friction

> **8. Coefficient of Friction (CoF).** ASTM C1028 is a test to determine how much traction a tile provides after installation, under both wet and dry conditions. A value of .5 for dry floors and .6 for wet floors are considered acceptable for most applications. Although a measure applied to individual tiles, the test can also be applied to an assembly of mosaic tiles (3 inches or less) and their grout joints. Values greater than .5 offer higher slip resistance, and values less than .5 offer lower slip resistance. To conform to world ISO standards, the ASTM minimum CoF standard may be raised to .6 in the near future. Tiles meeting the .6 standard should be used for bathrooms, shower floors, and exterior decks; tiles meeting the .5 standard should be reserved for dry interior areas only.

Because there are several test methods for gauging a tile's coefficient of friction (CoF), selecting a single method for determining this property is hotly contested by different countries. Nevertheless, ASTM C1028 is used in the U.S., and a minimum test value may be required as part of an engineer's or architect's project specification for floor tile. There are a number of commercial treatments (liquid applications) available that claim to increase a tile's CoF; most of these actually etch the surface of the tile. The same results can be obtained by abrading ceramic, stone, glass, cast, or other types of hard tile with diamond polishing pads, used in descending order of grit (from smoother to rougher) until the desired CoF rating is achieved. All such treatments tend to de-gloss a tile's surface, which in turn, tends to provide better traction —but at the expense of muting and diffusing colors and muddling the details of the tile. Also, matte finishes are usually not as easy to clean as a slick glazed surface. If the tiles you intend to install need reworking to meet the .5 standard, contact the tile manufacturer's technical service group for assistance with applied or etched techniques, or recommended grits when using abrasion

methods. Better yet, select a more appropriate tile.

One situation that completely overrides a particular tile's CoF in actual use is a lack of cleanliness. Tile makers who test for CoF generally post accurate figures that meet the needs of the building industry and consumers; nevertheless, so-called "slip-and-fall" lawsuits continue to be an issue for tile floors. Extensive industry reviews have shown that using a tile whose surface tests at below .5 (or below the project-specified amount) have been a causal factor in less than 5% of all cases. The prime causes of slipping in the remaining 95% of cases are water on top of a greasy or oily surface, and little or no soap used during the cleaning process. Especially in food service areas, enough cleaning agents must be used to remove slippery residues on floor (and wall) tiles. Traction matting may be required in areas that are constantly wet and oily, such as would be found on the floor of a commercial restaurant kitchen. Without adequate cleaning, even the most compliant tiles will be extra-slippery if coated with a thin film of oil or grease and splashed with water.

Bond Strength

> **9. Bond strength.** A measure of the ability of a tile to be bonded with portland cement adhesives, with test values (ASTM C482) expressed in pounds/square inch. The minimum value for this test is 50 psi. It is an important value for glass tiles, especially those with a smooth or coated back.

Bond strength is a measure of the grip of the adhesive between the tile and setting bed. It is based on 95% minimum uniform adhesive coverage. Ideal coverage occurs when the lower third of the tile is embedded in thinset, with no visible gaps or voids around the perimeter of the tile. Since the test uses regular dry-set thinset mortar, the minimum value of 50 psi can easily be upgraded by using latex- or polymer-modified thinset. Special care must be given to two of the most popular tiling materials: glass and porcelain. Both are in the impervious range and are likewise difficult to adhere, but there are numerous high-performance thinsets and grouts formulated for glass and porcelain.

Break Strength

> **10. Break strength. A measure of the breaking strength of tile with test values (ASTM C648) expressed in pounds-force. The minimum value for glazed and unglazed mosaic, quarry, and paver tile is 250 pounds. Minimum value for glazed wall tile is 90 pounds. Samples of non-ceramic tiles, made of stone, glass, metal, concrete, or other materials, can also be submitted for ASTM C648 testing and evaluation.**

This is a test of the stand-alone strength of a tile. Note the difference (above) in strength between floor and wall tiles. This test is also useful for testing nonceramic tiles prior to installation and is recommended for testing natural stone cut to normal tile dimensions. Strength tests developed by the stone industry on "dimensional stone" may not be accurate when the same stone is cut down to very thin tile sizes. ASTM C648 is a test developed for thin ceramic tile, but it can (and in my opinion, should) be the preferred ASTM standard for testing thin stone tiles. Stone less than 7/8-inch thick are not covered by the Marble Institute of America guidelines.

Crazing Resistance

> **11. Crazing resistance. Measured by a one-cycle, pass-or-fail test (ASTM C424) to determine resistance to crazing. The test uses staining dyes and steam to induce and identify thermal shock damage. Any tile claiming craze or crackle resistance should be able to pass the ASTM C424. There is no test value. The sample either passes or fails.**

Crazing occurs when extremely fine cracks begin to appear within the glaze. Crazing can be induced by covering a color glaze with a clear glaze having different firing characteristics and, for some applications, is used to create a desired appearance. When used in wet areas, though, crazing can lead to moisture penetrating the body of the tile, mold, discoloration, flaking glaze, and other problems.

Thermal Shock Resistance

> **12. Thermal shock resistance. ASTM C484 measures a glazed ceramic tile's resistance to thermal shock created by rapid or severe temperature changes. The test uses staining dyes and approximate 300°F temperatures to induce and identify cracks or other damage. There is no test value. The sample either passes or fails.**

Thermal shock resistance is an important property for any tiles exposed to the heat of a fireplace, stove surround, or other high-temperature applications. Most tiles can withstand gradual exposure to higher and higher temperatures, but when some tiles are heated to a high temperature quickly, they can crack or break. Resistance to thermal shock is one of two properties related to the effects of high temperatures on ceramic tiles; the other is thermal lineal expansion. Please refer to #17, below.

Moisture expansion

> **13. Moisture expansion.** A negative property, rarely found in ceramic tile, where prolonged moisture absorption causes a tile to permanently grow in volume. ASTM C370 is the test used to reveal this property.

Moisture expansion of tile is included here only to highlight that the phenomenon actually exists. This problem is mostly confined to non-vitreous and semi-vitreous tiles that are continually subject to high levels of moisture accompanied by hydrostatic or steam pressure.

Facial Dimensions

> **14. Facial dimensions.** A measure of the uniformity of size of a particular tile, determined by ASTM Test C499, with values found under "Nominal Size," "Caliber Range," and "Thickness," in ANSI A137, Tables 6 through 10.

An accurate understanding of the actual facial dimensions of an order of tile is important to an installer developing a bid proposa—the more uniform the tile, the easier it is to install. ASTM C499 provides more than just an average size, and included in the test results are minimum, average, and maximum sizes.

Warpage and Wedging

> **15. Warpage.** The curving of a flat tile surface, as measured by ASTM C485, with values found under "Warpage Edge" and "Warpage Diagonal" in ANSI A137, Tables 6 through 10.
>
> **16. Wedging.** A change in edge dimension, from one tile to another in a given lot, as measured by ASTM C502, with values found under "Wedging" in ANSI A137, Tables 6 through 10.

Warpage and wedging are two negative dimensional properties of ceramic tile that can affect the layout and look of a tile installation. Warpage is the curvature of the surface plane of the tile, while wedging is a measure of deviation from a perfect rectangle or square. Both are expressed as a percentage, with a 0.0% denoting a perfect tile.

Linear Thermal Expansion

> **17. Linear thermal expansion.** Determined by ASTM test C372.

The determination of linear thermal expansion is important for any tile exposed to exterior conditions, the direct rays of the sun, or to sudden or sustained high or low temperatures. Knowledge of changes in a tile's linear dimensions is critical for an installer and essential for the durability of an installation whose tiles expand and contract excessively. Glass tiles are an example of tiling materials known for their reaction to thermal expansion, which is greater than that of ceramic tile.

Thickness

> **18. Thickness.** The uniformity of thickness for a given lot of tile is determined by ASTM C499, with values found under "Thickness" in ANSI A137, Tables 6 through 10.

Another dimensional property important to an installer, thickness is defined by the ASTM C499 test. The results are expressed as minimum, average, and maximum major and minor thicknesses. The major thickness is a measure of the tile body and any protuberances on its back; the minor thickness is a measure of the thickness of the tile body only.

Evaluation for Defects, Shade Value, and Mounting

19. Evaluation for facial and structural defects. ANSI A137, 9.1 and 9.2 outline procedures for examining tiles for structural defects (such as cracks) and facial defects (such as discoloration or a chipped surface). The setup for examination of tiles can be performed on site or in a shop and requires no equipment other than a viewing board of a certain color (ANSI A137, 9.2.2), a stop watch, and reasonable lighting. These examinations—and their accompanying tolerances—are generally given if structural or surface defects in the tiles you want to install become an issue.

20. Evaluation of shade value. ANSI A137, 9.4, test method for evaluating ceramic tile, Class V0 to V4. Results from this test are helpful to consumers, designers, salespeople, and installers by assigning to a particular lot of tile one of four levels of surface appearance: very uniform (V0), uniform (V1), slight variation (V2), moderate variation (V3), and substantial variation (V4). Primarily an evaluation of color and texture consistency, the various V ratings give the installer a heads up regarding the style and level of finish required for an installation.

21. Mounting. ANSI A137, 9.5, an alternative test method for evaluating grout joint width consistency of some types of mounted mosaic sheets. This test applies only to mosaic tiles that are nominally square, no less than 1x2 and no greater than 3x3, not mixed in a pattern, and mounted on a sheet. Mosaic sheets are arranged on a viewing board and obvious joint irregularities are marked and counted. The maximum number of acceptable joint defects are 24 for a 1x2-foot sheet of 1x1s, 10 for a 1x2-foot sheet of 2x2s, and 6 for a 1x2-foot sheet of 3x3s.

These properties are determined by standardized visual test methods using specific test apparatus and samples, and apply mostly to tiles classified as V0 or V1(see ANSI A137, Table 3). The evaluation methods are used to identify surface and color-related defects on tile and mosaics.

Biographies

Michael Byrne has been a ceramic tile installer, contractor, consultant, and industry expert for over 40 years. He is co-founder and the first president of the Ceramic Tile Education Foundation, has been a board member of the Tile Council of North America and a voting member of the Tile Council Handbook committee, and is a voting member of ANSI and ASTM. He has written two other books and hundreds of articles on tile installation and has conducted countless seminars and educational events. Michael has provided consulting services in North, Central, and South America, the UK, and Europe. He is a partner in the Team of Ceramic Tile and Flooring Inspectors. Michael can be reached at www.tileconsultant@aol.com.

Michelle Griffoul is one of the most well-known ceramic artists in the tile industry. She received a Bachelor of Arts degree at San Jose State University, earned a Master of Fine Arts at the University of Puget Sound, and studied at the International School of Ceramics in Florence, Italy. Winner of four Spectrum awards, Michelle designs and manufactures handcrafted mosaic and decorative tile installations and specializes in Ceramic Art for Healing. Michelle can be reached at www.tileart4healing@aol.com.